Case

ME

Caleb Matthews, MD

To Mom,

Dedicated to the person

Who brought me into this world

And fought to keep me in it

Table of Contents

The Canary 1

Agrirama 7

Rite of Passage 23

Sleep Paralysis 47

Cardiac Surgery or Bust! 71

D-Day 91

Chance 122

Misdiagnosis 174

The Big Apple 214

Fried Egg 254

Pouched and Cracked 298

Heal Thy Self 335

The End's Beginning 391

1

The Canary

Whatever befalls, thee was preordained for thee eternity.
Marcus Aurelius, Meditations. Bk. x, sec. 5.

A cool evening greeted Indianapolis just as the leaves were beginning to betray their long-held green constitution into a plethora of turncoats marked by shades of reds, browns, and yellows. Intermittent gusts of wind stirred up fallen leaves and rattled them against the fading light sprinkling and scattering the last rays of sunshine. Indianapolis, Indiana, is quite a charming place, especially in the fall. After a scorching summer, fall was a welcome reprieve soon to be replaced by a harsh winter.

Of course, I among many others at the Simon Cancer Center (SCC) wouldn't be enjoying the changing of the autumn guard. I soon had rounds to complete in the postoperative Intensive Care Unit (ICU) for I would be taking care of some of the sickest patients in the Hoosier state that evening and into the next morning. Many of whom had an operation for some sort of malignancy, in other words, cancer. I would be on the 5th floor where thoracic and hepatobiliary (lung and liver with associated structures) postoperative patients were stationed, who not uncommonly require mechanical ventilation after a laborious and, oftentimes, lengthy operation. Patients came from all over the nation, better yet, the world, to be operated on here. Some as a matter of choice; others as a matter of necessity. Why? They simply had nowhere else to go as many a surgeon or doctor would deem an attempt at operating either too risky or futile.

Even though I would be spending the night at the hospital and much of the next day, as a budding Cardiothoracic surgeon, I wouldn't rather be anywhere else. I craved that responsibility. I had wanted to be a doctor my entire life. There was nothing else. There IS nothing else. I held that conviction as early as childhood, and it still rings true today.

I was accepted into a new and upcoming residency program, *where you go for practical training following medical school*, that combined general surgery (5-year program) and cardiothoracic fellowship (2-3 years). This amalgam was thus called an *integrated* cardiothoracic program that requires six years of training. In an effort to shorten the span of training and recruit more young people into the cardiothoracic trade, the *integrated* tract had mounted interest from some and criticism from others. For me, I had wanted to be a heart and lung surgeon for as long as I could remember. The quicker, the better in my eyes.

The *integrated* approach would call for some fundamental restructuring of training, unpopular as it was to some of the Old Guard. In the first couple to few years, you would focus on general surgery. In the later years, the emphasis would shift more into the cardiothoracic specialty. As this was a new program, and I being one of the first to participate, I was eager to perform and exceed all expectations. Especially in light of the fact that even in places where I interviewed for residency, some potential future 'bosses' would openly express their doubts in an *integrated* form of surgical training *within the interview itself.* Baffled at such an admonition and the lack of empathy for a struggling medical student, now having spent up to 10,000 dollars on travel expenses touring potential residency programs, not to mention my rising debt incurred from medical school and undergrad, I quickly struck some big names off my list even though their looming ivory towers were luring amongst the educational landscape.

Nonetheless, I found my Midwestern home after medical school, a literal hidden gem of a residency program. My intern year was probably not too unlike others'. Your intern year, *or your first year out of medical school beginning residency*, is mainly doing paperwork, learning how the hospital works, calling consults to other services, and communicating efficiently and effectively, *you hope*. Basically, learning how to tie your 'doctor' shoes. For about three months, you feel as if you are putting those shoes on the wrong foot. Let's face it. It feels like you are wearing someone else's shoes altogether.

Embellishment aside, intern year came and went, and I was now in my 2nd year, with much more responsibility. I had the privilege to take care of the intensive care unit (ICU) where a majority of patients are on ventilators or had received high-risk operations where bleeding and/or fluid balance are genuine concerns or at least needed to be closely monitored. I had some experience taking care of cardiac ICU patients during my first year being in the accelerated program where you quickly become aware of the importance of fluid mechanics. However, I was on call taking care of unfamiliar patients, across surgical services, and for physicians, I did not know personally, yet; presenting its own set of insecurities.

I had become pretty good buddies with the senior resident whom I was on call with minimizing the anxiety of my newfound responsibilities. Tyrone had an unmistakable cackle to his laughter that would relieve the stress in any situation. He also seemed to be perpetually sick, having the need to clear his throat multiple times in a sitting. I can't blame him; it was cold and peak allergen season.

Moving from Florida, I had my own suite of issues adjusting to the environment. Not only was it the cold of the Midwest, but I had a nagging dry cough that I couldn't shake. I also lacked a proper winter attire which required me to run clumsily from my car to the hospital at 5 am only to slip on the ice while wearing my yet to be, but soon to be, broken in Danskos, thick footwear suited to withstand an occupation that requires you to be on your feet for most of the day. I would purposely step on Tyrone's thin tennis shoes with those unforgiving Dankos as I walked down the aisle during weekly Wednesday morbidity and mortality (M&M) conferences. And in an effort not to disturb the speaker, he would be forced to silence his cringe and any expletives. Oh, the little things that can get you through a difficult residency! Needless to say, we were buddies, and I was glad and relieved to be on call with him.

Before I would be actively on call, when possible, I was trained to make my own personal rounds in the ICU early in the night after my daily duties were finished since the surgical ICU is usually filled with patients from different services. *During training, we rotate on various surgical services monthly or bimonthly to give us the experience and exposure we need for competency.* This practice allows you to get a feel for how patients are doing in a general sense, as well as looking for anything that may require your immediate attention. For example, labs that need to be followed, worrisome cases you are warned about from colleagues, addressing nurses' concerns,

4

essentially stomping out kindling smoke before they become full-fledged fires.

Moreover, this exercise affords you the opportunity to talk to patients and their families. I was soon becoming well acquainted with how busy doctors can be. So, when I would have a minute to shoot the breeze with the family or a patient, I was happy to oblige. It reminds you of why you had worked so hard to become a doctor in the first place.

As I made my preemptive rounds, I engaged in conversation with a family within a patient's room, "The operation went well, guys!" after having read the operative note from a differing surgical service, "the tube that's helping him breathe will come out tomorrow, and the specimen that was retrieved will be sent to pathology and further analyzed." I said assuredly as most patients follow a similar postoperative course, generally speaking. "I will be checking on Mr. "A" periodically throughout the night. I'm on call. My name is Dr. Matthews."

We exchanged pleasantries. Instantly, they noted my youthful appearance and red hair which inevitably led to them jokingly referring to me as Doogie Howser. Before residency, I had no idea about this popular TV show about the kid doctor. Soon, however, I would become well acquainted for jovial remarks from visitors and patients around the hospital who would remind of my youthful characteristics at least twice a month. It was and is always a reminder not to take myself too seriously.

The nurse for the evening asked me a question as I was leaving. I don't remember exactly what I said in reply. Or wanted to say. As I made my attempt, standing in the doorway facing the family and the nurse, nothing short of jibberish crawled out of my mouth. It was as if I knew what I wanted to say, something so menial and easy, but it came out as a hodgepodge of jumbled nonsense.

My speech returned quickly, however. But as you can imagine, I received some odd looks in return. Trying not to look too dismayed, I laughed it off and said, "Excuse me, that was strange." I continued to answer the question of the nurse and made my exit. I returned to the call room where an intense headache greeted me. One that I hadn't ever experienced before. Tyrone came to the call room with his devious grin to find me with my head in my hands. "Bro, what's wrong?" Thank God he had some Tylenol and had mercy on me as a senior resident to shield me from menial calls from the floor and ICU until the headache dissipated.

Little did I know, this pounding headache was the canary in the coal mine, a deep breath before the plunge into the dark waters of certain uncertainty. I would soon realize the fragility of one's mortality loosely tethered to the weathered strings of fate and faith. Awaiting my future was every flavor of pain that could be bestowed upon an individual; such is stated without a hint of embellishment. Through a continuum of suffer, a newfound appreciation of the ineffable reality for which we find ourselves was recognized. I pray any reader, from any belief system might happen across these pages and draw hope and inspiration through my experience. Perhaps, there is a greater underappreciated design that molds our life. In a little over six months, as I made the turn to twenty-eight years of age, I would find that I had a rare and advanced form of lung cancer testing my outer limits of strength, character, and spirit.

2

Agrirama

A brave man thinks no one is superior who does him an injury; for he has it then in his power to make himself superior to the other by forgiving it. Pope, Thoughts on Various Subjects.

Tifton, Georgia is a quiet southern town near the Florida state border adjacent to the metropolis that is Valdosta, Georgia. Those who are familiar with South Georgia, or nearby states, know I say this in jest. Tifton is positioned well below the *Fall Line*, a geographical boundary that formally represented a shoreline millions of years ago spanning from southwest Columbus, GA to northeast Augusta, GA. The Fall line is now signified by a marked by a rapid drop in elevation when traveling from north to south. One can appreciate it while traveling on Interstate 75 passing through Macon in the middle of the peach state. You might experience mild ear-popping upon the transition. I have always found it interesting how much a single factor like geography might shape the way a culture conducts itself.

Tifton is a cozy town where you would have no reservations in allowing your children to have free reign in engaging in unbridled play outside in the runway streets of Tifton's Historic District large enough to land a plane if need be. In this charming, pollen-stained neighborhood, everyone knows everyone else. Crime was almost nonexistent. The wide expanse of my neighborhood allowed my adolescence to be filled with constant street hockey games with ragtag goals swarming every which way across clear medians. The only real danger was an aberrant pecan that might have gotten jammed in your wheel sending your skates up and face down. Home to many kids of similar ages; it was a dream to spend my early childhood there, almost semi-charmed.

As you approach that *Fall Line*, you might note an exceptional uptick in a particular nuisance called the Gnat, a two-winged plague that consistently bombards South Georgia inhabitants until utter desensitization. For anyone not accustomed to their swarms, you are in for a most aggravating summer. Barring that pest, along with the heat and humidity, what remains are the most redeeming qualities of the South. Certainly, those features are the well-known southern draw and hospitality, not to mention sweet tea served over the rocks. Once that sweet, iced tea smacks across your lips, your location is unmistakable.

I am always happy to pick up those proverbial ya'll's, ma'am's, and sir's when I returned home from school it reaffirms my country spirit was still alive and well. It's a constant reminder and hallmark of the south. Most southerners find a point of pride within that culture and language. Many people are unaware that southern slang, or *cracker culture*, came from a particular part of Great Britain, an impoverished region, and Georgia was in fact a debtor's colony in its genesis.

Irrespective of its charm and checkered history, southern Georgia was not without its drawbacks as the tight-knit communities lent themselves to social despotism and hierarchies, as in any society of any race or creed. And I, being a child of divorce, encountered a suite of social implications, whether rooted in reality or self-perceived, due to having a less than nuclear family. My parents were divorced when I was three years old.

Before any semblance of abstract thinking for situational awareness, growing up in a single-mother family left me feeling estranged from other children with more traditional modes of growing up. A feeling of inferiority loomed heavy, whether consciously or unconsciously, and would shape much of my experience of early childhood.

However, it wouldn't be fair to make the presupposition that my parents' divorce directly resulted in those feelings of social ineptitude or that my father was never around. That is certainly not a picture I wish to paint; I think every child struggles to some degree in adolescence. My perceived difficulty was and is likely to be repeated for time immemorial; in all probability, millions of kids felt the same way. Scope in your worldview takes much time to develop. Nonetheless, I don't remember a time when my parents were together and the prospect that I could escape this deficiency in my home life would be ignorant for me to assume.

Indeed, any resounding difference in home life was undoubtedly lost on me until I began to compare my home life with others'. Until then I was a blissful kid, unaware, aloof. Comparison, indeed, is the thief of happiness. There may be situations in which parents should stay together for the sake of the family as almost 41% of first-time marriages end in divorce (divorcestatistics.org). Certainly, this was not the case with mine. If the fights that ensued during scheduled meeting times in child exchanges were any indication of what their tumultuous marriage had been like, I am very happy that they met their denouement. Having a schism such as a divorce afforded me an interesting dynamic during my upbringing that led me to develop diverse skills that most don't get the chance to develop.

9

Having divorced parents gifted me the opportunity to experience a childhood of dualism. My Mother is a loan officer; we lived within the city limits of Tifton. My Father is a forester living in the county. His profession involves evaluating the worth of trees by walking, or *cruising*, through the tall, planted pine tree forests, sometimes through unrelenting thick brush habitat doing his damnedest to avoid snakes and heat exhaustion. He tirelessly records the width and variety of trees to evaluate the value of a tract of land. After the trees are processed, he replants them to restore the natural beauty of the forests. Effectually between my mom and dad, one parent would provide the raw supplies for house development while the other would provide the financial assistance for people to purchase the property.

Even though I see the value now of my upbringing in a single-parent home (my beautiful stepparents on each side and my sister, and other advantages yet to be appreciated), it is harder to realize as a child dealing with all the other social confusion at that age. The constant back and forth between homes, between expectations, between norms of behavior. Despite having an excellent relationship with my father presently, it was difficult to know him with only seeing him every other weekend.

I fell prey to jealousy and envy as I would observe other fathers in attendance of soccer, baseball, and football games with constant encouragement coming from the stands. My father was rarely in attendance. I was skilled with most sports, so I would elicit encouragement from parents that weren't my own. A spur of resentment would bleed from the ranks of our little league bench as my fellow teammates wanted their parents' praises chiefly to themselves. Understandable, but it wouldn't be some years before I would develop any sort of emotional intelligence. Oftentimes, the ball wouldn't be passed to me even though I was the obvious choice. A challenging predicament as an adolescent who only longed for acceptance and fun competition but was consistently ostracized and sabotaged by fellow peers. Indeed, children can be cruel.

A prime example I experienced, unfortunately, came when I was around twelve years of age. I had invited a neighborhood friend from the same baseball league to come over to play and hang out. I wasn't aware but he already had a couple of kids over at his house, and he was within walking distance. My mom wasn't home, but, as previously mentioned, it was a very safe place for kids. I had just gotten out of the shower when I heard them coming down the road. Excited to greet them, I grabbed a towel and unlocked the door to let them in.

What happened next left a few scars. As if it was orchestrated, they rushed in and chased me to my room. In a split second, I knew what they had in mind. I was younger than other kids as I had started school a year early due to aptitude tests and overall growth but still being smaller than most in comparison. In other words, I was not as developed as other kids, I would always be a late bloomer in most respects.

The three or four kids, it's hard to remember how many there were as this was over twenty years ago now, commenced taunting me, removed my towel, rolled it up, and began whipping me repeatedly. I cried and pled for them to stop grasping at the bedcovers to maintain some sort of decency and privacy not to mention shelter from the lashes. I didn't know how long the humiliation would last. Likely only about a minute, but it felt like an eternity. Lying there shamed, littered in whelps upon my prepubescent body from a twisted intertwined towel, I was left in tears.

Years later one of the guys would make a sincere apology for the events of that day. I knew and know him to this day. He was going through some things at that time which made him a very unsavory child. Although I never maintained resentment toward any one of the kids that day. Nonetheless, the acute mortification made an appreciable mark on me. Seeding a constant sense of inadequacy, some healthy and some pathologic, within my psyche. I never told anyone about it until right now. I am thankful for it. Because a traumatic event like that, with all the embarrassment and shame, would provide me fuel to push myself well beyond my limits.

Guilt is the source of sorrow, 'tis the fiend, Th' avenging fiend, that follows us behind With whips and stings.
Nicholas Rowe, Fair Penitent, Act iii, sc. 1.

Georgia law stipulates, at least in my family's case, that, until the child is thirteen years of age, the child should remain with the mother. At age thirteen, the child can decide: mother or father. I emphasize *child.* During medical school, I recall learning that abstract thinking doesn't typically begin until after thirteen years of age. Asking a child to make a decision of that gravitas, especially amid the rocky tides of my parent's divorce, was no fair request. I loved both my parents dearly. The fear of disappointing either was more than palpable as I contemplated my decision at that age. How does any child make such a decision?

After all, even though it was just a town away, no more than 30 minutes, I had established an entire life already. Despite the unfortunate event I described earlier, I had no issues maintaining meaningful relationships with everyone. I was friends with the skaters, jocks, preps, nerds; you name it. Among the many cliques, I had none. I would tesselate throughout the groups seamlessly, belonging to no circle. Never meeting a stranger, I welcomed everyone. No stranger to social humiliation, I never wanted another person to feel like I had.

There was a kid in grade school named, coincidentally, Caleb. Caleb had a severe speech impediment. My heart broke for this kid. I'm sure he was enrolled in some form of speech therapy, but he still struggled daily. Part of his struggle, of course, was the banter received from children in their unforgiving and ruthless taunts. In addition, this poor kid was also on the heavier side, which wouldn't alleviate matters. He would stutter most commonly with his initiation of speech. Once he got the ball rolling, he'd continue more easily, although not completely.

Suddenly, an idea struck me. Because he was having so much difficulty initiating speech, "Well, why don't I just make my name a little bit easier to say?" "Instead of calling me Caleb, call me "Kay Kay," I encouraged him. I still get goosebumps about how much he blossomed thereafter. That one change allowed him, at least around me, to unravel his thoughts and words much easier instead of fumbling through them. His interactions with the other kids became night and day. And, of course, like Tom Sawyer and that white fence, everyone else started calling me 'Kay Kay." I didn't mind. Twenty years later after having brain surgery, I would lose all my powers of speech. If I hadn't had empathy for the 'other Caleb,' I sure do now.

So, the decision lay before me: should I stay with my mom, or should I go and move in with my dad? My brother, four years ahead of me, had already decided to leave and live with my dad. I did miss him, and he returned to live with mom and me before entering his senior year, for which he had his reasons. I felt like I owed it to my father that he have time with his son as I was three years old when my parents split. Moreover, I was always up for something new, an adventure.

One primary reason for making the ultimate decision to acquiesce to living with my father sacrificing many of the hard-won relationships that I had fostered for well over six years was guilt. I felt shame in not allowing a father to have a good relationship with his son. Even though it wasn't a circumstance that I created, I did have the power to rectify it. I desired retribution as well and the making up for lost time. Heartbreak goes both ways, however.

I can still hear the sobs from my mom on the evening I informed her of my decision. Her heavy steps down the hard floor hallway and the rapid shut of the glass door nearly cracking on her exit still makes me cringe as she wept her way out of our picture-perfect white house. Torn with conflicting emotions, there was no wrong choice; there was no right one either. Both decisions ended up in a parent being hurt. Should I be sad for abandoning my mother or happy to join my dad? The push and pull of emotions were callousing over time as this dynamic was repeated in more minor instances on holidays, birthdays, and what have you. For better or worse, it fortified me with an emotive shield helping me to stay focused in high-stress situations, i.e., operating.

These conflicting feelings, among other dynamics, caused me to always seek conflict resolution despite personal desires, which, I believe, led to the development of a Type 'C' personality, or Cancer personality. [1] As the name implies, a type C personality is a constellation of behaviors commonly found in people diagnosed with malignancy. There is some considerable debate in the literature about the actual existence of this entity. Like most things in sociology, they are tough to prove de facto. I consider Type C the quintessential people pleaser to a fault, so to speak, always looking to please despite any inconvenience to one's personal life. Persistent stress to please and keep the peace would have further implications down the road, as we will see. *This manifested in the inability to say 'no' for fear of letting my parents or anyone else down.*

Let us never forget that the cultivation of the earth is the most important labor of man.
Daniel Webster, Remarks on Agriculture Boston, 13 Jan., 1840.

Before I would go live with my dad in the next town over, Nashville, GA, I had my first healthcare experience in the most unlikely of places, the Agrirama. The Agrirama is a state-operated historical site set in the late 1800s that functions to give visitors, namely children, somewhat of a peek into what life was like back when subsistence farming was primarily the means to feed oneself and family. When steam engines and horse and buggy were a major modes of transportation. The compound was a blast from the past.

Walking through the Agrirama, you would pass an old country store where you could purchase giant hard candies and taffy to scintillate your tastebuds. After you buy your favorite treat, you visit the horses within their stables surrounded by the staunch smell of dried manure rustled up from a passing carriage. An occasional gust of hot, humid air would pass over the plowed fields as mule and man toil in solidarity with the burden of the dried earth in an effort to prepare for the season ahead. One would note century-old homes laid out among the modest tract of land. You were free to wander through the staged homes as the old wooden floorboards would crack and cackle beneath you like whining like old men having their bent backs pressed upon.

The surrounding schools would use this as a means to broaden children's horizons in remembrance of a bygone era. They split us between boys and girls to delegate our responsibilities for the coming day. Gender identity politics wouldn't be for another 15 years; I am sure that people at such a time in history would be utterly confused about all the fuss. More than likely, they would prescribe a shovel and just say, "Get on with your work."

The madams went to butter churning, quilt making, and cooking while the sirs went to the fields to turn the soil. However, no one volunteered to be the town doctor. I was curious about the occupation as I had already had my fill of working outside in the blistering sun at a young age. At my father's home in Nashville, we had cattle that required barbed wire fencing, corralling, and deworming. It taught me the value of hard work at an early age, but God did I resent it at times. You don't enjoy most things that are good for you, and I am so grateful to have had that experience. The experience developed a work ethic in me that was unparalleled. *Yes, I admit it, Dad, you were right.*

A town doctor sounded like a nice reprieve from what I was already well accustomed. Two other buddies and I made off with the town doctor who was a sweet older woman. We tended to her vegetable garden within the split rail fence where she informed us of her chosen plants' nutrition. This is where I was introduced to the idea that, as the acclaimed naturopath and proponent of the healing powers of wheatgrass, Ann Wigmore stated, "The food you eat can be either the safest and most powerful form of medicine or the slowest form of poison." I remember her commending me on how well I had folded up the water hose; her minuscule commendation made quite the impression on my adolescent psyche. Who knew I would do much of the same thing going on and off cardiopulmonary bypass, neatly folding up plastic tubing running to and from a beating heart, as a budding cardiothoracic surgeon?

The Coke Side of Life.
Coka-Cola Company slogan, 2006.

Now when I finally made the move, I would commence the dance between the two completely separate lives: efforts to maintain and keep alive those relationships in Tifton while beginning a new life in Nashville. Even though there weren't more than thirty minutes between the two, there were some appreciable differences: Nashville was far more *country* than Tifton led on. Nashville had twice the land area, but Tifton had double the people. The differences were reflected in what was required of my wardrobe during weekends. In Tifton, my attire would demand for whatever sport I would be participating in, likely soccer. Conversely, work boots, a tethered T-shirt, and hat were called for in Nashville. As I oscillated back and forth between two different lives, different homes, different personas, I would often miss out on life events shared by close friends as I simply couldn't be in two places at once. A certain resentment for my teenage pickle began to brew as the growing divide between former friends widened.

As previously mentioned, I had an issue saying no, acquiescing to obligations that far outweighed an average teenager capacity for work in a day. I played up to three sports at a time. In the fall, I would kick for the football team, ran cross-country, and played soccer for a travel team that was an hour and a half down away. In the spring, I would play soccer for the school. In the early spring, I would have to leave practice early to feed the cows as that was one of the deals I had to make with my dad. I had to keep up with all this, all the while maintaining academic salutatorian status. If the grades were inadequate, there would be no sports or allowance to fund my travel to and from the obligations mentioned above.

Spreading myself too thin would all come at a price, however. Amongst all the sports, soccer was my true passion having some marginal talent. As my physicality improved along with my dexterity and touch, I had impressed coaches from other parts of the state with my level of performance despite no traditional training. Subsequently, I was invited to play with their competitive travel teams. Unfortunately, practice was an hour and a half and a tank of gas away. Despite the inconvenience, what do I do? After begging my dad for extra gas money, I spread the butter a little more. Sign me up! Excited at the opportunity, I thought maybe playing ball in college was a possibility!? High school ball was nothing compared to travel ball, a wonderful opportunity to showcase my skills across the state.

My hands were, at this point, overflowing with responsibility. Sometimes I wouldn't get home until after ten o'clock in the evening. I could only make travel ball practice one day a week, unfortunately. I would load up my Landcruiser, which guzzled gas desiccated desert camel, practice, and return home to finish any homework I might've been unable to complete during lunch before all my practices began. This was a lot for a sixteen-year-old, but what can I say? I loved the beautiful game.

One evening, I was headed to travel soccer practice after football kicking practice (American) and cross-country. Despite my growing fatigue, I've maintained my rebellious attitude when told I was unable to do something even if the demand of the task was self-imposed. The fear of inadequacy pierced straight through reason and self-awareness as to my perceived limits. *Although, how do you ever know your limits if you don't push them?* I still remember the song playing when I fell asleep at the wheel in a top-heavy Landcruiser right next to a bridge embankment, Eric Clapton's "Tears in Heaven." In hindsight, the song selection was not the best when exhausted traveling on a dark, narrow country highway in southwest Georgia with low and unforgiving shoulders.

Looking at the evidence of the wreck, I should be dead. Going around 65-70 miles/hour, I met a bridge that crossed a creek with large embankments on either side. Fortunately, I collided with the aluminum shoulder, and my two right wheels were lifted popping both tires. After landing on the remnant tires and rims, I overcorrected and swerved across the road entering the opposing lane. When my deflated tires met the opposite side, they gripped the earth forcing the Landcruiser to flip at least for two revolutions. I was wearing no seatbelt. By the grace of God, I landed in the passenger seat with every other space in the cabin crushed like a coke can, especially the driver's seat. I stepped out of the Landcruiser with no more than a scratch on my right leg. Needless to say, the truck was totaled. *Indeed, fate would have other plans for my right leg.*

I am in, And must go on; and since I have put off From the shore of innocence, guilt be now my pilot.
Philip Massinger, The Duke of Milan. Act ii. sc. 1.

As my love for soccer grew, the larger my resentment grew for the duties out at the farm. I realized that in such a small town, there was no real chance to get the exposure I would need to play college soccer. Also, my relationship with my father had gotten increasingly rocky. We are much alike, both as hard-headed as the other. He was attempting to show me the value of hard work and the advantages of learning how to use one's hands. Something that served me well in the dexterity needed to be a heart surgeon. I was a short-sighted kid. *What teenager isn't?*

My father had been a junior Olympic swimmer in South Carolina. During a very important race, he failed to make a good turn on his last leg however maintained his slim lead. As he approached the finish line, the competing swimmer reached out to touch the wall only milliseconds before my father even though his body was clearly ahead. Milliseconds washed away the interminable hours spent in the pool preparing for the next level. Milliseconds. You can imagine the devastation felt by my father and how that would shape his view on sports, "No matter what you do, there will always be someone out there who is better than you." I resented that. I rebelled against that contention. Even though I knew it to be true, it didn't stop me from disregarding those hard facts and cultivating an unsurpassed work ethic that would serve me well in the years to come.

This rebellion fueled every extra mile and sprint, octane for every stair climbed and squatted, every pushup and sit-up outside of weight training. I'd study harder to remove any extraneous reason barring me from competition. Sometimes those words would keep me up at night, and I'd sneak out to the soccer field late at night just to get more touches on the pitch for fear of being ill-prepared. For fear of inadequacy.

Finally, my love for soccer led me to make one of the most challenging decisions of my life, save for leaving my mom's home. Despite having only three years with my father, I decided that if I wanted to have any chance of playing at more competitive levels, I would need to change my location to north Florida in Jacksonville. Opportunities were much more abundant, and I was much more likely to be seen by colleges and higher-level teams. I had only one year remaining in high school. If I wanted any chance to play in college, I had to leave right away. Fortunately, my mom had been remarried and moved allowing me to transition schools. This decision was not made without serious fallout in my dad and I's relationship. This dissension was seen as a deep betrayal and the reverberating guilt that haunt me forever. We wouldn't speak for some time.

Although I was chasing a dream; it came at a price of the ones I love.

1.   Amoros F, A.M., Esteve R, Lopez A, Ramirez C, *Is the type C behavior pattern characteristic of people with cancer?* 1st National Congress of Psycology . Madrid Spain; 1998, 1998.

3

Rite of Passage

Experience is the father of wisdom, and memory the mother.
Thomas Fuller, Gnomology. No. 1480

Pacing through the 4th floor of Methodist Hospital (MH) in Indianapolis, Indiana, alarms from a patient's room caught my attention. The 4th floor was where most, if not all, trauma or emergency general surgery (EGS) patients were sequestered suffering from all forms of penetrating and blunt injuries ranging in severity. The 4th floor was the floor as it was the most basic level of hospital care before a patient was either upgraded to an intensive care unit (ICU) status or discharged. Patients on the floor are generally stable making their level of acuity more forgiving to medical error lending opportunity to surgical interns like me to learn. The floor is where every surgical intern has his or her first swing at-bat in being a doctor.

MH is well over one hundred years old carrying no shame in showboating its weathered features through its many years of serving the Indiana townsfolk providing hospital services for many of the trauma and EGS patients in Indiana and surrounding states. The stale yellow brick of MH's walls was reminiscent of the Wizard of Oz's brick road, but a sore, festering version of the classic movie marked by windswept and rustic walls as it was constantly bombarded by the harsh Indiana winters in decades past. MH wears proudly upon its brow all the trauma and pain which constantly sifted through those halls. For many years, MH was the only level 1 trauma hospital in the state of Indiana.

Fortunately, I was just passing by and ran into the patient's room, where a nurse was desperately trying to set up suctioning. Alarms were sounding off. The patient had aspirated compromising her airway, evident by the vomit rapidly filling her mouth and nose. She was a large woman, probably 60 years old, who had an abdominal operation during her stay but wasn't clear as to what kind. Not that it mattered at that junction; if we didn't establish an airway, she would die within minutes.

Obtunded, her vitals ceased as soon as I entered. I began compressions while the nurse applied suctioning. Within seconds, the room was littered with people much more experienced than myself. Thank God, I said to myself. This, of course, was my first code on my first day on call. I continued my round of compressions as my arms burned with fatigue. Chest compressions, as I was experiencing, are far more exasperating than one would think. Sweat dripping from my crown, I was relieved when someone else volunteered. Just as I had stopped, the chief surgical resident strolled into the room in a rather nonchalant fashion.

His name was Adam; we were barely acquainted. He stood intimidatingly a few inches over 6 feet as a bald, burly man. He was oddly always in a jovial mood which was probably the product of him being on top of everything in the hospital from his many years and hard-won experience in healthcare. Not to mention, he had an innate personality of a leader. Heavier set, I would later find out that he had a less than traditional arrival into medicine. Originally from Canada, he was previously a

24

pharmacist but wanted a more hands-on approach to medicine, so decided to be a surgeon. You can imagine my sigh of relief when he walked into the room.

He steps in front of me on the patient's left side and waits for the anesthesia resident to establish an airway. I noticed he was gripping an unopened scalpel. "You go it?" he asks calmly to the resident trying to navigate through the particulates of undigested food and stomach juices to place an airway tube. "Yea, I got it," he shakily replies while oxygen saturations continue to tank. "If you don't get it, I'm going to cric' her," Adam decisively retorts.

He was referring to a cricothyrotomy in which you make an incision in someone's throat in a specific area to avoid copious bleeding to bypass any obstruction impeding normal airflow. The incision is made wide enough to place a breathing tube and establish a reliable means of oxygenation and ventilation. Your brain only has about 5 minutes of reserve before meaningful brain function is compromised and is sometimes never recovered.

The anesthesia resident secured the airway just as Adam was about to take the scalpel out of the sterile packaging. Sighs of relief emanated from the crowd of healthcare workers who had promptly gathered in response to the code when the cardiac monitor sprang back to life and oxygenation was normalized. The patient was sent to the ICU. Danger was averted, for now.

Adam looked over at his newly conscripted greenhorn, me, and said, "First lesson: as a surgical resident, you should always walk around with a scalpel in your pocket." He handed me the plastic-wrapped scalpel as I remained in shock from precipitously the events unfolded; the only reply I could muster was "Yessir," and placed my newly acquired scalpel in my front pocket.

The evening shifts for the surgical residents on call were typically setup in the following fashion: the intern would handle all floor calls and would consult higher-level residents or ancillary help staff (e.g., nurse practitioners and physician assistants) if needed, the mid-level residents would see all consults both in the ED and within the hospital, and the senior resident would operate and direct the lower-level residents accordingly. When level 1 traumas were sent to the hospital, those with the greatest acuity and injury, all residents, from intern to chief, would be in attendance within the trauma room in a concerted effort.

Despite what we were doing, when we are paged to a level 1 trauma, short of operating or yourself actively dying, you drop what you were doing and go directly to the trauma room. The intern would document everything on exam and assist whenever they could. The midlevel resident would do the complete physical exam according to the ATLS (Advanced Trauma Life Support®) algorithm. The senior resident would help when needed, and the attending surgeon would intervene when they saw fit. We all knew our roles, helping to orchestrate ourselves in the most time-efficient manner to provide the most effective means of response. The rapid, coordinated springing to action certainly appealed to my inner adrenaline junkie.

Later that same evening, I was up on the 4th floor seeing to the many floor calls, answering the never-ending stream of pages involving requests for pain medicine to the correction of electrolytes. My beeper sounded off with its harsh screech demanding attention. Trauma 1, again. As an intern, you were often interrupted from floor duties several times throughout the night. And when I had time, I would do my best to help the midlevel with the ED duties. With several unaddressed calls and requests piled up over the evening, another trip down to the trauma room was the last thing I had time for. But in the wise words of ultramarathoner Cameron Hanes, I repeated to myself, "Nobody Cares, Work Harder."

So that's what I did. I scurried down to the ED and began my documentation before the patient was in the hospital adorning required personal protective equipment (PPE) needed for whatever may be coming through the door. The trauma nurse announced, "Motorcycle accident, 5 minutes." I populated my pre-typed rubric for a trauma evaluation whilst trying to probe incoming paramedics as to any details of the accident.

"65-year-old male. High-speed motorcycle collision. Blood pressure 100/80. Heart Rate: 100. GCS (Glasgow Coma Scale): 3, with no pupillary response," exclaimed the paramedic as they rolled the patient into the trauma bay unbuckling the patient from the gurney but maintaining head stability. Unresponsive. "He got 1 liter of fluid before arrival with no analgesics administered." The paramedic and his partner summed up their report while trauma nurses descended upon the patient like buzzards over a carcass establishing venous access and drawing every lab under the sun. The midlevel resident, however, was wrapped up in an earlier trauma that had arrived, so it was up to the chief resident, Adam, to direct the exam. All these things were happening simultaneously, quickly, yet orderly.

Not a minute had passed after transferring the patient from the gurney to the trauma bed before we lost all vitals. There was no blood pressure and a thready pulse. Due to the nature of the man's injury and the observed abrupt loss in vitals, an emergent thoracotomy would be indicated: we would proceed to open the man's chest and internally massage the heart to save his life.

The attending surgeon called for the ED thoracotomy kit to open his chest to gain access to the heart and aorta to pump the heart manually. The trauma nurses returned his request with blank stares. One of the more experienced nurses ran off to retrieve one; seldom is one forced to open the chest in the emergency department. Time was ticking. We HAD to get the chest open expeditiously. Standing to Adam's left, in short recall of Adam's clinical pearl earlier that evening, I pulled the unused blade out from my pocket and whispered, "You know, as a surgical resident, you should always have a scalpel in your pocket...." Smirking, Adam grabs the scalpel from me, and he and the attending surgeon quickly incised the chest to find the culprit thoracic injury likely to cause such a rapid drop in blood pressure.

Oddly after opening the thoracic cavity with a bone saw, Adam and the attending surgeon were able to stabilize the patient noting no significant vascular injury that would have caused such an abrupt drop in blood pressure. There were no visible sources of major hemorrhage. As they closed the large, clamshell incision, we rushed the patient to computed tomography (CT) for a closer look. Baffling, the patient has suffered an internal decapitation; much of his cervical (neck) vertebra were simply not there. The amount of force subjected to the neck quite literally vaporized the neck bone. I can't believe it either. Needless to say, he did not survive, and I will never get on a motorcycle.

If you will let me, I will wish you in your future what all men desire --- enough work to do, and strength enough to do your work.
Rudyard Kipling, Address to Medical Students, 1908.

"We got another one for you!" exclaimed the junior emergency department (ED) resident matter-of-factly. Surely, he had noticed the checkerboard of patient labels, simply stickers, arranged on my back complete with patients' medical record numbers and names. Passerby's, from nurses to doctors, would stick these labels on my person so as not to interrupt the mountains of paperwork I was attempting to complete from previous traumas and surgical consults from earlier that night. They weren't trying to be rude; the goings-on's revolved at heightened RPMs in the ED. Moreover, I didn't have the patience or time to sit through an intern's presentation of the "chief complaint." There was simply too much to do. Information needed to be mainlined, central lined rather. I grew to prefer that expedited mode of communication; anything I needed to know could be found documented in the chart, for which I was going to double-check anyway. Trust but verify!

I had now assumed the role of mid-level resident (2nd year of residency) on the trauma and EGS service at MH for the entire month working from 5 pm to 6 am; MH was one of three level 1 trauma centers in the state. My responsibility entailed the following: seeing all surgical consults evaluated by ED physicians and throughout the hospital, all trauma evaluations designated as trauma 1's and 2's depending on the severity of injury, and, at the end of my shift, reporting to the day team. Throughout the shift, I would be constantly following up on imaging and labs, adequately documenting the nature of the injury and/or pain requiring surgical consultation, communicating with patients and nurses about plans of treatment, not to mention voicing any concerns to my superiors, in other words, the chief resident and attendings. There were shifts where my hands never left the keyboard save for when actively evaluating patients.

According to the Indiana Department of Health, injury is the leading cause of death for Hoosiers aged 1 through 44 and the 4th leading cause of death overall. According to the Fatality Analysis Reporting System (FARS), there was a total of 4,089 traffic fatalities within a four-year span. In 2018, nearly 33,000 people suffered some flavor of traumatic brain injury resulting in 1,313 deaths. All said, there are more than 500,000 ED visits due to injuries each year with around 11% of those visits resulting in hospitalization   (https://www.in.gov/health/trauma-system/injury-prevention/national-and-state-injury-facts/). The takeaway: we were busy. Extremely busy.

For the longest time, Indiana University hospital was reportedly the highest volume level 1 center (around 802 beds) standing alone as a bastion of aid serving a mostly impoverished and poorly educated population. It would only be joined by Eskenazi Hospital and St. Vincent's Hospital later.

The ED at MH must've been conjured from someone's ill-fated LSD trip. Rather than a spacious arena of functionality aimed at the quick delivery of healthcare, the layout was more labyrinth than ED. The physician working station was located literally in front of the patient intake

30

secretaries. Due to our intimate proximity, you had no need to call them to get their attention; in fact, a whisper would have sufficed. Directly behind me, within arm's length, were a few patients' rooms and unused beds arranged haphazardly. Sometimes complaints from more belligerent and inebriated patients could be felt, rather smelt, from right beyond my computer screen. Between belches, they would plead for food or water despite bowel rest orders. Constantly surrounded by screams and guttural moans of every stomachache and injury in Indiana, one can imagine the amalgam of putrid stirred into an unsavory milieu produced by public intoxication and seared crack pipes. Such was a standard night.

You might be wondering why didn't you just leave and complete your work elsewhere? As soon as I would seek out a hiding place to focus, I would be paged back to the ED for another trauma or surgical consultation. I learned quickly that the five-minute walk up and down the stairs was too time-consuming and an attempt at solace would drag me further behind in work. Work was constant until the morning came. You're lucky to remember to hydrate yourself.

As if the pandemonium couldn't spread any further, the halls were littered with patients and beds filled almost always to capacity making it difficult to walk at times. Bumping into the edge of beds accidentally left my thighs with gnarly bruises. Rooms were arranged like encircling wagons in some Western Film; however, there were series of beds with no rooms, just curtains to provide some degree of privacy. Any extra space more than two arm's length was populated by a bed. Sifting continuously and spilling out through the cracks between the beds were nurses, radiology technicians, lab technicians, students, et cetera, within the hub of activity.

You would find yourself in constant wars for computer access among nurses and fellow residents. And take it from me; you do not want to get on nurses' bad sides. Both my sister and mother are nurses; I didn't have to learn that lesson. Many of my budding doctor friends certainly did, the hard way. The worse thing a new resident could do is disrespect a seasoned nurse who knows more than any resident would understand in a lifetime. I pity the individual, whoever he/she is. Being marked as an unruly and disrespectful resident by the nursing staff is a stain that is rarely removed from your scrubs. Inevitably, there will always be a handful of residents who feel that the world owes them something because they wear the MD insignia on their left pocket. In reality, you have only just started learning. The hubris and disrespect I see in medical students now is unsettling, to say the least.

Night after night amongst the backdrop of chaos in the Methodist ED, I am constantly assured that I would not be able to make it through the night. There was too much to do, each night being busier than the one preceding it. Constantly juggling between any and everything begging for your attention, the art of proper triaging matters was never more paramount. "Hey man, would you please come lay hands on this patient?" my ED colleague would implore. "This is not a formal consult, but could you just lay hands and examine the patient...?" I loathed this request, not because I didn't want to do my job and provide greatly needed care to these people, but the sheepish and cowardly way of requesting services. What these ED interns didn't know is that if I see a patient, I must fully document everything. Period. Giving a cursory review with subsequent cursory advice is a huge no-no and leads to mistakes and poor patient care. Moreover, I could be heavily reprimanded.

"Is this a formal surgical consult?" I would say in reply. "Well, no," he or she would exclaim. I was not trying to be crass, only direct to the new intern. There was no time for anything but "Have there been any labs or imaging completed?" "No." I would politely ask them to do a more "complete workup, and I'd be happy to see them." I was on nights in August which was an important time in all residencies. Why? Because both July and August are when the new interns arrive at their residences fresh from medical school consequently increasing medical errors.[1] If you can avoid going to the hospital during those months, I'd recommend it.

But that is how you learn. All doctors are "practicing" medicine. "Practicing" medicine being the operative word. Physicians, and all healthcare workers for that matter, are people who succumb to all the same human fallacies that we all experience. Inexperience. Greed. Laziness. Fatigue. Anger. Ignorance. How you treat people who are lower on the medical hierarchy, so to speak, is reflective of who you are as a person. I withdrew numerous applications to residency programs at well-respected institutions because of how I saw them treat their subordinates with disrespect and disdain. That's why in response to a green feather ED resident without proper consulting etiquette, I would always, if time permitted, engage a small bit of teaching in the process perhaps alleviating the stress of a future poorly conducted consult. Downstream, it might make my job easier or someone else's. I am not infallible, however. The integrity of my character would be challenged when patience was in short supply.

Indeed, patience was challenging to practice with the nagging distractions yapping at your heels biding for attention. "Can I survive to sign out?" I would frantically ask myself. More often than not, I would be typing up my last note or seeing my last patient while racing to sign-out at seven in the morning. And in that small, decrepit board room filled with the commiserating stares of residents, nurses, and doctors arriving in the morning to seize the torch of the evening's endeavors, I would begin, with the chief resident at my side, morning report. With one piece of paper filled with medical speak complete with all the making of medical shorthand jargon and lab tables with optime values, I would begin my structured oratory for morning report.

Like a struggling news anchor, morning report was a challenge because, like most people, public speaking was never a strong suit of mine. The beauty of the overnight chaos, with all the stress of multiple traumas and urgent operations experienced in a single evening, would force one to formulate a coherent presentation of the significant overnight events. Painting an accurate and informative picture for at least over twenty patients required practice, medical knowledge, and confidence in your performance from the night before. Confidence would be key when held up to the scrutinizing looking glass of the incoming staff who are charged with evaluating the overnight teams' management decisions. Indeed, the residents often served as a medium between treatment philosophy or other menial inter-departmental politics among attendings. As one can imagine, the air could get a bit thick with resentment amongst the strong surgeon personalities.

Despite the stress of morning sign-out, after the third night on call, you were far too exasperated to care. I quickly became too engaged and too exhausted to be conscientious about my performance as a resident. The insecurity did not serve me as I did my job; I purged all my apprehension from awareness and began owning the night. Nervousness and hesitancy took too long to feel as I would peer into the small crowd with bloodshot eyes holding my single paper of notes with shaking caffeinated hands. Bashfulness became obsolete. The stress and focus of those shifts demanded squeezing all the indecision and unsurety from your job. No longer would I be a nervous intern, but finally, an effective junior doctor.

A scene from Fight Club starring Edward Norton comes to mind. "A guy who came to Fight Club for the first time, his ass was a wad of cookie dough. After a few weeks, he was carved out of wood." Therein lies an apt description of what that month provided for me; confidence that I could handle any amount of work thrown at me. I was always surprised by people who were tentative about having such a rotation. Don't you want to be tested? Wouldn't you want to know if you could perform at such a high level? (I am sure that some of the Old Guard would scoff at the notion that residents work as hard as they did in the past.) Having a month straight of overnight call early in my 2nd year set the stage well for future performance; I knew if I could get through a busy trauma/EGS month, I could do almost anything. Thus, why residents oft refer to it as a rite of passage.

Within that short month, the stark distinction between the best and worst of people were displayed on a revolving merry-go-round exhibiting the full scope of the human experience. Moans of suffering in one room contrasted greatly with the sighs of reprieve emitted from another. A joyous celebration from a misread scan could be heard from one patient's room while the wails of devastation radiated from another as they were just informed of an advanced stage of colon cancer. A mourning parent might be saying their last goodbyes to their son in the trauma bay as chest compressions are conducted; meanwhile, a child's knee might have received its last stitch closing a dog bite suffered earlier that day. Where else does one experience the intersectionality of the human experience between pain and relief? Where else do you respire the fullness of the human experience? In a cycle that never rests?

Moreover, the patient population I found to be near and dear to me as they reminded me of the good folks down in southeast Georgia. They served as a constant reminder of why I went into medicine, to serve those less fortunate and pay forward the knowledge that had been passed down. An adage from an old cardiologist in South Georgia rang in my ears, "Service Over Self." Every time I would complain about the heaps of work and frustrations of working in the hospital, I would remind myself that how I feel doesn't matter; the patient is having the worst day of their lives. I would soon be acquainted with those days repeatedly.

I saw, reflected in patients, my Grandmother who had taken a fall, my Father who had a heart attack, and friends who had died too soon in motor vehicle collisions. I wonder if effectually, we healthcare workers, are, indeed, treating, not only the patient in front of us, but also transitively our loved ones, or loved ones who have since passed, that are/were in similar unwanted positions. Indeed, the Hoosier landscape itself, other than those unforgettable and unforgiving winters, with its long stretches of corn fields, pine, and deer further served as a potent reminder of home and the people therein. Indiana would start to become my home away from home. As it turns out, I found I had family in Terre Haute, IN, whom I had never met prior to my move. How bout that!

At the edge of this beehive of activity was the trauma 1 rooms where everyone would coagulate and jump over one another to ready for whatever may roll into the room—all hands-on deck. As mid-level, you were in charge of the physical exam, many times shouting out your findings over the chatter and superfluous noise when conducting an evaluation. There is a very systematic way in which you retrieve and evaluate patients (according to the ATLS) who have undergone severe trauma. The surgical resident was charged with conducting the evaluation orderly and clearly without lapse in communicating the findings.

Don't get me wrong; I was not unsupervised. And you patients out there concerned that you are being treated by a bunch of kids barely able to stand alone on their "doctor" training wheels, do not fret. Every decision is cleared by the attending doctor within academic centers. Also, something I learned very early in residency is that someone is always watching. Always.

As residents mature, we are given the responsibility to evaluate medical students. I quickly noticed how much information I could glean from just observing a medical student from afar, unbeknownst to them. Many

37

evaluations actually came from aspects extraneous to any conversations we ever had but their interactions with patients which I had observed passively. That's how you know if someone will be a good doctor, what they do when no one is watching. I then realized that I must've been similarly scrutinized in medical school. Heed, medical students!

As I reminisced upon the scene from the vantage point of a small oasis of crackers and some ancient machine stationed in the middle of the ED that produced a lead-tinged hot liquid remotely resembling coffee, I took a mental note of the constant calamity. The stress, the work. The ludicrous characters you treated. The friendships forged amongst colleagues and superiors. They say that you become a doctor after four years of medical school. I truly became a doctor after one month as a second-year on Trauma nights at Methodist Hospital.

The heart of the fool is in his mouth, but the mouth of the wise man is in his heart.
Benjamin Franklin, Poor Richard, 1733

Yes, the Emergency Department could be a charming place where many a resident sees much professional growth, but the ED was not why I wanted to go into the medical field. Despite my early interest in being a good ole country Doc making house calls in southern Georgia, I wished to use my hands; I wanted to be a surgeon. Specifically, I wanted to work on hearts. Once I arrived at that conclusion, all my efforts from thereon were geared toward the practice and preparation to meet that end. Everything in life became superfluous if it were not to, directly or indirectly, somehow prepare me for the next step. One of my fellow cardiothoracic residents would often remind me, "The hardest thing about heart surgery is getting to the point where you can DO heart surgery." Of course, stated in jest, not all that wrong either.

At the University of Florida, my alma mater, I recall a lecture in medical school given by Dr. Thomas Beaver during my first year on the emerging technologies of heart surgery. Dr. Beaver would go on to be the Chief Cardiothoracic surgeon and a continued advocate for my career and health, as short as it would become. After the lecture, I inquired as to any way to become more involved with heart surgery, whether it be research or departmental events. "Why don't you drop by my office? Will we talk about it? In the meantime, feel free to drop by any OR! There's always someone operating." I can recall precisely what seat I was seated in when I received that invitation, top-right section. First-year, the first six months of medical school rather, I was already witnessing heart surgery. My excitement could not be contained.

Within a month's time, I was in Dr. Tomas Martin's operating room. Dr. Martin's upbeat attitude was as springy as the supported shoes he wore while operating providing support for his marathons standing unfatigued for hours on end. He offered a warm welcome into this hallowed ground where thousands of patients have greeted the skillful strokes of his surgeon's steel. Walking on eggshells hyperaware not to contaminate anything adorned in blue, I tentatively announced my presence in the room expecting only to observe.

"Scrub in," he declared in his shrill one-of-a-kind voice. The problem was that I had never scrubbed in before. Although, I had only reviewed the steps ad nauseam. My insecurity most have been written on my face despite the surgical mask. Fortunately, the staff at UF are some of the kindest people to work with, and a scrub tech politely walked me through my first scrub with blue kid gloves. After spinning me around and smacking on the last layer, I slowly approached the operative field where I could barely make out the heart squeezing within the chest cavity.

"Put your hands on the blue," Dr. Martin said referring to the sterile drapes over the entire patient. Gazing up at the monitor and back down, he had already gotten done with the case and was coming off the cardiopulmonary bypass machine, sometimes referred to as the pump. Of course, I had no idea that was happening at that time. The heart began to enter a strange rhythm, and he readied the paddles to deliver a shock. Hearts often encounter arrhythmias following a pump run when they have been kept cold to preserve the myocardial tissue.

Before delivering the shock, he asked, "What rhythm is that?" I hadn't the slightest; I still hadn't recovered from the acute mystification of witnessing an actively beating heart within the chest. An actual beating heart was in front of me! Being my first four months of medical school, we wouldn't encounter the subject of cardiology until the spring. In other words, I didn't know enough to come up with a stupid answer. Staring up at the cardiac monitor recording the squiggly lines, I tried to discern what these ancient hieroglyphics could mean. Despite all efforts to think of something clever, I remained silent as to not reveal my ignorance in full form.

Too late. The fact that I was even looking at the monitor was enough. The heart was right in front of me. All I had to do was look down. Even

40

under direct observation of the heart, I still had absolutely no clue the rate and rhythm. "A-fib!" he said, short for atrial fibrillation. He grabbed the pedals and shocked the heart right back into normal sinus rhythm.

After a few more minutes of normal cardiac activity, he began to skillfully remove all the octopus-like heparin-coated tubing from the chest, components of the heart-lung machine, a cardiac surgeon's best friend. After closing the sternum, he allowed me to close skin with his assistants and resident at the end of the operation. From then on, I was hooked. Thereafter, every waking minute in my education was just another step in preparing for my eventual profession of being a heart surgeon. Everything henceforward was just whatever I had to do to get back into that cardiac OR. My remaining years of medical school would involve bench research in Dr. Beaver's lab despite a full course load, attending conferences, and sneaking away from other rotations to jump into the OR, if only for a few hours unbeknownst to my other course directors. Without fear of respite, I was addicted.

Early, I would begin reading cardiac surgical texts despite the lack of having secured my place in residency or having passed the competency tests. I didn't care; I needed to know everything about heart surgery. I devoured cardiac critical care manuals having completed detailed outlines of both Paul Marino's ICU care text and Bojar's Cardiac critical care before I took my step 2 exam. Step exams are competency tests one must pass before practicing medicine in America. Gone are the days when you can show up with a large leather briefcase filled with snake oils and elixirs. These two books I highly recommend to any prospective resident.

I stopped attending class because I could get much more work done and cover more material when I studied on my own. My penultimate goal was to achieve the highest test scores I could manage so that I might be considered for a very competitive surgical residency, hopefully, one which employed an integrated tract that truncates the time spent in residency. These programs are a mix between general surgery and cardiothoracic fellowship which streamlined the production of the waning CT surgeon numbers nationwide. My thinking was: Why would I waste time in class filled with the presentations of some Ph.D.'s superfluous research when the only thing I truly needed was to perform well on the test? If I could cover more material and then some, why not take my education into my own hands?

My resident idol, Dr. Erol Belli, was a cardiothoracic fellow at the time I was a medical student. I found that he too played college soccer in Florida: I at Stetson University, him at the University of South Florida. Belli was fearless; I recall his hands moving swiftly around the heart manipulating carefully the heparin-coated tubing extending on and off the bypass machine. His athleticism and skill from the soccer field clearly translated to the OR which only served to motivate me much that much more.

Not to mention, his endurance as a CT fellow was unmatched as both fellows were worked to utter exhaustion despite not having slept for a matter of days. Despite fatigue, his positive attitude pierced through his bloodshot eyes; his endurance in performance was no doubt from his experience on the soccer pitch. Coincidentally, he had known my soccer coach, Logan T.

Fleck at Stetson University, my alma mater, when he coached at USF. My belief in coincidence was starting to wane.

Therefore, when he asked me to close the superficial layers as a medical student by myself, I did not want to disappoint. "You think you can do this on your own? I don't wanna have to come back here in the middle of the night because you did a shotty closure." I felt so honored that he would trust me enough to give that job to a medical student. "Absolutely!" I had been practicing knot tying and suturing so I was prepared.

In sailing o'er life's ocean wide, Your heart should be your only guide;
With summer sea and favouring wind Yourself in port you'll surely find.
W. S. Gilbert, Ruddigore. Act i.

I would go on to conferences to present research at my home institutions and away. I was honored to have the chance to go to Seattle to take part in the member for a day program hosted by the American Association for Thoracic Surgery (AATS) with my mentor being Sarah Shumway MD, cardiac surgeon in Minneapolis last I heard. Both residents and medical students could sign up for the program; I had already paid to go on a cruise with some of my best friends. However, I had been given the chance to see and meet one of the major players in the field; I could not pass it up.

After traveling across the country to Seattle, I walked to meet Dr. Shumway at the entrance of her hotel near the first Starbucks in the nation. She looked at me with a touch of bewilderment. She was taken aback by my youthful, Doogie Howser characteristics which had yet to be weathered by the onslaught of chemotherapy and radiation in the coming years. "What year of residency are you in?" she probed looking at me inquisitively. "I'm in medical school," I said bashfully, not quite understanding what she was

43

trying to get at. "Oh, that makes sense then; you look far too young to already be a resident."

We went on to the large expose' of emerging cardiac and thoracic technologies in a large conference hall orchestrated by the AATS. Everything appeared to have been sourced from one of the Star Wars movies. Walking through the many stands and kiosks, Dr. Shumway educated me on what the many devices that she used in her practice as well as ones that she didn't. Following our tour through the showroom, we attended a few lectures where people came from all over the world to exchange ideas and research. Between attending the AATS convention and Dr. Shumway, I experienced just how big the cardiothoracic world was, and it was exciting to see what my future might hold.

Invigorated by the day's excitement, I had dinner with Dr. Shumway and her fellows who had accompanied her. As a guest and youngest in the group, I had little to add to the conversation between her and her tight-knit team. Dr. Shumway turns to me and remarks upon the accelerated program I would eventually be accepted into. At this point, there was, and still is, much apprehension about these programs.

She brought up a very good point, "I am a little hesitant about those programs. You learn so much in general surgery, and how are you so sure, at such a young age, that you want to do CT surgery?" I thought back to my feelings at the Agrirama in South Georgia. "Another issue is that you, at a young age, will eventually be making some critical decisions, life and death decisions, as a cardiac surgeon. And much of that knowledge comes from life experience, not any textbook."

She was dead right. I heeded her advice well; slowing down and enjoying the process is what I needed. I had canceled a trip with my best friends throwing away a few hundred dollars to attend the AATS meeting in Seattle. As a medical student, cash was in short supply; I needed to press the brakes and approach life with a different attitude. Lift the sole focus on cardiothoracic surgery and remove the blinders on all other aspects of medicine, not to mention life.

Indeed, if you go too fast, you miss things. For example, I had no idea until I came back from Seattle that Dr. Shumway's father was the guy who pioneered heart transplantation. Norman Shumway MD was an iconoclast and pioneer, to say the least. Dr. Beaver chuckled at my ignorance on my return, and rightly so. What a historical figure so vital to the history of the field with his daughter carrying on his legacy in Minnesota! Thereafter, I sought to abolish my ignorance of the great history of cardiothoracic surgery so as to not to be found wanting again.

Towards the end of medical school after having passed all my qualifying exams, it became time to enact Dr. Shumway's advice. Subsequently, I halted all major studies in my last six months. Residency interviews were approaching, nonetheless. With the plethora of destinations on my travel schedule searching for the right fit, it was high time to kick back and enjoy.

1 .Phillips, D.P. and G.E. Barker, A July spike in fatal medication errors: a possible effect of new medical residents. J Gen Intern Med, 2010. 25(8): p. 774-9.

4

Sleep Paralysis

I could a tale unfold whose lightest word Would harrow up thy soul, freeze thy young blood, Make thy two eyes, like stars, start from their spheres, Thy knotted and combined locks to part And each particular hair to stand on end, Like quills upon the fretful porpentine.
Shakespeare, Hamlet. Act i, sc. 5, 1. 15. (1600)

I couldn't move. Frozen, my eyes climbed the terraced support of the bunked bed immediately above me. Still getting accustomed to my new living arrangements as welcoming and loving as they were, they remained foreign under less than desirable circumstances. Although the futon was mostly lacking meaningful lumbar support, my new bed was surprisingly comfortable despite its rigidity. Since, I have preferred a stiffer mattress finding comfort in its resolute constitution; however, not in the context of being immovable in my acute state of petrification beyond measure.

Close to 3 a.m., the fabled witching hour was upon me. Sleeping had been a struggle since the move, that night and the many preceding it. Drifting in and out of consciousness never receiving a fortifying night's rest, the sleep debt made me ill-prepared for the constant challenges awaiting my next days having moved to a brand-new school system in an unfamiliar state. I hadn't spoken to my dad in almost six months after moving to Jacksonville, Fl. The summer showers of northeast Florida at the beaches competed in frequency with the constant ebbs and flows of guilt that had consumed me for months.

Had I done the right thing? What if the relationship with my dad was irreparable? When would I see my little sister and my stepmom again?

Still immobile. My heart began beating louder and louder. I could hear the percussions in my eardrums, like a set of tribal drums. The ice in my muscles hardened still.

The move was not without much thought and deliberation on my part. I had moved to a new school system at Allen D. Nease High School, where Tim Tebow went to high school, also where their soccer team had won two state championships and positioned to win another. They had nearly all their starters back in that year; we were poised for a three-peat for the school. Moreover, the travel team was top class, perfect for me to get as much exposure as I needed in the recruitment from a college team.

Finally, I was positioned to compete properly. Perhaps I would discover the true extent of my abilities prior to embarking on collegiate ball. Indeed, both exciting and anxiety-provoking. However, what made matters worse between school and club ball, my presence was unwelcomed. Trifling the waters of long-held bonds amongst teammates who had played together since grade school, I disrupted their status quo. The assumption that their positions were safe without the need to compete was overturned. I refused to be outworked; it wasn't long before some unhappy players were riding the bench.

I couldn't help but be reminded of the childhood jealousy leered upon me from fellow teammates not a decade ago reverberated in my current setting. The result would be the same: further alienation from the team and other social circles. They would go as far as not to pass the ball despite my incessant pleas even when I was the obvious option.

The ceiling fan was oscillating making a slight ticking noise as if registering its revolutions. I still couldn't move.

Academically, I was struggling. Florida has some of the best schools in the nation, especially in Jacksonville. Many students had not 4.0 GPAs but 5.0 GPAs as they were enrolled in International Baccalaureate courses far superseding any rigor of academic discipline this dumb country boy had been exposed. I didn't even know what 'IB' meant until I arrived in Florida. I had been salutatorian in a 150-student class in Georgia. Now, I was barely ranked top 50 in a class of 500 graduates, and I was lucky to be ranked that high. A block off my ego tumbled into the salty Atlantic.

During calculus, we were given daily quizzes as warmups and extra credit. The problems I encountered didn't look like any Calculus I had ever seen. I had already completed the course but was forced to retake it due to the interstate move. I suppose they lacked confidence in the education I had received previously. And rightly so! Staring in bewilderment at the problems that lay before me, my confidence imploded before class even began. Each minute of the morning quiz, I sank deeper into my seat as that block became an iceberg breaking off a glacier into the dark waters of inferiority. Drowning in self-doubt, what have I gotten myself into?

My well-meaning southern hospitality didn't seem to resonate well with the beach population of northeast Florida. My thick southern draw was met with odd looks and taunts which forced me to betray my diction accordingly to avoid the mockery. The good ol' southern boy persona was not well-

49

received and drove me deeper into a guarded shell further adding to the stress. Despite my early efforts, I had no friends. During lunch, I would wander through the honeycombed outside hallways biding time before my next scheduled class or adding another workout to my schedule due to boredom.

Tick. Tick. Tick. Tick. Still immobile, unable to move an inch other than my eyes darting in all directions looking for some outside stimulation to pull me out of this trance. Heart pounding, deepening with each stroke, an unseen ominous presence crept into my room.

The transition was not without some perks; I had totally hit the lottery as far as stepdads go. He had been a track coach at Nease High School and coached track part-time at the University of North Florida, allowing me access to all the athletic facilities. I needed to be faster. Track was a way to work on my running form which served me in all forms of future athleticism, especially in collegiate soccer. If I wasn't the most skilled player, I was sure going to be the best conditioned. Moreover, my stepdad adores my mom and has the utmost respect for my dad; what more could I have asked for?

As my fear heightened, a heavyweight fell across my chest as if an ironclad rod was being pressed obliquely squeezing the desperate air from my lungs. Breathing continued to labor as I felt hot breath across my face. Still, I couldn't move.

Despite all the setbacks and constant battering of my ego, the isolation and rapid change in life circumstances provided me with an unwavering focus on my future. I had no choice but to trudge forward through whatever

50

personal pain I was experiencing, knowing that these things were only temporary. This remained only a steppingstone. After all, I had chosen this. For better or worse, I would need to see this through to the end—college ball or bust. If I wasn't all in before the move, I was all in now. Indeed, I had something to prove to myself and everyone else that this move was no fool's errand.

Paralyzed, the fear only intensified as the seconds passed. I then remembered the scene from the movie Kill Bill when Uma Thurman had woken up from a coma and couldn't walk. She hoisted herself up into the backseat of a man's truck who had done unsightly things to her while she was comatose. She sat there for hours telling her big toe to move. After several hours, her big toe wiggled, and she was able to restore her motor control for the rest of her body.

So that's what I did—the Kill Bill technique. And within seconds, I snapped out of this witch's trance. I had just experienced my first episode of sleep paralysis or SP, and it wouldn't be the last. Frightened from this first experience of SP, I was unable to return to sleep. The entire next day, I walked those honeycombed arranged hallways as a brainless zombie.

Fear is an instructor of great sagacity, and the herald of all revolutions. *Emerson, Essays, First Series: Compensation.*

After researching my experience, I found this to be a relatively common phenomenon with online forums teeming with frightening anecdotes resembling my own. SP is defined as a "transient state of conscious, involuntary, immobility occurring when falling asleep or waking up. Most commonly, SP occurs when lying in the supine position and transitioning from awake to asleep.[1-4] The overall prevalence is reported between 6 to 40% depending on the population you are referencing.

In a study including over 36,000 subjects reviewing over 35 empirical studies, the overall prevalence of SP was gauged to be 7.6% of the general population but likely underreported due to social stigma or shame [3]. However, higher rates are noted in the college-aged and psychiatric populations reaching incidences up to 30% or more.[3] Additionally, they are often accompanied by hypnogogic, *while falling asleep,* and hypnopompic, *while waking up,* hallucinations. Quite bizarre.

What's more bizarre than the tonic immobility while being fully conscious of your surroundings is the feeling of something evil or ominous lurking beyond the safe confines of your bedroom. One is overwhelmed with an almost irrational fear of someone, or something, readying to infringe upon your most intimate positions during sleep, commonly with heart up and arms out. An *intruder experience* is a distinguishing characteristic along with the *intense fear* felt by the victim upon initiation of the maligned stupor.[5] Admittedly, the few times I've experienced SP, I refused to go back to sleep.

Researchers have found SP to be associated with poor sleep, frequent nighttime disruptions, and, most relevant to my case, anxiety.[6] More frightening than the experiences themselves and the cycle of sleep deprivations which followed was the similarity in the reports. Understand that people with no real connection to each other would report comparable, if not the same, experience! What did these people have in common? And why were they experienced *cross-culturally?*

Olunu et al. conducted an exhaustive review of the many manifestations of SP. It would seem that SP knows no bounds as it has been noted commonly among African Americans, Cambodians, Canadians, Egyptians, Germans, Iranians, Japanese, Koreans, Mexicans, United Kingdom; the list goes on and on. Of course, this phenomenon is described differently depending on your geography, but all the accounts share a central theme.

For example, this nighttime intruder or incubus, *male form*, or succubus, *female*, is referred to as *'khyal'* in Cambodian lore which is associated with immobility and hallucinations. In Italy, in the Abruzzo region, they refer to them as the *'Pandofeche.'* The *'Pandofeche'* attack when its victim would be lying upward and would immobilize the individual by lying on his or her chest [5]. Mexicans report a dead body lying on top of them [5, 7] creating a feeling of suffocation. In Newfoundland, it is said to be an *'old hag'* who is thought to have had intercourse with the devil and could put you under her charm [8].

In the southeastern United States, where I am located, it is said to be a witch riding a broomstick while sitting on your chest. I saw no witch that particular night, but I would see that *'old hag'* several years later during my undergraduate studies.[8] Weighed down with a heavy course load as I was a Molecular Biology major and Chemistry minor at Stetson University just thirty minutes west of Daytona Beach, Fl, I was also recruited to play on their division 1 soccer team. My Florida gamble to move had paid off after all, and I was playing soccer at the next level. We would travel packed in buses for many hours getting minimal rest in shotty hotels prior to away games. My coach was well aware of my aspirations to be a physician, so he expected and required me to have a higher GPA than my teammates. If I didn't meet my personally prescribed goal, I didn't play.

Due to my heavy course load and the rigor thereof, the only way I could adequately cover the missed material during the travel season was to spend all-nighters studying before laboratory practicals and written tests. My professors would be forced to have me clean up and exit after my having spent the struggling waning last few hours of the night catching up on material the typical student had ample time to cover. Smelling of formaldehyde, coffee, and the remnants of some invertebrate freshly dissected, I would stumble back to my room after an early morning exam. My three roommates were what you would expect from a multicultural *futbol* team: a Mexican, Colombian, and a German/Peruvian/American. The latter would claim homage to whatever was most convenient in conversation. *He'll get a kick out of that*; he's my best friend, so he won't mind the good-natured ribbing. He did speak fluent German; so I'll give him that, but he's from Virginia.

I digress. You can imagine the quality of rest I would receive, however. After an early morning exam before I could even open my door, a barrage of Reggaeton music could be felt through the dormitories' old, tiled floors. Half-awake, I'd walk in to unleash all the intensity of a FIFA soccer game being played on the XBOX. My roommates' days were just starting; I hadn't been to bed in 24 hours. And it would only be another few before I had another class. Constantly sleep-deprived and stretching myself too thin, my performance on the soccer pitch also began to suffer. Convinced that I wasn't in shape, I would run extra sprints after practice punishing myself

54

for the lack of being in soccer shape. However, I was one of the fittest on the team. In retrospect, what I needed was rest.

As you have probably suspected, my next episode of SP would quickly follow my first year at Stetson. The stress and pressure I placed on myself to perform and my chronic lack of sleep served as fodder for another paranormal experience. An analysis of the risk factors predisposing to SP's overall incidence, I had all the kindling for the fire: supine position while sleeping with interpolated disturbed sleep-wake cycles, general stress and lack of sleep, and a belief in the supernatural. I was raised in Presbyterian and Southern Baptist Churches. [2, 5] The triggers were set. All that was needed was a spark.

We were traveling for soccer yet again. My memory is hazy as to the precise location, either South Carolina or Tennessee. Unfortunately, traveling forced me to bring work on the road. My course load wouldn't permit otherwise. Due to my poor tolerance of motion sickness, I was forced to sleep on the bus, skip out on team dinners, and study in the hotel. The welcomed quiet of an empty hotel room provided a foreign safehouse for me to digest the vast material required for me to gain proficiency. It also led to much-needed self-reflection. Unhappy with my lack of playing time, I, in turn, found comfort in my studies. One aspect of my life that no one else could touch where I had complete reign over performance. There was a direct 1:1 relationship between effort and reward.

My best friend and roommate for four years, Kai, the multicultural guy from Virginia, brought me some parcels of food from the team dinner. We are complete opposites in most respects, if not all. Myself religious, him agnostic, the best I can describe. Good ol' southern boy versus well-traveled hippie. Muscular and defined versus wiry and flexible. In the future, I would go to medical school, and he went to India to train under a Yogi master. The massive chasm of our differences was only equaled by our love and respect for each other and each other's point of view. We were the direct antithesis of each other.

As much as we differed, we worked incredibly well together. We composed a musical rendition of Telemachus' dilemma in the Odyssey, him on the guitar and me reciting our constructed monologue in one of our elective classes at SU. We would go to trivia nights and utterly wipe the floor clean with the competition. We had a knack for knowing just what each other was thinking. Guessing games? A resounding 'Donnie Brasco,' forget about it! You wouldn't stand a chance.

And just like most roommates, we were never shy to play practical jokes on our unsuspecting roommates. Flushing the toilet while taking a shower rapidly changing the temperature from warm to icy cold, for instance. Taking all the towels from the bathroom or rearranging the furniture within our dormitories while the others were stuck in class are just a couple of examples. Much of our perpetrating acts are too graphic to cite but know that it was never a dull moment living with four idiots, me included.

Therefore, I felt no surprise when I felt a slight tug at my hip nudging me towards the center of my hotel bed while attempting to sleep after a late-night study session. Kai and I were usually paired with one another while traveling, naturally, we were roommates when not traveling as well. Immediately, I was convinced Kai was just trying to freak me out. When I opened my eyes, however, I found Kai fast asleep on the adjacent bed. Confused, I shifted my gaze from Kai to the hovering apparition above me. A dark shadowy figure dripping wet with shaggy black hair was gripping me by the waist attempting to squeeze the air out of me. For some reason, I wasn't as frightened as in past episodes, only confused about its purpose. Instead, I was pissed that this old hag had woken me up. I was dead tired and had a game the next day. Once this incubus realized its loss of power over me, it vanished. *I can't discount a prayer or two.*

A few more episodes would occur with far less intensity until they were no longer. But I would reencounter the subject in another fashion during medical school attending a lecture exploring the spectrum of sleep disorders. I would find that *parasomnias* included disorders of arousal, rapid eye movement, or *REM,* disorders, and non-REM sleep disorders, including sleep paralysis, night terrors, among others [9]. During REM sleep, you naturally enter a state of paralysis so as not to act out your dreams putting yourself in danger or wandering into the neighbor's flower beds, or both. If you lose the ability to properly paralyze yourself in your sleep-wake cycles, you may have an issue with sleepwalking. The antithesis of sleepwalking is known as sleep paralysis, SP, where you maintain all consciousness but have no motor control. No motor control is fear-mongering in and of itself.

SP has plagued the human mind for centuries. The earliest mention of SP can be cited as far back as the late 1st century BC recorded by Themison of Laodicea, the founder of the Methodic School of  Medicine and even further in Chinese history extending back to 400 BC. Perhaps the most detailed description came much later during the 10th century AD with Akhawayni's *Hidayat al-mata'allemin fi al-tibb,* a voluminous work on heath, wellness, and physiology, not to mention the treatment of disease. Within this work, there is a whole section dedicated to SP. [5, 10]

Many throughout history would not see the significance of SP attributing its occurrence as the imbalance of gastric juices as the famed Galen contended in the 1st century AD, a Greek physician, surgeon, and philosopher among many other trades and fields of study.[10, 11] However, a swiss artist would soon capture the imagination of the *pop culture* of the time producing a detailed oil painting of a young lady suffering from SP. As featured, the incubus sits upon the victim's chest while her arms and legs are in a defenseless posture utterly open to the whims of the unwelcome nocturnal intruder. The weight of the incubus magnifies with each inspiration pressing on the diaphragm inciting a choking sensation and fear.

58

The incubus peers over at the voyeur of the scene with a disdained leer as the shadow of horns are outlined in the red tapestry in the backdrop suggesting its realism not just mere conjuring. There are insinuations of sexual violation in keeping with the myth of the incubus. The horse, or mare, in the background, added later, was meant to represent sleepers' torment.[12]

The Nightmare was painted by Henry Fuseli in 1781, who was an ordained minister in the Swiss Evangelical Reformed Church.[12] This portraiture, among its many renditions, left a demonstrable impact on the human psyche inspiring art and literature for hundreds of years. For instance, it provided inspiration to the writers Erasmus Darwin (Charles Darwin's grandfather) and Edgar Allen Poe, not surprisingly. Why has it had such a profound impact on our imagination inciting fear during unsuspecting slumbers? Moreover and again, why is this experience seen cross-culturally in people having had no direct contact with each other?[5]

Of course, there are some clever scientific explanations for the manifestations of SP along with the full spectrum of sleep disorders. As mentioned previously, SP is a form of a REM sleep disorder where instead of being appropriately unconscious and unaware of your nightly paralysis occurring during REM sleep, you are instead wholly aware. You lie motionless and helpless until you snap out of it. Researchers have identified the brain pathways involved and have suggested the culprit regions.[13] At-risk populations, like the mentally ill and medical students, have abnormally high rates of occurrence. [5, 14]

The question remains, why? Why does it manifest in a similar way with similar reports? Across space and time? A shared distant memory, perhaps? Is it a shared defense mechanism keeping us safe within our caves away from the lions, tigers, and bears that may lurk during the night, a protective mechanism for our species? Or is it a cross-section between a biological basis of behavior and a glimpse into a phenomenon more preternatural and abstruse? Proof of something outside our bounds of accepted reality?

Give to faith the things which belong to Faith.
Bacon. Advancement of Learning. Bk. ii.

Located in Deland, Florida, Stetson University (SU) is a gorgeous, quaint institution thirty minutes west of Daytona Beach. Before its conception, Deland Hall stood in the heat of middle Florida amongst the tall palms of campus providing much-needed shade to escape from the sweltering summer afternoons. First opened on October 13th, 1884, it stands as the oldest educational building in Florida remaining in active use. In fact, the first lecture was given a year earlier at the local Baptist church before the official school being built. (https://www.stetson.edu/other/about/history.php)

Despite its history steeped in Protestantism, over the subsequent century, SU's roots would become rot with, for lack of better words, *woke college culture,* encouraging an uncompromising sense of secularism without regard to tradition and values that had long shaped its history of success. Not that I am in favor of an overly religious education, one should have a well-rounded worldview, but not at the defamation of another.

60

Flowing down from the educational ivory towers, a pompous disregard for how the past has shaped the future has seemed to have gripped academia. Such is apparent in the current trends of belief. More and more, we find ourselves in a crisis of belief and faith.

National data supports this trend. Surveys funded by the Public Religion Research Institute, or PRRI, located in Washington, DC, tracked religious affiliation from 1972 to 2016 recognizing a dramatic increase in those 'unaffiliated' persons around 1991. The most precipitous increase was found in young adults: nearly four out of every ten (39%, 18-29 years of age) individuals claim no religious affiliation compared to only 10% in 1986.[15] A difference of almost thirty percent! This was mainly experienced in white Protestants and Catholics rather than non-White and non-Christian counterparts, and 12% more common in children of divorce. These trends are not promising for the future of a nation whose ideals depend on the inherent morality of its constituents.

Indeed, my religious and existential crisis occurred during my time at Stetson. I had held true to my strong religious tendencies up until about my sophomore or junior years in college. Growing up, I had gone to vacation bible school, multiple church retreats, attended church every Sunday, and gave to charity. Even though I attended a Baptist church, that quintessential Catholic guilt reigned powerfully in my mind steering my moral compass left and right. I felt a resounding guilt (*there's that word again*) when I had done something wrong. For example, when I pulled the fire alarm at school as a child, maybe 8 or 9 years old. Instantly my daring modus operandi quickly changed into my head in my hands begging for forgiveness from the supreme being before the teachers had a chance to arrive. Looking back, I cannot stop laughing. I maintained a mischievous streak but nothing to call any serious concerns for delinquency.

Back at Stetson, I had fallen on what I would perceive as hard times. *Hardly.* My girlfriend at the time had broken up with me; to add insult to injury, I would find out that she had been cheating on me. My performance on the pitch was less than I had hoped, receiving minimal playing time despite my best efforts. I got mononucleosis, also known as the 'kissing disease,' which is more commonly contracted by single people, no surprise there. Mononucleosis can cause splenic rupture in athletes of contact sports excluding me from practicing for a couple of weeks. [16] As soon as I returned to practice, I was met with a minimal head injury leaving me unable to practice. That was a rough couple of weeks, so I thought.

Meanwhile, my relationship with God was suffering. I had begun taking courses on Islam and Christianity's history challenging my fragile and narrow worldview. I would find that many books of the Bible were struck out at the council of Nicaea in 325 AD (a second was held in 787 AD) in an effort to unify the Christian canon and clear up conflicting messages in doctrine. But I wondered, how could one rule out the legitimacy of a consecrated book of the bible with absolution of authority?

For example, the Infancy Gospel of Thomas, a so-called heretical book of the Bible, describes a miracle that Jesus conducted as a child.[17] Most, if not all, stories of Jesus which are accepted by mainstream Christianity are well beyond His childhood. Further, I discovered the plethora of disagreements on the nature of Christ compelling and thought-provoking as

62

they were, but, in the end, unsettling. Was Jesus human or divine? If He was first man then made divine, when did His transition occur? At birth? Or at His baptism? During His crucifixion as he held humankind's sin upon his shoulders? What about the prophet Muhammed? Was his message less legitimate just because it came later? In fact, what about all other religions? Were these people doomed even though they were never exposed to Christianity? That hardly seems fair or just. Clearly, my head was spinning.

Subsequently, I would seek council from one of my professors who taught religious studies who was previously a preacher for well over 30 years. He was the obvious choice for counsel for these matters. "How do you teach this stuff if you know all the arguments that can be made against it?" I eagerly inquired. "You can effectively punch holes in the logic of these teachings. Certainly, over several hundreds of years, the true meaning of the teachings is likely to be subject to gross misinterpretations, fueled by ignorance or ineptitude, from personal desires or false teachings; how can one be confident in any of this stuff?" My professor reassured me that this was not uncommon for someone to have an existential crisis like this at my age, especially if someone had a potent religious upbringing, which was comforting to hear, in a way. He continued, "You must search for the true kernel of what can be distilled from these teachings. Realize that God does not exist. He is beyond our understanding. God just simply is."

I walked away more confused than I walked into his office. This idea I would ponder for many years to come. "God just is…?" I was happy to be at least questioning things as I maintained I might achieve a more profound respect and reverence for our understanding of God. *Such wouldn't come for some time.*

Religion is like the fashion. One man wears his doublet slashed, another laced, another plain; but every man has a doublet. So every man has his religion. We differ about the trim-ming.
John Selden. Table-talk: Religion.

In the meantime, I would synthesize a clever, but coarse explanation of the nature of God and existence which combined some elements of my newly acquired scientific background and appreciation for theology. Note that according to the 1st law of thermodynamics, energy or matter in a closed system is conserved or constant; and cannot be created nor destroyed. Subsequently, I posed that there was a central balance and dichotomy in everything. Look around. There is no shortage of examples. Sky and earth. Fire and water. Roots and shoots. In organic chemistry, an example is the concept of chirality in which stereoisomers of compounds are mirror images of each other. This idea in action can be understood by Le Chatelier's principle, all chemical reactions move to a state of thermodynamic equilibrium, or a relaxed energy state, at the expense of entropy or disorder.

The most straightforward rendition of this idea is a positive and negative charge. When positive and negative charges meet, it yields neutrality, or nothing. Existence is, thus, the stretching out of these charges to allow for matter to manifest. Taken as a whole, however, we are a zero-sum game. The mechanism of this stretching, the force that allows for existence, is what we understand as God. Many people have different modes of appreciating and reflecting on that reality, Christianity, Buddhism, Islam, etc. In essence, we are everything, and we are nothing. This seemed to agree with what my professor/preacher was discussing, "God doesn't exist; God just is."

Suffice it to stay that I had fallen from conventional belief. However, I didn't think I was in direct contradiction either. I found this to be a happy compromise marrying science and religion in a neat package that wouldn't torment me at night. Moreover, as long as you do right by people, what was the real harm anyway?

I would continue not getting the well-deserved playing time I wanted in college despite my best efforts and performing well on a PDL (Premier Development League) the prior summer. Subsequently, in my Junior year when a freshman started over me who was clearly not as skilled, I decided to quit soccer. However, other things went into that decision, not just my discontent with the coach's management. I needed to focus on the MCAT (Medical College Admissions Test). Even though my dreams of playing soccer at a higher level were dying, my determination to become a doctor was quite alive.

Quitting a game that had given me so much inspiration and spurred me to go beyond what I thought were my physical limits brought me much sadness. But it was not without purpose. Never stagnant, I became involved in plant ecology research with my college mentor who would turn out to be a mentor for life, even throughout my cancer journey. She even accompanied me to a few doctors' appointments in the future. With her, we would revitalize the greenhouse on campus where we researched the *Passiflora incarnata,* more commonly known as the passionflower. Instead of soccer practice, I would take courses in preparation for the MCAT in conjunction with my college courses. Joined and eventually would be the president of AMSA (American Medical Student Association) chapter at Stetson. One of the most rewarding experiences was joining 'The Kilometer Kids,' a program teaching kids at a local school healthy eating and exercise habits. Indeed, I had no issue keeping myself busy.

After my hiatus from the soccer team, I was asked to rejoin my senior year. Having done well on my MCAT the summer between my junior and senior years, the clouds of uncertainty loomed not so ominous. After a memorable senior soccer season, all clouds parted when I was accepted into University of Florida's College of Medicine for the class of 2013 but not before I graduated Magna Cum Laude majoring in Molecular Biology and minoring in Chemistry at SU. I was honored by a biology departmental research award with my work with the Passionflower, which further reinforced my love for plants and medicine much like the country doc at the Agrirama a decade prior.

Beginning medical school in the fall of 2013, the quintessential college town of Gainesville, Fl is where I would call home for the next four years and where I'd experience some of the happiest years of my life. I would take long runs around the entire campus noting the moss-laden oaks and occasional willow trees casting refreshing shade along the sidewalk. Venturing past the bars in midtown, one could smell the beer and spirits lingering in the early morning humid air before the heat of the coming day would attempt to nullify the debauchery of the preceding evening. Turning on 34th street, I would march past the painted wall commemorating the five students who were murdered in cold blood in August of 1990. The perpetrator is not worthy of mentioning. I would cut through Shand's Hospital campus crossing the DNA bridge returning home, sometimes hurling alligators scattered around the campus warming in their sunbath.

During the fall, or football season, the entire city would be geared for game day, save me. The hectic activity on campus left a void of peace and solitude further downtown. The placid quiet that fell upon the surrounding town on gameday gave the sensation of being stuck in time. Any additional time that I spent studying on gameday, I imagined, was time that no one else had access giving me a friendly leg up on my competition. Indeed, a conjured mental edge gifted me with extra confidence. Crazy, I'd admit, but one step closer to being a cardiothoracic surgeon, yes.

The relationships made in medical school would have far-reaching effects yet to be seen, not the least of which included saving my life or providing the opportunity to write this account. My roommate, Michael, all throughout medical school, would have a vital role in making that happen. In fact, one of his recommendations would have an immense effect on my overall survival during treatment.

Near the conclusion of my time at UF, we were required to attend lectures from visiting professors to broaden our educational experience. One of the lectures at the McKnight Brain Institute right across the street from the medical school building discussed REM sleep disorders for which, as previously mentioned, I was well acquainted. The speaker described a study where they hired a police sketch artist to draw what a handful of patients described during their SP episodes. These people didn't know each other; the only thing in common was perhaps being from the same region.

The study created a composite drawing from the collection of descriptions of what was observed during SP. They projected what was described on the large PowerPoint screen leaving me with chills on its unveiling. The gnarled incubus apparition appeared vividly depicted on the widescreen, identical to Henry Fuseli's, *The Nightmare,* staring right through me.

Of course, I had to ask at the lecture's conclusion, "What do you think about the cultural and pathological implications of having a shared experience despite these study participants being blinded to one another?" I wouldn't receive a satisfying answer that day or any day following. Probably because I already knew my answer, and it was comforting. If I had experienced a manifestation of *evil,* rest assured its antithesis is alive and well, *good.* Sleeping was never easier.

1. Nan'no, H., et al., *A neurophysiological study of sleep paralysis in narcoleptic patients.* Electroencephalogr Clin Neurophysiol, 1970. **28**(4): p. 382-90.
2. Cheyne, J.A., *Situational factors affecting sleep paralysis and associated hallucinations: position and timing effects.* J Sleep Res, 2002. **11**(2): p. 169-77.
3. Sharpless, B.A. and J.P. Barber, *Lifetime prevalence rates of sleep paralysis: a systematic review.* Sleep Med Rev, 2011. **15**(5): p. 311-5.
4. Takeuchi, T., et al., *Factors related to the occurrence of isolated sleep paralysis elicited during a multi-phasic sleep-wake schedule.* Sleep, 2002. **25**(1): p. 89-96.
5. Olunu, E., et al., *Sleep Paralysis, a Medical Condition with a Diverse Cultural Interpretation.* Int J Appl Basic Med Res, 2018. **8**(3): p. 137-142.
6. Sharpless, B.A., *A clinician's guide to recurrent isolated sleep paralysis.* Neuropsychiatr Dis Treat, 2016. **12**: p. 1761-7.
7. Jiménez-Genchi, A., et al., *Sleep paralysis in adolescents: the 'a dead body climbed on top of me' phenomenon in Mexico.* Psychiatry Clin Neurosci, 2009. **63**(4): p. 546-9.
8. Ness, R.C., *The Old Hag phenomenon as sleep paralysis: a biocultural interpretation.* Cult Med Psychiatry, 1978. **2**(1): p. 15-39.
9. Wills, L. and J. Garcia, *Parasomnias: epidemiology and management.* CNS Drugs, 2002. **16**(12): p. 803-10.
10. Golzari, S.E., et al., *Sleep paralysis in medieval Persia - the Hidayat of Akhawayni (?-983 AD).* Neuropsychiatr Dis Treat, 2012. **8**: p. 229-34.
11. Nutton, V., *The fatal embrace: Galen and the history of ancient medicine.* Sci Context, 2005. **18**(1): p. 111-21.
12. Paulson, D.N. *Henry Fuseli, The Nightmare.* [oil on canvas] 2015 August 9, 2015 [cited 2021 October 18]; Available from: https://smarthistory.org/henry-fuseli-the-nightmare/.
13. Hishikawa, Y. and T. Shimizu, *Physiology of REM sleep, cataplexy, and sleep paralysis.* Adv Neurol, 1995. **67**: p. 245-71.
14. Fraigne, J.J., et al., *Mechanisms of REM sleep in health and disease.* Curr Opin Pulm Med, 2014. **20**(6): p. 527-32.

15. Robert P. Jones, D.C., Bestsy Cooper, and Rachel Lienesch, *Exodus: Why Americans are Leaving Religion-and Why They're Unlikely to Come Back.* Public Religion Research Institute (PRRI), 2016.

16. Balfour, H.H., Jr., S.K. Dunmire, and K.A. Hogquist, *Infectious mononucleosis.* Clin Transl Immunology, 2015. **4**(2): p. e33.

17. Assgaard, R., *The Childhood of Jesus: Decoding the Apocryphal Infancy Gospel of Thomas. .* 2011, Lutterworth Press Lutterworh Press pp. 255.

5

Cardiac Surgery or Bust!

Man is only truly great when he acts from the passions.
Benjamin Disraeli, Coningsby, Bk .iv, ch 13

The harsh winter wind bit my cheek as I stood upon my second-story stoop in the brisk early morning. An autumn-type glow emanated from the streetlamps sharing in the illuminating reflection of scurrying snow flurries too premature to take advantage of the coming daybreak. At the tail end of November, it was four-thirty in the morning in downtown Indianapolis on North Alabama street, and my southern bones were chattering against the wintry. I needed to get moving. I dared to brave running to work despite my cold intolerance and needed to get a move on if I was to make it to rounds. Before you Yanks scoff me, remember I hadn't owned a proper winter coat, or even gloves for that matter, the winter before. This was progress.

I had stashed all my toiletries in the call room at Methodist Hospital (MH). All that remained was peeling myself off my newly purchased down comforter, change, and begin my early morning plod through the icy slush hardened overnight not yet ameliorated by the early morning salt dispensary. Unfortunately, I would miss the lowered freezing point and the much-needed salty friction due to my early rise. Slipping and sliding on icy sidewalks was as stimulatory as a hot cup of coffee. Luckily, no one was awake to watch me eat it a few times on my way to the hospital.

71

Coming off an exhausting month of night shifts during my '*Rite of Passage,*' so to speak, I struck off my porch invigorated with the anticipation for the month to come. I was finally here. IT was finally here. My rotation on my home service, the entire reason I had left the beaches of Florida to come to this northern tundra that is Indiana's winter, cardiac surgery.

As not to lose you to the significance of this occasion for me, we may need to examine what I had done to reach this point in my training. This was the culmination of all my work up to this point; my dream was, at last, alive!

Recall, I had wanted to be a doctor since that day at the Agrirama, although I hadn't envisioned in what capacity or form. After shadowing a general surgeon in Tifton, Georgia during high school, it became clear that I wanted to sew and tie! I knew it to be a long shot in preparation, but what else was there? Working long, arduous days at the farm tending to a bunch of stubborn cows? I'd rather work long, tiresome days in air conditioning with stubborn nurses. At least there were rules about them kicking you in your shins indiscriminately.

Every summer or break was solely focused on my dream to play soccer in college and the penultimate goal of becoming a surgeon. As much as I wanted to play in the Premier League somewhere overseas, my delusions only ran so deep. Whether I was aware or not, I had a long road ahead. Most of my activities would be geared, not entirely, but certainly motivated, by that end goal. An impressive resume is required for one to embark upon a career path such as cardiothoracic surgery. Although my resume paled in comparison to some of my competition having much work to do, I internalized the advice from Dr. Shumway, "Don't grow up too fast." Some of the angst lifted in light of those words, and I began to find joy in the process.

Regarding research activities, I was part of the CRISP (Clinical Research Internship Study Program) at the Mayo Clinic in Jacksonville, Florida, in the transition from high school to college. As mentioned, I was involved with Plant Ecology Research at Stetson University resulting in the Departmental Award for Research in Biology. I researched the Passionflower whose leaves have a high content of cyanide for which the plant employs as a biological defense mechanism. Another interesting property is its ability to be used as an analgesic and sedative.[1, 2] Quite noteworthy!

Once in medical school, I steered my research efforts toward cardiothoracic surgery early in my first year up and beyond my matriculation into residency authoring several Pubmed searchable articles, some not. Admittedly, some were composed during my treatment; I wasn't clinically active. It's far less impressive when you aren't carrying full clinical responsibilities. Anyone can sit in an infusion chair and write. I'd refer the reader to the following article written shortly after D (diagnosis)-day (*next chapter*): *Thirty-three, Zero, Nine*. [3]

Concomitantly, I played soccer as much as possible. Playing had morphed into training. As previously mentioned, I would sneak onto my high school field to play under the lights when I could not sleep; cops would wave as they patrolled the area late at night. After I made my transition to

Florida during my senior year at the expense of my father's relationship, I would spend any extra time training and conditioning either at the University of North Florida or Nease High School in lieu of hanging out with friends in hopes of being picked up by a college squad. My hard work and sacrifice would pay dividends as I was accepted to Stetson University (SU) soccer team. When my assistant coach delivered the news, I ran down the street in jubilation vindicating my sacrifice. At SU, three hours a day was devoted to training rarely with interluding breaks. We won the Atlantic Sun Championship my freshman year; I was awarded all-academic conference every year. Summers were consumed by more training in the Premier Development League.

Cease not to learn until thou cease to live; Think that day lost wherein thou draw'st no letter To make thyself more learned, wiser, better.
Guy De Faur Pibrac, Collection of Quatrains.
(Joshua Sylvester, tr., c. 1608)

During athletic endeavors, I maintained good standing in the education realm. Despite graduating from high school as a fish out of water, I still was top forty in a class of about 500 students after moving to the Sunshine State. I was consistently on the Dean's list in college and tutored biology. Scoring well enough on the medical college admission test (MCAT) to be accepted to the University of Florida's College of Medicine, I was consistently in the top middle third of my class. *I'm no savant like some of these folks.* Additionally, I prepared cadavers for dissection every summer during medical school which allowed me to learn more detailed anatomy.

Also, I was a member of several professional societies: AAMC, Phi Eta Sigma, AATS, ISHLT, and STS candidate member. I performed well on

74

the USMLE (United States Medical Licensing Exam) steps 1, 2, and 3 exams. This test evaluates readiness to become a practicing doctor; I took them all early to gear my studies toward cardiothoracic surgery. My scores were adequate for me to be honored with the opportunity to be one of 37 matriculating medical students in the country to be accepted into an Integrated Cardiothoracic Program despite all the uncertainty it provoked within the specialty. Within residency, I was awarded excellence in teaching medical students, counseled medical students, and gave over eight lectures for the institution at Indiana University.

Before departing to residency, I read a multitude of cardiothoracic textbooks in preparation. If you are interested in becoming a CT surgeon, I would highly recommend the following: Bojar's Manual of Perioperative Care in Adult Cardiac Surgery, Marino's ICU book, Sabiston and Spencer's Surgery of the Chest, and Fiser's ABSITE (American Surgery In-Training Examination) review; as a primer. The strength, some say the downfall, of the integrated programs is that you have to study both general surgery and cardiothoracic surgery simultaneously, i.e., the necessity of the ABSITE review. Additionally, some must-reads are 100,000 Hearts by Denton A. Cooley, a pioneering heart surgeon, as well as King of Hearts: The True Story of the Maverick Who Pioneered Open Heart Surgery by G. Wayne Miller.

You also acquire a profound amount of imposter syndrome when accepted into higher education. I feared incessantly that I was going to be found out! "How could a dumb country boy make it here?" I would imagine my attendings asking themselves as my southern draw laid thick on their ears—anxiety-provoking almost to the point of mental illness. There is a higher incidence of sleep paralysis among medical students with rates well above 20% compared to ~8% of the general population. For comparison, the prevalence is over 30% in schizophrenics.[4] Indeed, the continual waning of the mental health in both medical students and residents is alarming as we enter a national health crisis demanding more from our active and employed healthcare workers.[5]

Not only is your psyche twisted and stressed during your time in medical school, so too is your pocketbook. The Association of American Medical Colleges (AAMC) started in 1876 in Washington, DC, includes 136 accredited schools in America and 17 in Canada. Participating institutions number in the 400s and report yearly their cost of attendance. The average tuition at an in-state public institution, like the University of Florida where I attended, was *$32,384* per year in 2020 – 2021 (x4 years, *$129,536*). If you are out-of-state, *$54,502* (x4, *$218,008*). Compare these figures to just 25 years before in 1995-1996, *$7,917* and *$23,171*, respectively.[6] Inflation does not explain the uptick; unnecessary administration costs, perhaps?

Notwithstanding the interest accrued on loans required to ultimately pay for medical school, many have outstanding and unpaid loans from undergrad. FAFSA, or Free Application for Student Aid, is the primary federal institution that allows for funding for higher education. According to their website, the going interest rate for Direct Subsidized and Direct Unsubsidized Loans, i.e., Undergraduate loans, is 3.73%. For Graduate or Professional degrees, the interest rate is 5.28%, and 6.28% for Direct PLUS loans.[7] According to an article published in 2021 by *U.S. News and World Report*, the average undergrad student debt is nearly $30,000 and rising as evidenced by the last ten-year trend.[8]

Note that throughout this process, there is no time to hold down a job to have some semblance of an income. Without the support of my family, none of my goals could have come to fruition. Nonetheless, I still managed to accumulate over 100,000 dollars in debt. I spent over 10,000 dollars in travel expenses for interviews among different residencies around the country before landing on Indiana University. Debt continued to accumulate during three away rotations during medical school, each a month in duration: Vanderbilt in Tennessee, Emory in Atlanta, and MUSC, or the Medical University of South Carolina. No telling how much that costs between lodging and travel. Oh, and food is a necessity.

Most medical doctor candidates are not aware of what exactly they're signing up for. Many students are often disillusioned; they desire title and privilege which is misplaced. Seemingly, becoming a physician is the next logical 'Type A' step in one's education, but many individuals have failed to complete any honest self-scrutiny through thoughtful self-examination. Such introspection should be emphasized before diving into an ocean of debt and committing oneself to a near-decade of post-secondary education before receiving a decent paycheck. The amount of debt accrued is staggering and certainly worth a small conversation with yourself, including the question, "Hey, why are you doing this? There are easier ways to make money." "Am I going to be happy with waking up at all hours of the night to manage a sick patient with having a full day of work the next day?" Many doctors, when asked if they would choose the same profession again, across specialties, sadly nearly half said 'no.'[9, 10]

In an article published on CBS's website in 2013, Kathy Kristof, editor of *Sidehusl.com*, financial journalist, and author of *Investing 101*, reported from Christina Lamontagne, vice president of health at *NerdWallet*, that "administrative tasks account for one-quarter of a doctor's day," and less than half of physicians would opt for the same career. Kristof goes on to cite that a doctor new to the workforce has around $166,750 in medical school debt at a time when reimbursement is declining. And with most residents having to defer loan repayment until after they complete their final bit of training, you are looking at close to *half a million dollars* in debt at interest rates between 5-6% or more. Notwithstanding previous student loans from undergrad at 3-4%.[7] All said, according to Kristof, it takes "between 11 and 14 years of higher education to become a physician."[9]

With compensation falling and more time spent on painstaking paperwork [10], and although the electronic medical record seems to be curtailing some of that frustration despite the perceived hassle [11], physician *burnout* remains a significant issue. *Burnout*, previously a drug addict slang term, was coined in 1974 by Herbert Fraudenberger, a clinical psychologist. He worked in a free clinic in New York about a decade before the crack epidemic of the mid-1980s. [12, 13] Fraudenberger was cited by Reith as describing the occurrence of "*burnout* [as]…excessive demands on energy, strength, or resources," and Reith describes further clinically exhibiting "a set of symptoms including malaise, fatigue, frustration, cynicism, and inefficacy."

Regarding *burnout,* psychologist Christina Maslach at the University of California in Berkeley with Susan E. Jackson further refined the definition into a triad: "emotional exhaustion, depersonalization, and a diminished sense of personal accomplishment."[14] *Burnout* is on the rise, especially in particular specialties.[15] *Burnt*-out doctors make more mistakes and have been associated with increased clerical and bureaucratic tasks like charting and note writing.[13]

An average of 2.6 hours per week are spent on paperwork equating to nine additional patients that could be seen. [16] In another study published in the Annals of Internal Medicine in 2016, doctors spend only 27.0% of their time in face-to-face interactions with their patients and 49.0% with the electronic medical record and clerisy.[17] If you are ever upset about waiting to be seen in the doctor's office, you can know what to blame: *required* paperwork. And if you think, "Well, they can just take their unfinished work home and not waste my time." They do. The average doctor spends one to two hours at home each night working. This is referred to as *pajama time*. [17] Indeed, it is a thankless job.

Why? Why would you sacrifice so much? Sacrifice relationships in order to study, to stay focused? Thousands of hours of study? Missing out on life events, family, weddings, trips? Sacrifice your early and late twenties in medical school and residency only to fall deeper into debt? Stunt your growth in personal relationships for the sake of education? Sacrifice prime birthing years as a female physician? If a female dares to have children, they are awarded little maternity leave, or be criticized for taking it? [18, 19] Literally, risking mental illness due to stress and anxiety?

79

Having an incessant feeling that life is passing you by as you bury your nose in books? Why?

Every physician must answer that for him or herself. That's what makes being a physician still a noble profession. You work and toil for something greater than yourself. Personally, I felt it a great exhibition of self-sacrifice. As one cardiologist said to me during his last years in practice, a practitioner who still gave his personal phone number out to patients, "Service over Self." And I would repeat those words to myself whenever I fell prey to negative self-talk or being less than grateful for being in a position to help people. I have a looming fear that the next generation of doctors are more concerned about money, status, and time-off than they are about healing the sick. Many senior doctors would likely concur with that observation.

Superimposed on all the obstacles necessary to hurdle on the way to becoming a cardiothoracic surgeon, I was constantly reminded that "Cardiac surgery is a dying field." Such a prospect was laughable to me even in medical school. I was happy to let other people believe that as that was less competition for me. Cardiac surgery was indeed changing, but in no way was it dying.[20] With the opioid epidemic of recent years, highlighted superbly by Sam Quinones's book *Dreamland,* massive spikes in intravenous drug use have led to a concomitant increase in bacterial endocarditis, a heart infection, usually only amenable to open surgical debridement or heart surgery.[21-23] Not to mention, the role of less invasive means of cardiothoracic surgery in the future is being heavily investigated.[24-26] I'd predict that the specialty is here to stay.

Enough of Science and of Art; Close up those barren leaves; Come forth, and bring with you a heart That watches and receives.
Wordsworth, The Tables Turned. St. 8.

So…I was finally here! From the backwoods of the gnat-ridden Peach state below the fall line to a Midwestern residency with a steadfast history in heart surgery. I hope I have adequately expressed to you how big of a deal this was for me. This had been my life's sole focus for as long as I could remember. My stepmom always said, "Remember, never put all your eggs in one basket." Clearly, I had done the exact opposite.

After making it through a formfitting and tumultuous intern year as a cardiothoracic surgery resident, my sophomore or 2nd year, I began to feel more like an actual surgeon. Still at the bottom of the totem pole, no doubt, but receiving some good touches in the operating room, finally feeling comfortable coming on and off the cardiopulmonary bypass (CPB) machine. Understanding and properly manipulating CPB is fundamental in becoming a heart surgeon because working in a near bloodless surgical field is paramount. Additionally, the CPB pump requires close communication with a perfusionist while the surgeon operates controlling temperature, blood flow, pH, among other metrics, while the heart is shut down. Blood is rerouted to and from the body to maintain homeostasis while whatever pathology is addressed. I must consciously force myself not to expound on the wonders of this machine and how revolutionary it is to the field at large. Arguably, CPB is one of the greatest medical achievements of the 20th century.[27]

After showing the ability to come on and off CPB with confidence, I was given multiple opportunities to complete the crux of the operation or correcting the primary pathology. For example, replacing a diseased heart valve or performing coronary bypass. *A bypass of the coronary artery, or the artery providing oxygen-rich blood to the heart muscle itself, with either an artery from up under the breastbone or a large vein harvested from the legs, is a common, if not the most common operation done in cardiac surgery.*[28] Bypassing heart arteries clogged with years of poor life choices and/or genetics provides much-needed perfusion to areas of the heart that are starved for oxygen-rich blood. Ultimately, this operation extends the life of many patients worldwide, if not, at the very least, improves their quality of life (QoL).[28]

Even though I was working well over 80 hours a week, I found it immaterial. Never did I feel as if time was all that important when you are dealing with life and death situations. My QoL never factored into the equation. What about the QoL of the patient who was literally having the worst day of their life having their chest cracked open and insides prodded? I caution medical students who have expressed interest in cardiothoracic surgery whose first concern is QoL; you are already entering the field in the wrong state of mind. This is a calling and passion. If QoL is a major concern, I'd suggest another specialty or an entirely different career.

Moreover, there is great satisfaction in having done good work and making a tangible difference in someone else's life. Oddly, I liken the fulfillment analogous to mowing the grass. With every full cycle around the yard, you slowly become the harbinger of order, with each passing round of the mower calming the chaos that had become your yard. Where the grass was misshapen and asymmetrical with some patches overgrown and others not grown enough, you bring about a balance to your small kingdom. The newly primmed grass stands proud and even with the freshly imprinted green shades from the mower impressed in the yard. A similar feeling was elicited with each throw of a stitch during surgery. Imagine that fulfillment each day.

Rounds in the cardiac intensive care unit were also invigorating. *I realize; I am a huge nerd.* I had been reading about this stuff for five years prior to residency and seeing it in action only made my job that much better. Having spent immense time understanding pathophysiology, operating, and observing patients postoperatively, I saw all my hard work come full circle both personally and professionally as a cardiac resident. This thrill was reinforced daily. Directly after a valve operation, for instance, one could appreciate gradients visibly drop providing escape from future symptoms like dyspnea, angina, or possible heart failure. You can actively mow those blades of grass, and there is always more to cut.

One of my favorite things to do was to observe a patient who had just come back from the operating room. They are often coagulopathic (still bleeding) after being cooled down for extended periods and having heparin (an anticoagulant) pumped through their systems. After coming off a pump run, a patient's clotting mechanisms aren't entirely intact. You must support them with fluid and blood to keep them tanked up, so to speak, until it corrects. At times you must take them back to the OR to identify an aberrant bleeder, which is mainly in the middle of the night. That's never a fun phone call to make to your attending! I must pay homage to my attendings at Indiana University. They never lost their temper with me when they certainly should have at times.

For example, while learning the ropes during my intern year, I was late to a case, which is a huge no-no. I scurried around the scrub sink after gowning, having haphazardly placed my headlamp and loupes around my noodle. Sweating to take my place on the assistant side, my attending's disapproval was silent but palpable. As we were opening the chest, I kept bumping into his headlamp. After about 10 minutes of frustration, one of the scrub techs says, "Caleb, your headlamp is upside down." Flushed with embarrassment, the first thing this attending said to me during that case was, "Yea, you should probably go change that."

Are you familiar with an old cartoon called Doug? Well, Doug used to have an alter ego called Quailman with his dog, Quaildog. Quailman would wear his underwear over his pants and his belt around his head with the belt buckle on his forehead. My headlamp was sticking up just like Quailman's belt, and it kept bumping into my attendings light every time he or I bent forward. I turned to stone with embarrassment, and now I can't stop laughing. I would write a few papers with that particular surgeon, and he would always be willing to make accommodations for me during treatment. He was one of the many people I am indebted to when sickness struck.

During the months on the cardiac service, I wasn't getting home before eight O'clock most nights, still having the time of my life. I reveled in the challenge; however, my appearance was less than inspiring. Many scrub nurses had commented on how beaten down I looked. Sunken and sullen behind bloodshot eyes despite my overall happy disposition, I felt an odd sense of pride in their concern. People could actually visualize how hard I was working. My red eyes and fatigue were hard-won, and I wore my weariness with pride. Being a resident was temporary; I only had six years of residency to take my future patient safely through a heart operation. The way I saw it, that's not much time. Unfortunately, this led me to ignore some early warning signs of my waning individual health.

God keeps a niche In Heaven to hold our idols; and albeit He brake them
to our faces, and denied That our close kisses should impair their white,
I know we shall behold them raised, complete, The dust swept from their
beauty, ---glorified, New Memnons singing in the great God-light.
E. B. Browning, Sonnet: Futurity.

Sharing my love for cardiothoracic surgery by teaching medical students further bolstered my love for the field. Distilling complicated pathophysiology into ways that could be easily understood was a fun exercise; I loved to see the lightbulbs illuminate above their heads when they reached a new level of understanding. Nothing is so difficult that it cannot be taught. I am convinced. I'll say this until I expire: I am a dumb country boy, and anything can be learned. I guised my ignorance with relentless study. Nothing came naturally to me but manual dexterity and operating; all subjects had to be beaten into submission. I was convinced that if I could understand something, the medical students could too. I would always tell them, "Never underestimate the POWER of incremental progress!" Keep reading! Large surgical textbooks can be intimidating indeed. If you read every morning for 30 minutes to an hour, you would be surprised how many textbooks you can read within a few months, even with a busy resident's schedule. That's the only way to establish long-lasting knowledge, taking notes and firsthand experience.

During my second year, I was finally feeling a little more like a surgeon and, more importantly, an effective resident doctor. I desired the responsibility from all the attendings that if they wanted to know how their patient was doing, all they needed to do was ask me. I aimed to prove myself worthy of their trust in managing all aspects of ICU care: fluid balance, pacemakers, wound care, etc. When not actively operating, they could trust I had knowledge of all overnight events and consistently provided updates throughout the day. On-call, I didn't want my attendings to lose a wink of sleep. In the evening, I'd make it a habit to call the surgeon I would be operating with the next day to review any concerns or pitfalls we'd encounter.

I would leave the hospital each night looking at my bumper sticker that read Cameron Hanes's, elite ultrarunner and bowhunter, adage, "Nobody Cares, Work Harder," when I decided not to run in the morning. When tragedy struck, I couldn't have been surrounded by a more supportive faculty and staff who would bend over backward accommodating to my future dilemma. The integrity exhibited by both IU and UF during my treatments was unyielding, not to mention the family of residents and nurses who rallied my cause. There are very close ties between the two institutions; such was well demonstrated in events to come forming a wide net of support.

When I was clinically active, I remain eternally grateful for every patient I had the pleasure to treat, not to mention every mentor who guided me throughout my surgical education. The fulfillment has been beyond measure. My eyes well up when I reminisce on my short tour as a cardiothoracic resident. Nothing compares. Now, I can only continue to dream, as I have for the better part of twenty years. I am unsure how to fill the void that remains. Paintings of anatomically correct hearts were gifted to me throughout my treatments; now, I can't bear to look at them. Every beat of my heart has been permanently intensified by the lack of a large portion of my left lung. Like an internal thoracic subwoofer, its absence constantly reminds me of my trenching loss.

I used to say in jest amongst other residents, "The only thing worse than death is not being a cardiothoracic surgeon!" It seems absurd, but a part of me legitimately felt that way. I found it necessary to assume that attitude. Having a plan B would distract from plan A. Best go for broke and fail rather than be left to wonder.

Sometimes I wonder if I hadn't romanticized cardiothoracic surgery to the extent that I have, if I hadn't prioritized the central goal of becoming a heart surgeon forsaking everything else, would this have happened to me? Am I being punished for making cardiothoracic surgery a god rather than focusing my praise on God? Was I guilty of idolatry? Would I have made it as far as I did without being unapologetically driven? *I don't know.*

Lastly, in the fall of 2018, I discovered David Goggins' book before my diagnosis. Mr. Goggins lived a significant part of his life in Indiana, and after reading his biography, Can't *Hurt Me*, I found motivation in the fact that I was running on the same paths that he traveled in the frigid winters. Although I hadn't worked my way into jumping into an iced-over lake, I certainly aspired to in an effort to edify the mental fortitude necessary to operate for long hours. I admired his focus, relentlessness, and tenacity, relinquishing nothing to supersede his limits. He was and continues to be a major motivation in my life, and I hoped to reflect that same warrior ethos in my career as a budding cardiothoracic surgeon. Make no excuses, not even cancer, "Stay Hard!"

1.   Hay-Roe, M.M. and J. Nation, *Spectrum of cyanide toxicity and allocation in Heliconius erato and Passiflora host plants.* J Chem Ecol, 2007. **33**(2): p. 319-29.

2.   Kim, M., et al., *Role Identification of Passiflora Incarnata Linnaeus: A Mini Review.* J Menopausal Med, 2017. **23**(3): p. 156-159.

3.   Matthews, C.R. and P.J. Hess, *Thirty-three, zero, nine.* J Thorac Cardiovasc Surg, 2020. **160**(3): p. 871-875.

4.   Olunu, E., et al., *Sleep Paralysis, a Medical Condition with a Diverse Cultural Interpretation.* Int J Appl Basic Med Res, 2018. **8**(3): p. 137-142.

5.   Brazeau, C.M., et al., *Distress among matriculating medical students relative to the general population.* Acad Med, 2014. **89**(11): p. 1520-5.

6.   Colleges, A.o.A.M. *Data and Reports.* 2021 November 3rd, 2021]; Available from: https://www.aamc.org/data-reports.

7.   Aid, U.S.D.o.E.o.o.F.S. *Federal Student Aid.* 2021 [cited 2021 November 3rd, 2021]; Available from: https://studentaid.gov/.

8.   Wood, E.K.a.S. *See 10 Years of Average Total Student Loan Debt.* 2021.

9.   Kristof, K., *$1 million mistake: Becoming a doctor*, in *CBS News.* 2013, CBS Interactive Inc. All rights reserved. : Money Watch.

10.   Tanne, J.H., *Income and job satisfaction fall among US doctors.* Bmj, 2012. **344**: p. e3109.

11.   Robinson, K.E. and J.A. Kersey, *Novel electronic health record (EHR) education intervention in large healthcare organization improves quality, efficiency, time, and impact on burnout.* Medicine (Baltimore), 2018. **97**(38): p. e12319.

12.   Cornish, J.W. and C.P. O'Brien, *Crack cocaine abuse: an epidemic with many public health consequences.* Annu Rev Public Health, 1996. **17**: p. 259-73.

13.   Reith, T.P., *Burnout in the United States Healthcare Professionals: A Narrative Review. .* Cureus, 2018. **10**(12).

14.   Jackson, C.M.a.S.E., *The measurement of experienced burnout.* Journal of Occupational Behaviour, 1981. **2**: p. 99-113.

15.   Dyrbye, L.N., et al., *Association of Clinical Specialty With Symptoms of Burnout and Career Choice Regret Among US Resident Physicians.* Jama, 2018. **320**(11): p. 1114-1130.

16. Casalino, L.P., et al., *US Physician Practices Spend More Than $15.4 Billion Annually To Report Quality Measures.* Health Aff (Millwood), 2016. **35**(3): p. 401-6.

17. Sinsky, C., et al., *Allocation of Physician Time in Ambulatory Practice: A Time and Motion Study in 4 Specialties.* Ann Intern Med, 2016. **165**(11): p. 753-760.

18. Potee, R.A., A.J. Gerber, and J.R. Ickovics, *Medicine and motherhood: shifting trends among female physicians from 1922 to 1999.* Acad Med, 1999. **74**(8): p. 911-9.

19. Juengst, S.B., et al., *Family Leave and Return-to-Work Experiences of Physician Mothers.* JAMA Netw Open, 2019. **2**(10): p. e1913054.

20. David Yaffee, M.a.M.W.M., FACC, *Cardiac Surgery and the Future.* American College of Cardiogy, 2015.

21. Cooper, H.L., et al., *Nationwide increase in the number of hospitalizations for illicit injection drug use-related infective endocarditis.* Clin Infect Dis, 2007. **45**(9): p. 1200-3.

22. Østerdal, O.B., et al., *Cardiac surgery for infective endocarditis in patients with intravenous drug use.* Interact Cardiovasc Thorac Surg, 2016. **22**(5): p. 633-40.

23. Starakis, I. and E.E. Mazokopakis, *Injecting illicit substances epidemic and infective endocarditis.* Infect Disord Drug Targets, 2010. **10**(1): p. 22-6.

24. Melfi, F.M., O. Fanucchi, and A. Mussi, *Minimally invasive mediastinal surgery.* Ann Cardiothorac Surg, 2016. **5**(1): p. 10-7.

25. Kilic, A., et al., *Operative Outcomes of Concomitant Minimally Invasive Mitral and Tricuspid Valve Surgery.* Innovations (Phila), 2019. **14**(5): p. 412-418.

26. Soltesz, E.G. and L.H. Cohn, *Minimally invasive valve surgery.* Cardiol Rev, 2007. **15**(3): p. 109-15.

27. Hessel, E.A., 2nd, *History of cardiopulmonary bypass (CPB).* Best Pract Res Clin Anaesthesiol, 2015. **29**(2): p. 99-111.

28. Bachar, B.J. and B. Manna, *Coronary Artery Bypass Graft*, in *StatPearls.* 2022, StatPearls Publishing
Copyright © 2022, StatPearls Publishing LLC.: Treasure Island (FL).

6

D-Day

Pride goeth before destruction, and a haughty spirit before a fall.
King James Version, Bible, Book of Proverbs, 16:18

Something was wrong.

A visceral, cavernous fatigue had fallen over me. Despite adequate rest from being on less busy clinical rotations in the months following the *'Rite of Passage'* and being on my home services, no amount of sleep seemed to quench my lassitude. Sure, I had worked my butt off that fall and winter working greater than 80 hours a week, testing my outer limits of sleep deprivation and work capacity. But there was no explanation of why I hadn't recovered. *I always recovered.*

I would awake more tired than when I went to sleep, finding it more and more difficult to crawl out of bed. Additionally, I had developed a dry nagging cough that had lingered since my time on my home cardiac service. At the time, I was only twenty-seven, almost twenty-eight years old, when I noted this chronic fatigue and cough. Despite my growing concern, I continued to ignore these symptoms, just like the brief moment of aphasia where I had lost all powers of speech while on call in the ICU earlier that year. "You're just getting older...." I would tell myself. *Yea, right.*

I would go on longer protracted runs on the weekend where time allowed traveling ten to twenty miles on a single run. Instead of powering through my route down the Monon trail dissecting Indianapolis north and south, the last energizing kick for which I always held in reserve was no longer present. I would search in vain for the final surge of vigor in those last few miles as I switched on the afterburners at the run's culmination, but my tanks were tapped dry. Something had robbed me of my preexisting and abundant vitality.

This unexplained lethargy loomed largely yet was ignored. After a busy fall and winter, I figured I needed to expect some element of chronic fatigue requiring me to give myself some rest and grace. Pride, however, would restrict me from giving myself a break. Refusing to accept any lapse in performance, I was convinced these barriers were purely mental. As a firm believer in the power of the mind to overcome physical obstacles, I would decide when to stop, not my body. However, this weariness was of a different kind, deep-seated. I found myself walking back home on several occasions as I overestimated my capacity for enduring my decided distance. I wasn't the same college soccer player in his late teens and early twenties anymore with an endless battery pack strapped to my shoulders. No longer was I immortal.

Ignoring my prior episode of aphasia and my incessant fatigue, my rotation schedule was filled with lighter services allowing me to take time for self-care and sleep. Thus, I expected my fatigue to improve; it didn't. If resting didn't work, I decided that it was just something I needed to train through. It just comes down to a decision I would ask myself: "Are you going to *will* yourself through training?" Overcoming obstacles is a decision; plateaus were a natural part of maturing in training. "Nobody Cares, Work Harder," Cameron Hanes's adage continued to ring in my ear.

In rebellion against my waning performance, I decided to give myself the lofty goal of completing the Monumental Marathon held in Indianapolis every year. I had run marathons before, but I wanted to perform well. In the months leading up to the run, I would train tirelessly; however, never fulfilling my expectations. Usually, my goal was to complete a handful of twenty-mile runs before race day. Leading up to my last marathon, I was unable to finish one.

Having signed up for the marathon months before, not knowing the ever-fluid call schedule for the week of the race, I was fortunate enough to be assigned in-house call at the Veterans Administration (VA) hospital the night before the race covering consults from the emergency department, floor calls, intensive care unit (ICU), and operating rooms. Usually, this would have been fine; but that evening was hectic. I constantly had issues with the ICU and, oddly enough, conducted an appendectomy on a thirty-year-old. The typical age for someone presenting with acute appendicitis is around that age, [1] but not for a patient at the VA whose average age, according to 2017 data, is 65 years.[2] What were the chances?

While conducting the appendectomy with my attending, my pager was constantly sounding off. I couldn't be in two places at once and was the only surgical resident in the hospital. I fielded calls the best I could while operating; however, I still wound up with a write-up from an unsuspecting nurse. They must've been under the impression that I was hiding away in the call rooms, neglecting my responsibilities. Residents are powerless to the whims of an employee with an ax to grind. This is not uncommon.

93

Having not gotten a wink of sleep and barely arriving at the beginning of the marathon on time, I saw this as an excellent opportunity to discover how mentally resilient I was. Running at a record pace for myself was far beyond a possibility being dehydrated and sleep-deprived having been awake for 24 hours already. I saw this as practice for when I would attempt ultra-marathons where athletes complete 100-200 mile runs, sometimes taking days to complete. This would just be one of those types of challenges.

I remained strong for fifteen miles until I caught my first cramp, heralding a tortuous next ten miles. From all my experience in running, I was aware of how easily I cramp despite all efforts of hydration and electrolyte replenishment. I lose water and salt effortlessly despite ingesting energy packs and salt packets every three miles. I knew it would be a battle to finish with over ten miles to go. I practically walked the last five miles, carefully maintaining one configuration of my arms and legs during my gait to avoid inciting widespread spasms. I crawled across the finish line and slept into the next day.

There are two tragedies in life. One is not to your heart's desire. The other is to get it.
Bernard Shaw, Man and Superman. Act iv.

Proud of my resolve but surprised by how much the race took out of me, I grew increasingly concerned, especially when I began to experience headaches on top of the dry cough and fatigue. Still, under the impression that I was invincible, my headaches became severe enough to force me to lay down for short naps until they dissipated. In hindsight, all the signs were present; the issue was I appeared too fit, too healthy. *Some intuitive physician I was! Although, we are typically our own worse doctors.*

Despite my abrupt run-in with aphasia, headaches, fatigue, and cough, months would pass before I would finally see a doctor, and I almost didn't even do that. Why would I? Other than these badgering concerns, I was still in stellar shape, loving life, and had just started a relationship with my ex-fiancé. What more could I ask for?

Nonetheless, after I walked over to the resident family medicine clinic in my spare time one afternoon while covering Eskenazi Hospital's (EH) ICU to schedule an appointment or at the very least get an order for a chest X-ray and possibly a brain scan, to my astonishment, I was turned away because they didn't have room on their schedule that day or any date in the foreseeable future. I was simply told, "The clinic was full." I was flabbergasted about how fast I was turned away. I was an incredibly busy surgical resident getting turned away from their own institution! We squeezed people in all the time in the surgical clinic; how could this be any different? I may get two days off a month, making it incredibly difficult to carve out times of the day to devote to self-care. Pissed, I stormed out in dissatisfaction.

After attempting to go through the usual channels in vain, I stomped my way across the campus in the cool crisp air of late spring, where parkas and gloves were no longer necessary to don. My thin blue scrubs provided plenty of ventilation from the heated exchange that I had had with the front desk at the family medicine clinic. I marched past Riley Children's hospital, reminding me of my secret ambition to be a congenital heart surgeon if I proved skilled enough to do so. My inspiration stemmed from another mentor of mine, Mark Bleiweis MD, a congenital heart surgeon at the University of Florida, who had an infectious personality, was outgoing, and full of energy. "Be like Bleiweis" was one of my many positive self-affirmations to make manifest my goals. Repeated affirmations had worked well for medical school examinations; why wouldn't it continue to work? Visualize and execute. Visualize and execute. Visualizing brings birth to the idea. It is up to you to execute. In fact, "Be like Bleiweis" was a post-it note on my bathroom mirror for a couple of years, reminding me to start each day emulating his positive attitude.

Approaching EH, I notified a fellow surgical ICU resident that I needed to inquire about a quick scan from one of our colleagues working in the emergency department. If anyone could understand how busy surgical residents were, it certainly would be those who consult us nonstop. I walked into the ED, and, surprisingly, one of my former classmates from UF was working as an ED resident. There were several residents from UF who had transplanted to Indiana. "Boy, I lucked out!" I said to myself. She was not originally part of our matriculating medical school class as she was one of the first students to be admitted to UF's Juris Doctor program. She spent three years in law school and returned later to complete her medical doctorate. Although we weren't intimately acquainted, we knew *of* each other, and I respected her devotion to her education.

I recall her affinity for homemade baked breads with ornate fruity fillings. Her Instagram was littered with these tasty treats, and I wondered how she would ever have time to bake in residency. I was then quickly reminded that she was an ED resident; they typically have more generous schedules among residents comparatively. From my experience, they are typically more interested in quality of life, searching for administrative-type roles, which was perfect for someone with her educational background. However, I find that hardly filling, unlike her savory baked goods. To each their own, I suppose.

Nonetheless, I approached her with my hopeful request for a chest X-ray and perhaps a head scan. Desperately, I needed to return to a busy ICU where I had left my partner to handle all concerns. As capable as she was, it was still bad form to leave her stranded in the trenches taking grenades. In requesting this quick favor to streamline a couple of scans, my former medical school comrade denied me quite bluntly. It wasn't like I wasn't going to pay for it; I had the IU's institutional insurance, after all! I was quickly reminded why she didn't have more friends in medical school and why she made pastries as a pastime.

I returned to the ICU in much of the same disposition I had left the family medicine clinic: pissed. I began to loathe every time I had taught an ED resident how to do a proper abdominal exam. Moreover, my frustration with the lack of accommodation for someone prepared to give their entire life to medicine was boiling over to stay the least.

"Get your ass to the beach. I'll be there waiting for you and I'll tell what to do. There ain't anything in this plan that is going to go right." *Colonel Paul R. Goode, in a pre-attack briefing to the 175th Infantry Regiment, 29th Infantry Division*

The following day I would have much better luck as you were guaranteed to have a different suite of ED residents from one day to the next. Fortunately, I was surprised by another former medical student colleague whom I respected immensely. He had come from a broken home, emancipated himself, and put himself through medical school. Oh, and he was nothing short of, in my mind, a genius. Eccentric as most geniuses are, but a genius nonetheless. He was smart enough to choose emergency medicine because, as he put it, he didn't want to work that hard. He had former aspirations to be a neurosurgeon, for which he had the salt to do. And I am not saying in any way that ED doctors do not WORK HARD, but they can, if they want, formulate their work schedules to work as hard or as little as they wish. Not all specialties have that luxury, leaving room to assume administrative roles, for example. We need people with those aspirations, the need to feel in charge because I certainly don't want to do it. I just wanted to operate and leave bureaucracy for the birds.

Skinny, scraggly bearded, and short in stature, I was relieved to see him. "Josue'!" I exclaimed, "So good to see you!" We had shared a few suds back in medical school and were well-acquainted. He was someone I wished I was better friends with, but the demands of medical school kept a cap on meaningful friendships. Time was limiting. After we exchanged pleasantries, he walked me through the ED admissions after introducing me to the attending, expediting my processing. Josh and I worked in the Methodist ED during the *Rite of Passage;* he always did an exemplary job evaluating surgical patients. He and I worked well together, however disconcerting as he was to some. When asserting their exactness, savants are off-putting at times; I suspect that's what most people found crass. Conversely, I enjoyed it, speaking the unabashed truth.

I sat in a patient's room for a few minutes observing all familiar devices: otoscope, hand sanitizer, soap dispenser, along with a couple of pamphlets informing of the various hospital services. Following my chest X-ray and computed tomography (CT) chest, I strolled through the hallway, greeting the familiar faces of nurses and physicians. The modern décor accentuating bright shades of green and blue on the clean linoleum floors lined the hallways in an interdigitating fashion, assuming a stance of simplicity in style. Sidney and Lois Eskenazi hospital had a long history dating back to the Civil War era and aiding in ameliorating the smallpox epidemic in the mid-1800s. Also, City hospital, as it was called in its early days in Indianapolis, treated those patients afflicted with tuberculosis and polio in the early 1900s. The hospital went under a couple of different names until it was finally dubbed Sidney and Lois Eskenazi Hospital when the Eskenazi family donated forty million dollars in 2011 to construct its downtown campus, opening in 2013.[3] Importantly, and most notably, they had the best salad bar on all of campus. I was a frequent customer.

Due to its recent opening, one can imagine how many improvements had been made in the overall design for the ED layout streamlining workflow and properly separating emergency rooms from trauma rooms. The updated floor plan made for a less hectic and more orderly work environment contrasting greatly from the haphazard design of MH devised a century earlier, not a mile away. The intensive care unit was stable, and I was in the ED if any traumas arrived. My time to fulfill this simple chore was secure. All that was needed was for me to step out of my patient room and evaluate a trauma if necessary. A bedside ED nurse assured me that Josh and the attending would return shortly.

99

A few minutes turned to thirty. Reassuring myself that these things take time, I asked myself a tantalizing question, "Why haven't I been paged yet?" If it was taking up to an hour to read a CT, there must have been an overload in demand for a radiologist's reads'. However, I hadn't been paged for any consults or trauma, making me doubt the on-call radiologist was all that busy. An uncomplicated read wouldn't take so long.

Moreover, Josh would have checked in by now. As a cardiothoracic surgery resident looking at almost fifteen chest X-rays a day before seven in the morning, a simple read of an X-ray wouldn't take this long. The longer I waited, the more anxious I became.

The door to my ED room crept open slowly as Josh did his best to meander the cow, or computer on wheels, with his small, wiry stature directing the screen where I could see the images clearly. Josh avoided eye contact at first; the room's mood sank heavily. I noticed a redness about his eyes that could only result from allergies or a rapid effort to wipe away tears. "Josh, what's wrong, man?" I said. Directing the cow towards my view to show me the brain scan, I realized he didn't have allergies. "Caleb, we don't know what this is yet, but it doesn't appear to be good." "Let me take a look," I replied, sure that he was overreacting.

He wasn't. Littered throughout much of my brain were small, maybe half a centimeter spots, too many to get an accurate count, but not quite miliary (*millet seed size*) for the medically inclined. Additionally, the chest X-ray was less than inspiring. A significant consolidation was revealed in my left lower lobe of my lung, approximately 3 cm in diameter, with associated lymphadenopathy (*swollen lymph nodes*) throughout my chest

100

and into my neck. Moreover, whatever was inhabiting my chest, was more or less *centrally located*, meaning that instead of it being towards the periphery of the lung, it was positioned more towards the hilum or closer to the heart. Not to mention, there was a large lymph node right at my carina or the bifurcation of the trachea into the left and right main bronchi, which was likely the culprit of my inconsolable cough acquired over the past year. *In other words, small spots were seen in my brain, and a sizeable unexplained mass was inhabiting my left chest with bulky lymph nodes throughout.*

"We want to get a dedicated chest CT scan to take a better look at the mass in your chest," Josh said. "I don't have to tell you about the differential (*a term doctors use to discuss what a myriad of findings may indicate as far as possible diagnoses*), but obviously, I am worried about cancer, although there are many other things we need to rule out. Because at 27 years old and how healthy you are, it's hard to believe." "Hell yeah it is," I said to myself.

"We need to admit you and run further tests. We have a range of consulting services already arranged to evaluate you," Josh continued, "Meanwhile, we can get that dedicated CT done, and we will figure things out as we go." Morose, Josh was still tearing up as he and I continued scanning the images. He already knew what I already knew but would not admit it to myself for another week. Well-read, Josh knew the data, and his medical judgment and knowledge were tip-top. His initial assumption elicited tears because he knew how unlikely another diagnosis was. I found myself consoling him in light of my scan, reassuring him that we don't know anything yet; best not to jump to conclusions. Despite my being the one with the possible metastatic cancer, oddly, I was comforting him in true denial. I was hopeful that there was a better explanation. In my heart, I knew what it was, even though it would take a week for me to accept. *Some days I still don't believe it.*

My girlfriend, Jen, had been waiting in anticipation as I updated her consistently about the afternoon and evening events. Our relationship was in its infancy, barely two months old. Coincidentally, not only was she a nurse, but she was also next-door neighbors with the attending ED physician in charge of resident Josh who had ordered my scans. Dr. Beam was an uber good guy and an excellent doctor, always having a great rapport with residents and patients. Relieved that Jen and Dr. Beam knew each other, living only a couple of doors down from each other within the same cul-de-sac, this happenstance reassured me. He was hopeful that we would have a better plan of action once we had more information the following morning. I wasn't working the next day, so I had 24 hours to figure this out before my next shift.

Jen had arrived once my scans revealed some worrisome findings, and she had stayed throughout the night until she was forced to leave. Before Jen left my patient room, we sat on the tenth-floor perch overlooking the expansive lamp-lit parking lot illuminating the adolescent trees placed after the hospital's construction five years prior. The dim lights barely caught the White River adjacent to the Hospital feeding the Indiana Central Canal dug in the 1800s to facilitate interstate commerce and the current site of the NCAA headquarters. The mile-and-a-half canal provides an enjoyable tourist destination, a pleasant venue for pets and family, and, believe or not, and gondola rides, to name a few amenities.

Together, looking out over the parking lot at the very beginning of our relationship, I expressed that I didn't know what was going to happen, but she was under no obligation to stay. She responded, "I don't like you any less just because you '*maybe*' have cancer." Nearly a year later, we were engaged to be married. What was to come, though, would test a young couple beyond what was fair and reasonable. However, cancer could care less about fair. Cancer cares nothing of your best intentions or desires. Cancer is the consumer of dreams; an insidious sycophant digesting one's hopes and wishes of a life yet lived.

"The first time I saw a poster wanting men to sign up to be paratroopers and heard how hard it would be to make it in, I knew that was for me. I wanted an elite group of soldiers around me."
Staff Sergeant Frank Soboleski

The next day a gang of doctors was consulted from multiple fields of medicine, from infectious disease to neurology, to attempt to ascertain a compelling differential that did not involve malignancy, i.e., cancer. The team was baffled by my case. How could someone as seemingly healthy as I was, at my age, present with widespread cancer? Nonetheless, the constellation of signs and symptoms was hard to excuse: unremitting dry cough, lymphadenopathy with an associated centrally located lung mass, and worsening headaches. In search of the most likely culprit, excluding cancer, we landed on Histoplasmosis.

Histoplasmosis is a dimorphic fungus endemic to the Ohio and Mississippi river valleys, i.e., Indiana. The fungus is aerated from the soil

103

after topsoil disruption and is inhaled by the host, humans. Usually, this is not a problem. Our immune system is competent in taking care of this pathogen we encounter daily. But in severe cases where there is some predisposition or hypersensitivity, your body could react with severe inflammation of the lungs resulting in knotty collections known as granulomas. Granulomas are pockets of inflammation responding to an insult to your body's defenses where your body attempts to quarantine the pathogen.[4] Its reminiscent of consumption, or tuberculosis, in its clinical presentation. Treatment is usually antifungals and surgical intervention if necessary.

'Histo' was a great alternative and potentially not deadly. I was new to the Midwest, so it was plausible. I was happy to leave the hospital with that explanation, although many more studies needed to be conducted before we could be sure. Labs to check for 'Histo' take a few days to be processed. It was almost noon the next day, and all that I desired was to sleep in my own bed.

Sure, there were other infectious causes, however less likely: Cryptosporidiosis, Blastomycosis, and other granulomatous diseases. At that point in time, I already knew it was cancer before I left the hospital. My heart knew, sending its visceral information flooding through my gut neurons, churning my stomach in nervous anticipation. I knew. A disseminated fungal infection usually occurs in immunocompromised patients, like those actively undergoing cancer cytotoxic therapy or those with inborn genetic diseases like Severe Combined Immunodeficiency Disease. [5, 6]

104

One of the older infectious disease doctors was convinced that it was 'Histo.' In fact, he was so convinced that he recommended no other studies or labs. "Classic Histo," he said. "As long as I was clinically fine, continue about your business as if things were normal. If you become symptomatic, then we will treat." If it came to that, they would recommend oral itraconazole, an anti-fungal, with success rates of over 80% for pulmonary histoplasmosis.[7] Seems like an outlandish proposition in hindsight, although. Many years ago, he may have been right.

Cancer incidence is a tricky thing to remark upon. Like most things, it depends on scope. Currently, we are at an increase in cancer incidence. Most attribute the uptick to early cancer recognition and screening initiatives; as healthcare technology develops, fewer people are dying from heart disease and stroke, thus living longer to experience cancer.[8-10] Westernized societies seem to be victims of our own success, but we are no closer to solving the cancer dilemma despite our efforts.[11] The International Agency for Cancer (IARC), funded by the World Health Organization (WHO), reports in their GLOBOCAN studies (Global Cancer Incidence, Mortality, and Prevalence) reporting on 36 cancers in 185 countries. In 2018, lung cancer was the most common cancer overall for both sexes accounting for 11.6% of the cancer incidence and responsible for 18.4% of the cancer deaths, only to be followed in frequency by prostate, breast, and colorectal cancer. [8]

Again from a GLOBACAN study in 2020, lung cancer was surpassed in global *incidence* by breast cancer. However, lung cancer has remained the leading *cause of death,* with an estimated 1.8 million deaths worldwide.

In men, it remains the most lethal. [12] Although, according to the SEER database (Surveillance, Epidemiology, and End Results Program) following United States national trends, we are at a current downtrend of new cases of lung and bronchial cancer, at 50.4 new cases per 100,000 persons in 2016, the lowest since 1975.[13] Admittedly, somewhat reassuring.

However, we still haven't begun to approach the 'single digits' per 100,000 persons seen at the start of the 20th century before the Sugar and Industrial Revolutions,[14, 15], although we are better at screening these days.[9, 10] But an aging population and the height of cigarette smoking in the 1950s cannot alone explain the increase in childhood solid organ malignancies from lymphomas to germ cell tumors that have increased in incidence since the 1970s.[16] Additionally, the production of synthetic chemicals has risen exponentially since the 1930s,[17] a majority of which are carcinogenic. Causality is difficult to prove, however, with epidemiological data.

What I aim to express is that cancer of the chest was much more plausible than what my infectious disease (ID) doctor might've been hoping. The ID doctor, who was highly experienced and knowledgeable due to his decades in the field, was living in a different world now. The landscape of the standard differential was shifting; continents of differential probability were shifting. But I was eager to get out of the hospital; I accepted a more hopeful explanation and skipped away from the hospital in hopeful denial.

Once place there is --- beneath the burial sod, Where mankind are equalized by death; Another place there is --- Fane of God, Where all are equal who draw a living breath.
Thomas Hoode, Ode to Rae Wilson, 1. 133.

Trotting out of the hospital at a rapid clip at about noon the next day after the barrage of consults and visitors, I climbed into my car, intent on going right to bed for sleep and hospitals should never be used in the same sentence unless describing how they should never be used in the same sentence. Before igniting my engine, my cell phone indicated that Mimi Ceppa MD was calling me. Deliberating on whether to answer the phone as I was dead tired, wanting no conversation with anyone before I got some zzz's, my wiser head prevailed. I would never ignore an attending calling me, and she wasn't the one to start.

Dr. Ceppa was junior faculty at Indiana University, trained at Duke University, and specialized in minimally invasive thoracic surgery (lung surgery). Not only did she have an impressive academic pedigree, authoring countless PubMed searchable articles, but more importantly, she was a caring and attentive mother and wife. *To this day, I don't know how you women do it.* As a patient, if your goal is to leave the operating room with a small incision, she's your surgeon. Standing at five foot nothing, her height was inversely proportional to her domineering attitude in the OR and in life. A champion for female surgeons everywhere, I was proud to have her as an attending and fellow James Franco fan. Although the nature of minimally invasive surgery, her technique, in particular, left little room for a junior resident to assist to a great extent. However, I was allowed to man the radio, which was satisfying enough for me. I studied her technique and

107

had detailed notes on how she did things; when my time came, I'd be prepared.

A note to residents: never feel entitled to operate. Operating is earned, not given. Indeed, the operation begins before the OR. One must master perioperative care by displaying the ability to care for patients outside of the OR. Prior to actively scrubbing into the operating room, a resident must know how the room is set up, how the patient is positioned, and care to avoid essential pressure points prone to skin breakdown—an *important consideration that will come to play later.* Moreover, knowing the main indications for the operation and its pitfalls, or common problems encountered, are the resident's primary responsibility before knife breaches skin.

Moreover, realize the attending has a fiduciary responsibility to the patient who has agreed to allow the surgeon to penetrate the most intimate confines of their body to correct whatever pathology ail it. A sacred agreement is struck between surgeon and patient as ancient as the times of Galen and Hippocrates, extending beyond the white sheet of paper issuing informed consent. Residents, in order to get the training they need, squeeze right in between this agreement, allowing for this consecrated art of operating to be passed down from surgeon to surgeon. But not without trust and confidence at the base of that understanding. Why would you expect to man the scalpel if you don't know how to position the patient properly?

Dr. Ceppa's tenacity is only matched by her caring for her residents. And I was no stranger to a strong woman being raised by a tiger mom myself who remarked upon her difficulty in a male-dominated business; her intensity was nothing new to me and was clearly demonstrated in the events to come. In my humble evaluation concerning female surgeons or any high-ranking females within a male-dominated field, if I am allowed to comment, a fallacy exists in the assumption that a female must assume a hard-ass male persona in order to be respected. Where our differences should be celebrated, they are believed to be undesirable. This perceived obligatory behavior, indeed, propagates resentment between the sexes, at least in the workplace.

Moreover, a presupposition exists that all aspects that define one's femineity must be forsaken to legitimize career advancement in the *"male hierarchy."* The general assumption is that if you are too assertive as a female within said field, you would be regarded as well, for lack of better words, a bitch. However, the same boldness of action through the lens of a man is considered as strong-willed leadership with no negative connotation. *I conducted a personal poll of several female colleagues, each with similar concerns.* Whether this assumption holds up to scrutiny is quite inconsequential; however, the perception is truth enough.

What choppy waters to navigate for all female professionals; I can only attempt to empathize with their imposition! Many have called for a significant change in our social consciousness regarding gender equality and parity, or the numeric equality in the representation of the sexes.[18] However, why must the social tides between the sexes have similar trends? I would argue that a male's journey through an occupational experience *should differ* from a female's. A woman's experience provides a unique outlook that a man's viewpoint, dictated either by our biological basis of behavior or social construct, cannot provide, highlighting the necessity of the women's perspective. Of course, gender equality under the law embracing similar reimbursement practices for services rendered by accepted standards is of no question. But why would we assume or even strive for identical experiences between the sexes? Moreover, why would we want them to be the same? Fodder for a boring workplace and an even more boring world.

There are 631 results after searching "gender inequality in medicine" on Pubmed.gov (an NIH-funded website where you can search peer-reviewed studies) since 2000. Indeed, this has been a hot topic. However, the cause of gender inequality is subject to manipulation and subsequently aberrant conclusions that cultivate animus among the sexes. The fact is that there are inherent differences among the sexes that dictate vocational choices that have been well documented since the early 1900s and have remained conserved.[19] It does not indicate the existence of baseline, purposeful, and directed discrimination among the sexes or even race.

Su, Rounds and Armstrong from the University of Illinois at Urbana-Champaign and Iowa University, respectively, in their 2009 study, *"Men and Things, Women and People: A Meta-Analysis of Sex Differences in Interests,"* published in Psychological Bulletin, remarked upon the vocational choice differences between the sexes. This comprehensive meta-analysis involving multiple personality scales and inventories revealed that at the extremes of vocational preferences, men are more likely than females to be interested in the STEM fields (science, technology, engineering, mathematics) especially at the extreme ends of a normal distribution.

110

Women are likely to strive towards more artistic and social interests. The sample involved over half a million respondents. [19] Realize that these personal interests exist on a continuum and are not valid for everyone. Still, men's interest tend to cluster to ideas and data while women cluster towards interests in people.

Thus, is it any surprise to me that there would be historically a higher number of male surgeons than female surgeons? Not at all. Does this indicate a cabal of sinister women-hating patriarchs yanking on the strings of our higher institutions? No, it doesn't, even though higher education would have you believe that. Are we to compel free-minded men and women to be anachronistic to their wants and beliefs to maintain an institutional quota? I certainly hope not. My anatomy professor in medical school was from the Soviet Union, where she was forced to be a family physician rather than a surgeon. I certainly hope we don't devolve into a society absent of free will or are forced to meet consequences for not maintaining exact proportions of occupational ratios to stay 'woke' and 'equal.' Differences are the spice of life and should be embraced and accepted, not discouraged.

I digress.

Nonetheless, Dr. Ceppa personifies the duality between surgeon and femineity, more aptly motherhood, as she impressively juggled her responsibilities throughout the day. I admired her immensely, and as tired as I was, not answering was not an option; she was like my residency mom calling to check in on me. "Hey, Kiddo!" she responded. I caught here up on the events of the evening. "Do you mind if I take a look at your scans?"

She politely requested. "Of course not! Show them to everyone." I was an open book.

"I'll call you back!" she said directly. I got in my car and headed home, only a few miles away. Not half a mile down the road, Dr. Ceppa was calling be back. "Caleb, we need to make an appointment for clinic," she declared with urgency. "They're thinking it's Histo at Eskenazi," I said, "Do you really think it's necessary?" still grasping at this delusion that nothing was wrong. "Caleb, don't argue. You need a tissue biopsy; that's the only way you can be sure of what this is. There will be no guessing with you!" "Yes, ma'am," I said reluctantly. I could hear the urgency in her tone. "I'll set up a time for you to get a biopsy with one of our interventional pulmonologists." "Sounds good, Dr. Ceppa. I'll see you soon."

I celebrate myself, and I sing myself, And what I assume you shall assume, For every atom belonging to me as good as belongs to you.
Walt Whitman, Song of Myself. 1. 1.

I was scheduled for a bronchoscopy, where, under sedation, a camera is fed through your airways to visualize the area of interest. The operator can then safely take biopsies of the mass or lymph nodes in question. The 3-centimeter mass in my left lung was too peripheral to reach with the bronchoscope as it sat right in the superior aspect of my left lower lobe. Swollen lymph nodes were consistently scattered throughout my chest but not in a pattern consistent with lymphoma for those who are oncologically inclined. The largest lymph node sat at 3 centimeters at the carina, or bifurcation of the left and right airways. Sampling that lymph node, among a few others, would be sufficient to prove any diagnosis and lay concerns and speculation to rest.

(Lymph is fluid that all your cells are bathed in, and this interstitial, in between cells, fluid is constantly being circulated around your body. Lymph contains many things: protein, fat, and even bacteria. Lymph nodes are houses of lymphatic vessels and channels serving as an integral component of the immune system. They also develop in predictable and conserved way, allowing us to map the flow thereof. Due to this conserved anatomy, a deep 3-centimeter mass in my left chest unreachable without surgery could be assessed by taking a sample of a draining lymph node. The principal node was positioned at the carina, explaining my persistent nagging cough.) [20]

One of the reasons I was adamant about getting back home quickly as I had transitioned to overnight call covering ICU for the preceding week at EH. Therefore, my normal circadian rhythms had finally been adjusting to the new schedule while working nights. Usually, I enjoyed monitoring the ICU at night, having time to study the patients' physiology as it meandered through its course at night, giving a bolus of fluid there, extra electrolytes here. When I arrived on my nightshift that following evening with my biopsy appointment scheduled for the next day, I was given ample opportunity to mull over my imposition, alone, amongst the sounds of breathing machines and beeping IV catheters which was the only reprieve from the eerie silence that fell solemn over the unit.

The previous week I had taken care of a guy who had gotten into a treacherous motorcycle accident. I had admitted him directly to the ICU, placed all monitoring lines, including arterial and central venous lines, and was designated my sole responsibility as his resident doctor. Despite my and consulting services' best efforts, his condition failed to improve. Along with several long bone fractures, which required multiple fasciotomies, opening the compartments of muscle fascia to relieve the mounting pressure produced by blunt trauma to save the muscle, he had a severe head injury. So severe that the resultant pressure within his skull remained erratic and extremely difficult to control medicinally. Intracranial pressures (ICPs) had been climbing all week long, becoming more unwieldy with each passing day. According to the neurosurgeons, a craniotomy to relieve the ICP, given the extent of other injuries, would be ill-advised. Any meaningful brain function was unlikely to return. Each mmHg rise in pressure further bolstered that conclusion. By the end of the week, there was no brain activity.

His face still haunts me. His eyes appeared the way a goldfish would if you held the poor creature in the palm of your hand and squeezed. There was hardly a bone in his body that wasn't held in some sort of traction; no portion of his anatomy was not covered with a bandage or cast. The skin you could observe was taut with the many liters of fluid infused in order to maintain blood pressure and sedation. Over the span of the week, this goldfish had transformed into a blowfish, swollen and lifeless, washed up on the end of life's shore.

We had discussions with his family throughout the week, preparing for the inevitable conversation to come. Family members shuffled in and out of the ICU room all week, politely asking for updates as to his condition. That weekend, the weekend of my personal visit to the ED with dismal scans, his sweet mother agreed to withdraw care. His injuries were not survivable. The tears streamed vivid in my mind as I told her what she needed to hear. "He had been doing so good!" She cried, "He had a job, going to school, and he had just purchased the motorcycle in celebration." "He was just doing SO good; I am so proud of him."

Detaching myself from the reality of the situation is the only way I have found to cope with such situations. But in this particular instance, with this particular patient, I couldn't manage to create the distance. As much as there are happy moments like graduations and weddings, there are equal amounts of tragedy. Since I admitted him, I had been his doctor, catering to all that was necessary, conducting all bedside procedures, mediating communication between all the treatment teams, and providing continual updates for the family. After two years of clinical experience as a surgical resident, this one patient allowed me to showcase all my clinical skills, *unlike the 'Rite of Passage' within the Methodist ED, which mainly tested work capacity.* I felt confident I could handle anything in that ICU setting. I made every clinical decision; my attending merely sat back and allowed me to be the physician.

Some contend that you become a doctor when you receive your white coat or, perhaps, when you graduate from medical school, or even when you have passed all your examinations required from the accrediting bodies. But the moment I truly felt capable as a physician was treating that patient. From the Agrirama where a dream of being a doctor had germinated to letting go of all trepidation in its self-recognition, I had finally accepted, in my heart, that I was a physician. Imposter syndrome had fled from my consciousness. [21]

I had returned to my ICU shift for my overnight shift; unbeknownst to me, it would be my last day as a practicing doctor. Dr. Ceppa had scheduled my bronchoscopy for early the next morning; I was somewhat excited to fall asleep with a bit of help from anesthesia. Before doing so, the night before, I had ample time to be with the family whose boy I had taken care of for the greater portion of a week as we commenced to withdraw care.

At nearly 3 am, the patient's closest family members entered the intensive care unit room. I remained a quiet presence in the room as they all said their goodbyes. The mother was kind enough to invite me into their prayer circle as the family bowed their heads in unison in honor of the soon-to-be departed. When the prayer was done, the tearful mother motioned to me their readiness; I turned off the respirator. Leaning over the casts, wires, and monitors, I placed my stethoscope on his swollen chest and thought about my upcoming biopsy in just a few hours. I gazed upon his lifeless, waterlogged eyes, bloodshot and fixed, attempting to maintain any semblance of composure as I listened for breath sounds. I couldn't help imagining my own heart being auscultated. The family encircled me in anticipation of my next words.

As his heart sounds began to fade into a distant thumping, the silence was deafening amongst the members of his family. He would be the first person that I pronounced dead as a sole physician, and he would be the last. Belief in coincidence continues to wane; he was 27 years old, the same age as me. Through the arms of my stethoscope, I followed his diminishing heartbeat until its last threads were torn. As he slipped into the ineffable void and peaceful stillness, I was overwhelmed with the notion that we shared a similar trajectory. I was not far behind him.

Hope is a good breakfast, but an ill supper.
Francis Bacon, Apothegms. No. 95.

I began walking across campus from Eskenazi Hospital to the Simon Cancer Center where most of our thoracic surgery operations are conducted. Every step across the green plush lawn released a flurry of butterflies loose within my stomach. After arriving to a familiar waiting room and walking through the preoperative area, I traveled directly back to the bronchoscopy suite, where I had been many times before. Dr. Ceppa, among others, was waiting. That's the last thing I remember until I woke up from the anesthetic.

"It's cancer," I don't know who told me, but the message was clear. Dr. Ceppa was hugging me as tears were welling up in my eyes. Still emotionally labile as the sedation had barely worn off when I came to, I was sobbing as they rolled me back to the post-operative area. A couple of puzzled faces would cross me while being escorted to the post-anesthesia holding area; familiar faces of colleagues and friends who were bewildered as to what was happening and why I was in such an emotional state.

The exact pathology wouldn't be confirmed for at least another couple of days, only that it was clear that it was cancer. Meanwhile, my family made a trip from southeast Georgia to Indiana. Other than anxiety and angst, the next few days were also met with a hopeful apprehension that this was all but a bad dream. Maybe, I would wake up and continue with my next scheduled rotation, for which I was excited to begin in the cardiac intensive care unit for an entire month with one of our best ICU doctors. As much as I was happy my family had come to support me, I hoped they wouldn't be there when I awoke. Their presence was validation of reality. The next morning, my brother was on the couch in my condo, solidifying that conclusion. I realized I wouldn't be returning to any scheduled rotation for many moons to come.

The final pathology on my bronchoscopic sample taken from the lymph nodes in my chest draining the primary mass in my left lung would result within a few days. My mom and I were at my condo on 13th and Alabama in Old Northside when Dr. Ceppa called me to request if she could come by. Immediately, these sent bells ringing in my ear: if it were good news, why wouldn't she just call? The fact that she wanted to speak face to face did not bode well. "Of course!" I said, ready to squash the mounting anticipation hopefully revealing a miracle.

As if to soften the blow of the coming news, the spring afternoon couldn't have been more beautiful. I met Dr. Ceppa in my condo courtyard, which was well-manicured and orderly, with perfectly trimmed bushes lining each of the two-story units. The diamond-shaped arrangement of the complex welcomed visitors through a black iron fence, and the dark green grass contrasted well with the newly painted pale blue exterior. I was proud of the investment I had made in equity during the six years I was committing to residency here. "Maybe I would keep it?" I would say to myself. Indianapolis had become a home for me; I had gotten used to idea that I might be here for a while. Of course, that future never came to fruition with the news I was about to receive.

I led Dr. Ceppa up to the condo entrance and introduced her to my Mom, who was anxiously awaiting. My two tiger moms, one natural, one adopted, finally meeting. I scurried over to the kitchen to heat a batch of green tea as if to delay the inevitable. As the bronze kettle simmered, so did the feeling of fearful trepidation. We sat on my already worn couch where I had spent many nights sleeping, too tired from work to champion the stairs. Steam from the tea was still rolling surface of our blue mugs; my mom and I were gripping our chairs, awaiting the verdict...

"Small Cell Lung Cancer," she said.

"Uhhh, what?!"

1. Moris, D., E.K. Paulson, and T.N. Pappas, *Diagnosis and Management of Acute Appendicitis in Adults: A Review.* Jama, 2021. **326**(22): p. 2299-2311.
2. (VA), U.S.D.o.V.A. *National Center for Veterans Analysis and Statistics* 2017; Available from: https://www.va.gov/vetdata/docs/QuickFacts/2017_Veterans_Profile_Fact_Sheet.PDF.
3. Health, E. *History of Eskanzi Health.* Available from: https://www.eskenazihealth.edu/about/history.
4. Akram, S.M. and J. Koirala, *Histoplasmosis*, in *StatPearls*. 2021, StatPearls Publishing
Copyright © 2021, StatPearls Publishing LLC.: Treasure Island (FL).
5. Chinn, I.K. and W.T. Shearer, *Severe Combined Immunodeficiency Disorders.* Immunol Allergy Clin North Am, 2015. **35**(4): p. 671-94.
6. Wheat, L.J., et al., *Histoplasmosis.* Infect Dis Clin North Am, 2016. **30**(1): p. 207-27.
7. Wheat, L.J., et al., *Clinical practice guidelines for the management of patients with histoplasmosis: 2007 update by the Infectious Diseases Society of America.* Clin Infect Dis, 2007. **45**(7): p. 807-25.
8. Bray, F., et al., *Global cancer statistics 2018: GLOBOCAN estimates of incidence and mortality worldwide for 36 cancers in 185 countries.* CA Cancer J Clin, 2018. **68**(6): p. 394-424.
9. Hoffman, R.M. and R. Sanchez, *Lung Cancer Screening.* Med Clin North Am, 2017. **101**(4): p. 769-785.
10. Aberle, D.R., et al., *Reduced lung-cancer mortality with low-dose computed tomographic screening.* N Engl J Med, 2011. **365**(5): p. 395-409.
11. Howe, G.K. and R.W. Clapp, *Are we winning or losing the war on cancer? Deciphering the propaganda of NCI's 33-year war.* New Solut, 2004. **14**(2): p. 109-24.
12. Sung, H., et al., *Global Cancer Statistics 2020: GLOBOCAN Estimates of Incidence and Mortality Worldwide for 36 Cancers in 185 Countries.* CA Cancer J Clin, 2021. **71**(3): p. 209-249.
13. National Cancer Institute: Surveillance, E., and End Results Program, *Cancer Stat Facts: Lung and Bronchus Cancer.* 2019.

14. Spiro, S.G.S., G.A. , *Centennial Review: One Hundred Years of Lung Cancer.* Am J Respir Crit Care Med, 2005. **172**: p. 523-529.

15. Cordain, L., et al., *Origins and evolution of the Western diet: health implications for the 21st century.* Am J Clin Nutr, 2005. **81**(2): p. 341-54.

16. Steliarova-Foucher, E., et al., *Geographical patterns and time trends of cancer incidence and survival among children and adolescents in Europe since the 1970s (the ACCISproject): an epidemiological study.* Lancet, 2004. **364**(9451): p. 2097-105.

17. Davis, D.L. and B.H. Magee, *Cancer and industrial chemical production.* Science, 1979. **206**(4425): p. 1356, 1358.

18. Raj, A., et al., *Achieving Gender and Social Equality: More Than Gender Parity Is Needed.* Acad Med, 2019. **94**(11): p. 1658-1664.

19. Su, R., J. Rounds, and P.I. Armstrong, *Men and things, women and people: a meta-analysis of sex differences in interests.* Psychol Bull, 2009. **135**(6): p. 859-884.

20. Swartz, M.A., *The physiology of the lymphatic system.* Adv Drug Deliv Rev, 2001. **50**(1-2): p. 3-20.

21. Thomas, M. and S. Bigatti, *Perfectionism, impostor phenomenon, and mental health in medicine: a literature review.* Int J Med Educ, 2020. **11**: p. 201-213.

___7___

Chance

Probabilities conduct the conduct of the wise man.
Cicero, De Natura Deorum. Bk. I, ch. 5. sec. 12.

Shellshocked and pouring tears, my mom and I were seated together on my living room couch beyond consolation in my small studio condo in downtown Indianapolis. I had purchased the condo expecting to live there for a minimum of six years, the duration of my residency; I thought it would prove valuable in gaining equity while embarking on my future life. Building a reputation as a talented young surgeon with skill and knowledge exceeding my current post-graduate years, my future as a surgeon quickly evaporated. My mom, barely comprehending the implications of four words, I, knowing all too well what they meant. Less of a diagnosis and more of a death sentence.

Small Cell Lung Cancer (SCLC).

How? I can grasp that cancer, in and of itself, wasn't beyond the realm of possibility, but how could it be *THIS* diagnosis? At 28 years old, no less? As a physician, you are taught how to rank possible diagnoses based on all the information at your disposal. Chief among them is *age*. Depending on age, your risk for certain illnesses can be properly stratified by your physician. And for me, SCLC would have been at the bottom of that list if it had even made the list at all. The average person diagnosed with SCLC is around 65 to 75 years old with an extremely heavy smoking history![1, 2] Allow me to elucidate to explain how farfetched the proposition.

When you think about lung cancer, think about it in two major divisions: Non-small cell lung cancer and small cell lung cancer.[3] SCLC is the *MOST* aggressive form of lung cancer, accounts for 14% of overall lung cancer cases and affects 30,000 Americans each year, 0.01% of the general population. Most have *extensive* disease[4] by the time of their diagnosis, attempting curative resection untenable, unfathomable even. [5-7] There are two major reasons to operate to resect cancer: cure or palliate. Cure is obvious. A palliative operation might relieve an obstruction in a major organ or vessel, i.e. a tumor obstructing the flow of the intestine or the blood flow of a major blood vessel. Tumor debulking can be another reason, but let's keep it simple. Otherwise, why go through all the trouble? And at this point, I was no candidate for either a curative resection or palliation *yet.*

The way we discuss SCLC is also telling. I'm sure you've heard of the different stages of cancer. One, two, three, and four. This refers to the tumor, node, and metastasis (TNM) schema for the classification of cancer. We characterize each cancer with these three aspects, which indicate the severity and extent of disease, thus directing treatment and research efforts accordingly.

For example, my *primary tumor* was 3 cm in diameter, thereabouts, positioned in my upper portion of my lower lobe of my left lung (*say that ten times as fast as you can*). As far as we could tell, lymph nodes were involved throughout my chest crossing my midline, left to right, from the position of the primary tumor. There remained the possibility that it already had reached my brain, i.e., having gone to another organ system or *metastasized.* T (*tumor*), N (*node*), M (*metastasis*). Makes sense, right? If it hadn't gone to the brain, I was stage 3B. If it had, I was stage 4.[8] Stage 4 cancer! *Obviously, there is nuance to staging that I was inclined to rescue you from. And me, for that matter.*

There was deliberation on the findings in my brain. Much deliberation, in fact, even at the national level! My case was presented at an infectious disease (ID) conference where the best minds in their field would discuss the imaging findings as an interesting vignette. *From doctor to an interesting case now. Oh, how wonderful!* The central question posed was, "Did the imaging findings have an infectious etiology, and thus nothing to do with the findings in my chest?" I imagined a conference room full of doctors stroking their beards at my silhouette produced via computed tomography (CT) scan and brain magnetic resonance imaging (MRI).

"Did it represent a past resolved infection that I could've contracted at a young age being from endemic parts of the southeastern United States?" For example, other than the fungus Histoplasmosis as previously mentioned,[9] the intracellular parasite known as *Toxoplasmosis gondii* was suspect. The parasite induces behavioral changes in its host as it enters the brain, making the host less risk aversive. Mice infected with *T. gondii* do not find cat urine anxiety-provoking, in fact, sexually arousing, increasing the chances of the rodent being eaten by its secondary host, the feline. Cysts can be found in human brains from a previously resolved *T. gondii* infection.[10-12] My brain scan revealed similarly shaped minute cystic lesions puzzling the conference room full of ID physicians somewhere in Texas. "Or was it cancer that had traveled to my brain?" Thankfully, *it would prove very important for my survival that these questions were NOT answered at this time.* Due to the current sizes of the brain lesions (<5mm), a biopsy was virtually impossible. They were aptly referred to as *punctate.*

I shall show the cinders of my spirits Through the ashes of my chance. *Shakespeare, Antony and Cleopatra. Act v, sc. 2, 1. 173.*

Let's move on. At this point in time, it didn't matter, but this debate would come into play later. Note that I used the word *extensive* to describe the current state of my cancer, both clinically and radiologically. This is not without purpose. Although the medical community has decided the formulation of the *TNM* classification to describe most, if not all, cancers, when describing SCLC, most practitioners still refer to this particular lung cancer as *limited* and *extensive.* Why do they reduce this classification to a simple dichotomy? [6] Most often, at the initial diagnosis, the cancer is already at advanced stages not amenable to surgical correction. Due to the simple specimen unavailability, we are left with scant data for in-between stages. In other words, *limited-stage* disease is seldom observed. Moreover, if you do catch it early, it almost always comes back![5]

Let's recall that a cancerous cell is one that loses its ability to steward its own growth properly. Either through loss of function or gain of function, a cancerous cell proliferates unchecked and, after multiple divisions, culminates in a mass of cancerous cells, in other words, a tumor. (*According to the germ cell theory of cancer, we will return to the metabolic theory later.*)[13, 14] SCLC is a champion at this. How come? Well, it has critical mutations in its DNA, which yield its destructive power. Those genes: TP53 and RB1 (Tumor Protein 53, Retinoblastoma 1).[6, 15, 16] TP53 is known as the 'Guardian of the Genome.'[17] This name is apropos; a loss of function in this gene leads to a litany of cancers. For example, a familial loss of this gene, one that you inherit, is known as Li Fraumeni syndrome, where patients are plagued by a range of soft tissue neoplasms, e.g., breast cancer. [18]

DNA, or Deoxyribonucleic acid, is the molecule that stores the information for every cell in your body to follow. It's like a script that becomes unraveled to reveal a particular cell's destiny. Depending on the portion of the script that is unraveled, an undifferentiated cell, one that hasn't been read its personal script yet, will be dictated towards a particular function once the script is revealed: muscle cell, bone cell, gut cell, etc. Amazingly, every cell in your body has all the information to form every other cell. It depends on what portion is read or expressed! From DNA through messenger molecules, a protein product is created carrying out desired functions. Viola! You have learned the 'Central Dogma of Molecular Biology.' [19] And TP53 and RB1, if functioning correctly, are the major players, or stewards, of this process.

Thus, a deformity in TP53 sets the stage for many downstream mutations to occur throughout the life of the cancer. Whoever was charged with carrying the scripts for your cellular machinery one day had a tumble down the stairs and, like an unraveling toilet paper roll, exposed your delicate genetic code to a dirty bathroom floor in an old 7/11 gas station. Regarding SCLC, TP53 and RB1 genes were out for prolonged smoke breaks instead of tidying up as the scripts were soaking up the filth and acquiring additional mutations from each revolution. There are four times as many mutations driving SCLC's growth compared to breast cancer and almost ten times as compared to prostate cancer. [20] The *mutational burden* of SCLCs could thus be described as quite heavy. *Disclaimer: mutational burden doesn't necessarily correlate with severity of disease.* Some nasty cancers are driven by just one or two mutations; [21, 22] it can indicate the degree of disarray and tumult within the genome.

SCLC belongs to a spectrum of cancers that derive their lineage from *neuroendocrine cells*. [2] *Neuroendocrine cells. Neuroendocrine cells.* A discussion about the various functions of neuroendocrine cells is well beyond the scope of this book but know that they are abundant throughout your entire body serving to integrate neural information with your endocrine (hormone-producing) system, including your lungs. Although they make up less than 1% of lung tissue, dubbed *pulmonary neuroendocrine cells* (PNECs), they play essential roles in physiology, protection from pathogens, and reaction to allergens. [23, 24] All this information will come back around to make sense. I promise.

When PNECs become cancerous, they are called *pulmonary neuroendocrine tumors*, or PNETs. SCLC is a type of PNET. PNETs are responsible for 25% of lung cancers. [25] The number one reported presenting symptom is cough. *That explains that nagging cough.* Others include shortness of breath, fatigue, and other signs of distant metastasis when involving other organ systems. *For example, my headaches with the brain and the brief episode of aphasia as mentioned in the foreword. [6, 26] Things are coming together.* In retrospect, the signs were all there, insidious and nonspecific as they were. In fact, the reason why many present so late in their course and with *extensive* disease is because the warning signs are seemingly innocuous.

The outcomes following diagnosis and subsequent standard of care (SOC), chemotherapy and/or radiation, are not the least bit encouraging. Less than five percent of people are alive after two years.[6, 27] Since the early 1970s, survival has not improved demonstrably despite our best efforts. Median survival in extensive-stage SCLC is reported to be 7.0 months and 8.9 months in 1972-1981 and 1982-1990, respectively.[27] And after three decades of medical advances, there has been no appreciable progress in treating this particular cancer, landing it on the Recalcitrant Cancer list in 2012.[5, 6] Recalcitrant Cancers have less than 50% survival at five years.[28]

Again, returning to the central question…how could it be THIS cancer? As previously mentioned, this cancer occurs in elderly heavy smokers. As one of my oncologists would say in the future, Charles Rudin MD at Memorial Sloan Kettering in New York City, "You have to earn this diagnosis." What he meant was that you got to do a lot of smoking for a long time. Like two packs a day type of smoking for thirty years! I had been exposed to secondhand smoke all my life and as much as any good-time Charley, but this would not explain such a dismal diagnosis. The United States Preventative Task Force (USPTF) of 2014 doesn't even suggest screening asymptomatic adults until 55 and 80 years of age; and only if they have a 30-pack-year smoking history, have quit in the past 15 years, or who currently smoke.[29]

I was dismayed to learn of a small population with little to no smoking history who are found to have this unsettling diagnosis. The numbers are staggering. In a retrospective multicenter cohort study published in Chest journal in 2020 by Thomas et al. reviewing electronic medical records of 5,632 patients diagnosed with SCLC, 1.8% were never smokers. [30] *I should play the lottery; maybe that would've helped with medical bills.* Although, I did win a brand-new bike after only selling one raffle ticket in third grade in a school-wide competition. They had to pull me out of detention to award me the bike. I was a rambunctious child of divorce; give little ole me a break. But imagine my confusion! It still cracks me up to this day.

Even though I was devastated by this news, I was flabbergasted by the sheer improbability. Someone must not want me around! This stuff I briefly described about SCLC was fresh in my mind. It was my job to know things like this. My job as a cardiothoracic resident was partly to counsel and inform patients with diagnoses like these.

For example, I was working on a surgical service during my 2nd year of residency, which focused on the hepato-pancreato-biliary (liver-pancreas-biliary, HPB) system. A common operation is removing the gallbladder (gallbladder = biliary). My major responsibility at this point in my training was to see consults and to report back to the OR, only helping operate when the opportunity presented itself. I loved all aspects of surgery: cardiothoracic, HPB, breast, you name it. As long as surgical steel was involved, count me in.

In fact, a word to all those aspiring surgeons, get all the touches you can on whatever service you are on. Handling any type of tissue only makes you better and better. You will never be *that* good that a seemingly menial operation is not worth your time in training. Imprint that in your mind. You will never *deserve* this despite all the schooling and research that you've done. Never take it for granted. *Heed my words.* You'll never know when that privilege is no longer.

I was paged to see a consult towards the end of the day. Dissecting the patient's chart, it was clear from her labs and imaging, this sixty-year-old woman had pancreatic cancer—another cancer on the list of Recalcitrant cancer list with a dismal prognosis.[28] I finished my review and walked to the patient's room, making sure to note all the tell-tell symptoms of pancreatic cancer: yellowish coloring of the skin (jaundice), itchy skin (hyperbilirubinemia), diarrhea (malabsorption), abdominal pain, nausea, vomiting, weight loss, etc. [31]

Upon entry into the 2-person patient room, it was clear that her case was extensive, instantly noting the discoloration of her skin. You could have told me that she just had just gotten out of a bath of iodine, and I would have believed you. I closed the curtained division in an attempt to gain more privacy so I could speak with her and her husband, undoubtedly in vain, as the chatter from the other patient's family was hard to ignore. Their hands were interlocked forcefully, evidenced by the whites and reds of the finger's creases. I assumed their primary team had already informed them of the findings as they had ordered the labs and imaging. *Never assume.*

I introduced myself and began to explain how we would address pancreatic cancer. "You see," drawing her a picture of the anatomy we would be resecting, "we will likely remove the pancreas at these sections, here and here...." I stopped abruptly when her bewilderment became obvious. Confused, she replies, "I have cancer?!" Alarms began sounding off in my head like a Soviet prisoner had just escaped the Gulag! You would think the primary medicine service would have informed them before calling a surgical service. Lesson: *Never assume.*

As a junior doctor, I would reserve those conversations for the attending. It's polite, and they have more experience in breaking bad news. I would be in quiet attendance taking note of their eloquence and delivery. I hadn't quite mastered my personal approach to breaking bad news to patients even though we had down this countless in-patient simulations in medical school. I wanted to find my own way, more artfully than what a rubric required. Instead, I carelessly had thrust myself right into the thick of a tough conversation.

Holding back my frustration at the primary service neglecting their duty to the patient, I calmly replied, "Yes, ma'am. The cancer is blocking the normal drainage from your pancreas and other organs and causing many of your symptoms that brought you in." Wiping her eyes, cutting right to the chase, "How long do I have?" she asked behind her shaggy hair made frizzy and grey from age and cigarette smoking. I had been studying up on HPB pathology while on the service, so I was prepared for this question. "Well, the five-year survival for someone in your position can be as low as 6%, ranging from 2% to 9%."[31]

There it was…my ignorant mistake. I walked away from that patient's room, thinking I had done my job. I had informed the patient, right? I was proud of myself for doing my duty as a doctor. However, that pride was misplaced. What's the old adage? "Pride comes before the fall." Although, my fault would not be in my courage to be able to softly and kindly '*inform*' this poor lady of her prognosis. And make no mistake, there was no pleasure and no shortage of empathy on my part in its delivery. But these cold figures were insinuating that I had the power to predict the future! No one. And I mean NO ONE can tell you how long you have on this earth. Here was this young, cocky doctor with barely an inkling of life experience, '*informing*' the patient on something he had read in a book. How audacious! Without a thought of the downstream effects that this may have had on her life and overall survival…

PsychoOncology is a relatively new field in medicine exploring the relationship between the mind and patient outcomes with cancer. In 1989, one of the first investigations into the mental state of a patient and subsequent outcomes was conducted. Metastatic breast cancer patients who received weekly counseling sessions lived 18 months longer than controls, which was not explained by disease severity or differences in treatment.[32, 33] Along with improved survival, psychosocial counseling has been shown to reduce relapse in breast cancer at 11-year follow-up. [34, 35] A similar study was done in bronchial carcinomas, a type of lung cancer.[36]

How can this be? The mind and body are more interconnected than the westernized world appreciate. We know one of the main pathways of this connection: the hypothalamic-pituitary-adrenal (HPA) axis. In short, this is a major pathway for this communication mediated by many vehicles, namely cortisol.[32, 37] Perturbations in this pathway (e.g., stress) can lead to abnormal metabolism and depression.[32] High levels thereof have been linked to increased cancer cell turnover and metastatic spread in animal models.[38] Stress can increase the amount of epinephrine circulating which increases vascular endothelial growth factor, increasing the blood supply to tumors.[39]

There are more examples of this biological connection, but you get the point.

This brief moment in my medical career would be one of my biggest regrets. In a short conversation, I completely turned this lady's world upside down. I regret not telling her what I needed to tell her. That there are things that you can do to curb your fate. What I would soon tell myself. What I had to be reminded of throughout my future treatment. I am not a statistic. I'll decide when to lose hope. I will fight this. I will find a way. Despite my current resolve, I am reserved to have that woman's tears seared into my memories until an early grave. I never saw her again save for her tears seared into my memory.

All the affairs of men hang by a slender thread; and sudden chance brings to ruin what once was strong.
Ovid, Epistulae ex Ponto. Bk. iv. Epis. 3, 1. 35.

Dr. Ceppa had left. Neither of us had touched our tea which by now as lukewarm at best. All my family would subsequently travel up to Indiana. Even my dad would make the trip, who never ventured more than 100 miles from our farm in South Georgia. As a family, we were convinced the cows were cognizant of when daddy traveled, always managing to escape to roam the country highways. When he traveled outside that allowed radius, it never failed that he'd receive an unwelcomed phone call, "Hey Joe, the cows are out," sending my dad into a hurricane of discontent and expletives. The fact that my dad was now in Indiana was no small gesture.

Unfortunately, my small studio condo did not lend itself as an adequate space to host much of a crowd. As cozy and hospitable as my one-room palace was, only my brother and I would be able to maintain any degree of comfort in the week following. In my mind, that condo had served one purpose: provide everything I needed to come home and study to be a heart surgeon comfortably. Nothing else mattered. Positioned so close to the hospital, my commute was minimized to less than three minutes. Perfect for being on call. Located downtown, I took a hit on space, leaving little room for visitors. Although in the coming months, that capacity would be tested.

News of my potentially terminal diagnosis spread like wildfire, and not without me fanning the flames. Certainly, my sobbing in response to the confirmation that I had cancer following the biopsy didn't help matters, nor did the disinhibition provided by anesthesia. In fact, two of my best resident friends would coincidentally stop their morning duties consenting patients and opening for their respective attending's cases to visit with me. They had seen me being rolled down the hallway following the procedure. The cat was out of the bag, so to speak, and the condo would become a revolving door of friends and family providing their support. All of which was profound in retrospect, as you never know how much people care for you until tragedy strikes. I felt undeserving, nay unworthy, of the geyser of affection unleashed before me.

That same evening after the confirmation of cancer, I called many of my best friends in Indy at the time. Explained the situation. I informed them that the best thing to do was to go to my favorite pub and play my favorite pub game: shuffleboard! The game required finesse, planning, and no shortage of sabotage of your opponents! Oh, it's good fun! In no way did I want to be solemn. Physically, I felt fine. There would be time for moping later. I wanted to celebrate life. Assuredly, bad times were soon to come. *I was safe in that assumption as time would tell.*

We had a big night filled with laughter and cries. From the short two years, I had been in Indiana up to the D-day, it was evident how many altruistic people I had met and befriended. I knew there was a reason why I had chosen IU as my residency of choice. The people. No other residency struck me in the same manner; I felt like I was home. And I almost didn't take the interview; I was exhausted after a lengthy interview season. Indiana University was the second to last program I interviewed. It would have been doubtful to have gotten the degree of support if I chose a residency anywhere else. *Clearly, I am biased.*

Indiana University reopened their research track in response to D-day, so that I could possibly rejoin the integrated Cardiothoracic track once I had kicked the cancer. Although, they weren't obligated to do anything at the end of my *per annum* contract. I was officially diagnosed on May 31st, 2019, towards the end of the school year. They allowed me to work on my own time, publishing over eight peer-reviewed studies during my two years undergoing extensive cancer treatment. And when they were forced to let me go, they ensured that I would always have a home at Indiana University. I am forever indebted to the administration and faculty who helped me stay afloat both intellectually and financially.

Not only did I work for some top-notch and good-hearted cardiothoracic surgeons and other surgeons involved in general surgery, but I made life-long friends with fellow residents. I cultivated relationships that I will cherish for the rest of my life. Shortly after the diagnosis, they were planning fundraisers for medical bills, purchasing reading material for long days in infusion chairs, and any other creature comforts you could imagine: blankets, supplements, food, juicer, you name it.

Moreover, in the coming months, friends from each significant stage of my life would reach out to show their support: grade school, high school, college, and medical school. In no way could I ever fully express my immense gratitude and how appreciative I am to have such amazing people in my life, too many to count. Moreover, I am fortunate to have the opportunity, the ability rather, to praise and pay homage to those who stepped up when they felt the need to. Me writing these words wouldn't have been possible without you.

Soon after starting chemotherapy, a gang of friends from medical school actively in their respective residencies would travel from all over to Indy to see me. Well over ten dear friends! Words don't really encapsulate how much that meant. You don't have much time in residency to even go home to see your family! They chose to come to see me! There aren't words, and I am forever thankful for their friendship.

I wrote a gang of letters to my family, friends, and coworkers to be sent on my demise. It took me over a week. I entrusted them to my dear friend Sam. It was like a goodbye letter before I went off to war, knowing the likelihood of me returning when that ship had pushed off was unlikely. I was aware that I might not always have the energy to express my gratitude and love. Postage was purchased and everything. Two rubber bands tightly embrace my affectionate wishes for their futures; however, I hope they never see the inside of a mailbox.

Some might think it imprudent to put your life on display as I had. And I will be honest; after a couple of months of constant texts and voicemails, I was exhausted. Emotionally exhausted. Each person I talked to took me right back to D-day. And I would cry all the same, flushed with all the fear and heartache reliving that day that changed my entire life.

But then something amazing happened. It was as if a switch turned off. I had talked about it so much that it no sway on my emotions any longer. I recall talking to one of my childhood friends who was in bitter tears when he first heard about it a few months later, and he asked me, "Dude, why are you not more upset? I mean, I'm a mess!" I replied matter-of-factly, "It just is what it is. Just gonna do what I can to beat it." I had to spend the rest of the phone call telling him it was going to be okay. Kind of a weird position: consoling another about your own cancer. But each conversation with old friends would be a reminder of why to fight forward. Reminiscence would be fuel.

(Aside: If you are caught in a similar situation for whatever reason, cancer or other crises, never feel obligated to have a certain emotion for the sake of others. If you are a well-meaning friend wanting someone you care about to open up, you should understand that it is exhausting, sometimes even fearmongering, to go back to that dark place again. If you are genuinely that well-meaning supporter, I shouldn't begin by asking, "How are you?" or asking about the condition itself. Restore some sense of normality with menial conversation. Talk about what YOU did that day and invite them to share. They may have a lot to unload but just aren't ready. End the conversation in a subtle way making a point to remind them that you are here for any support.

If you feel like you aren't doing enough, don't worry! Simply being there, present, speaks volumes. You don't even have to talk about anything. Your presence is a gift. Remember, they know you love them. A simple message, "I love you, and I am here if you need me," goes a long way. I promise, in time, they will get back to you. And hopefully with good news. Remember that a lack of response may be for practical reasons. There may not be any information to share for updates. The journey through cancer is met with multiple periods of limbo. Between waiting on scans and test results, cancer patients are in a constant purgatory of uncertainty. It took me some practice to be comfortable in that uncertainty.)

Chance is a word void of sense; nothing can exist without a cause.
Voltaire, A Philosophical Dictionary

Early on, I didn't see the utility in trying to hide this information. It felt better to let it out. Relieving. Therapeutic. If you know me, you know I'm an open book. *Clearly, I am writing this.* The chances of me keeping this information quiet were slim to nil. Moreover, it would be challenging to cloak when I stopped showing up for work. But in some odd way, I thought that if I did not fear the news and embraced the challenge, I could possibly change the overall trajectory. Defense mechanism? Likely. Instead, I regarded this strategy as akin to the principle of distribution of responsibility. The more people I leaned on to make sense of what the Hell was going on, maybe it would lessen the blow. In retrospect, it may have been a little more than I bargained for.

The outpouring of love from my colleagues and faculty, extended family, and friends, both childhood and new, was unsurpassed. A more supportive foundation to fight this cancer could not be found. Even my teammates from my collegiate soccer years came to get a few last touches with me on the pitch before entering treatment. Reminiscing with old friends would inevitably conclude with, "If anyone can beat this, you can!" Encouraging, no doubt! Deep within, I knew the foe that I was up against. Vindictive, harsh, unrelenting. The same attributes I would have to adopt if I had a prayer at surviving. I would make every effort to make my body incredibly inhospitable to cancer, not only in the traditional standard of care treatments but also through dietary modifications via juicing or hyperalimentation of nutrients and supplements.

After the first couple of months following D-day, that welcomed support became progressively challenging to manage. However, I wouldn't dream of discouraging anyone from contacting me to extend goodwill. Phone calls, text messages, and mail were constantly pilling up. I recall spending entire days on the phone: updating, explaining, planning dinners, brunches, etc. I didn't want to let anyone down; all these wonderful people just wanting to help. What a profound gesture! I tried to satisfy everyone to my own detriment. And we have come full circle (Type C Personality).[40] Eventually, I had to change my phone number.

Strangely enough, the best flavor of support was when people gave me room to breathe. That space nominally stemmed from close friends and family who were well acquainted with my personality. As outgoing as I am, I am an introvert that replenishes the vitality for life by ironically being alone. However, I did not wish for people to mistake me for being rude and ungrateful. I now realize how ridiculous a proposition that is, but, at the time, it made sense. Outcome: Spent more time with acquaintances and well-wishers instead of time with family and close friends. I regret those minutes I cannot get back. Regrets and guilt yet again. Lesson: Protect your time! Circle the wagons!

The summer before my *Rite of Passage* (2018) and *D-day* (2019), I had just finished the autobiography of David Goggins, *"Can't Hurt Me: Master Your Mind and Defy the Odds."[41]* I found his story extremely motivating, reading it twice, back-to-back, in rapid succession. If you are unfamiliar, Mr. Goggins is an ultramarathon triathlete, former Navy Seal and Army Ranger serving in the Iraq and Afghanistan War, in active military for around 20 years, philanthropist, and all-around badass. His multitude of achievements is incessant, like his personality.

His warrior ethos and determination are as alive today as they were in his earlier years. His Instagram account, for which he follows no one, is littered with motivational videos and challenges for his subscribers. For example, a particular task he challenges his subscribers annually is running 4 miles every 4 hours for 48 hours. He was the sole reason I was inspired to stop driving to work and start running, or in spite of the weather rather, as a resident at Indiana University.

He lived a good portion of his life in Indiana, and the thought of he and I running on those same trails was inspirational. I wanted to emulate his mental resilience applying the same discipline to my daily life and future practice as a cardiac surgeon striving for excellence despite the cost. I had begun to and paid the price. *Recall my running a marathon after a twenty-four-hour call night?* That was a struggle but good for building mental resilience. What if it were a patient in my operating room on cardiopulmonary bypass and the procedure wasn't going well? Are you going to fold just because you are tired? Failure isn't an option. Nor is being tired.

Not only is Goggins's capacity for pushing his physical and mental limits unparalleled, but his compassion and charity also know no bounds. In response to the tragedy that befell marines on a reconnaissance mission in 2005 during Operation Red Wings[42] during the War in Afghanistan, later popularized by the movie starring Mark Walhberg, "Lone Survivor" in 2013, Mr. Goggins began long-distance running to raise funds for the Special Operations Warrior Foundation raising millions of dollars for educations of those children of fallen service men and women. These ultramarathons span a couple of hundred miles and take days to run.

His altruism wouldn't stop there. Shortly after my grave diagnosis, I was convinced to go and retrieve a second opinion at a different institution requiring me to hop on the earliest flight out of Indianapolis. As the engines purred idly on the plane and people were still loading into the cabin, I had a call from an unknown number. I never answer those, but that day I felt inclined to do so, "Hello?" "Caleb, what's up?" an unfamiliar voice rang. "Hey, who's this?" I replied. Mr. Goggins replied in his usual fashion, "Who the fuck do you think it is?!"

I'm still unsure who told him about me, but I am happy they did. A simple phone call made a world of difference, reinvigorating me to stop at nothing in seeking a cure or at least an effective treatment. He and I would periodically remain in contact. I then decided that as long as I was breathing and could move, I would not stop. Cancer or not. And in keeping with Newton's Laws of Motion, an object in motion will remain in motion unless acted upon by another force. So, all I had to do was remain in motion.

All the affairs of men hang by a slender thread; and sudden chance brings to ruin what once was strong.
Ovid, Epistulae ex Ponto. Bk. iv. Epis. 3, 1. 35.

A major reason I shared my diagnosis and subsequently bore the consequences of making it abundantly public was due to the many influences, unsuspecting even, throughout my life that aided me in becoming a physician. I appreciated every ounce of encouragement, realized or unrealized. You never appreciate the significance you may have played in someone else's life. Only in retrospect can one fully appreciate one life's power on another. And out of respect for that impact, I thought it only courteous and dutiful to inform these game changers in my life.

Chief among them, even more than Goggins, was a guy I grew up alongside in South Georgia, which I had mentioned previously had no shortage of social despotism and hierarchies. With a single mother, I hardly fit the quintessential southern aesthetic with a nuclear family. However, a dear childhood friend fit that mold seamlessly.

His name is Chance Veazey. The last name Veazey is a household name in the area and very well-known in the community, a blue blood, so to speak. The root of the name, 'enveisié,' is Anglo-Norman French, and, in articulation, its pronunciation forces the facial muscles into a smile, precisely telling you everything you need to know about him. His captivating grin and relentless unfeigned positivity in all endeavors, social and sport, made him an infectious personality. His golden-brown hair and olive skin brought him under the sights of all the girls. Like bees and honey, people buzzed around, hoping to get stuck within his sphere of influence and warming energy. He, the Sun, and us, the mere planets orbiting around him. Some people have an innate ability to bend space and time in that way. Indeed, he is a born leader.

Chance was destined to do great things. Although an all-around 4.0 scholar multisport athlete, his passion was baseball, where he exhibited great skill far outweighing his peers, including me. Such was evident at a young age, and soon the entire community would come to the realization that this *game* wasn't just a game to this youngster. At ten years old, he was vital in securing an All-Stars Championship to South Georgia.

143

Always keeping his nose clean despite ample opportunity to do otherwise among the mountains of Natural Light cans that stack up yearly in the south, he was steady in focus. I was there to see it. When not playing in organized high-school leagues, weekends were filled with baseball tournaments and training out at the *Field of Dreams*. The *Field of Dreams,* obviously named after the 1989 film starring Kevin Costner, was a baseball field at his house on the west side of town which had room for a batting cage and much more. Coach Todd, his father, and my little league coach at one point held practices on their property occasionally. A dream to me at such a young age, but a working reality for Chance; his sights were always aimed at loftier aspirations.

All his hard work and focus would lead him to attaining a full ride on a baseball scholarship at the University of Georgia in the fall of 2009. He impressed the coaches to such an extent that the starting 2nd base position would be his for the taking as long as he continued his meteoric trajectory. His aspirations to play in the major leagues soon became realized as scouts had shown keen interest in taking him early from collegiate ball.

Moreover, he is most deserving of every bit of praise and admiration, hard-won and hard-earned. Throughout his success, he never allowed his ego to over-inflate to an unsavory level and always gave his time to others. Never meeting a stranger and accepting everyone, Chance would lend encouragement to anyone who needed it. For me, as an insecure kid from a broken home, Chance unwittingly provided much-needed encouragement on the *Field of Dreams* one afternoon. We couldn't have been much more than ten or eleven years old.

We were playing a simple game of catch, warming up our scrawny pre-adolescent arms. For whatever reason, I was off that day. My poor aim forced him to make great strides to complete the catch as we increased the gap between us. As the distance increased, as did my frequency of mistakes. Being my own worst critic, I spiraled into a cycle of negative self-talk and frustration with the fragile confidence of youth being chipped away with each unredeemable failure in the form of a wayward throw. Sullen, I was embarrassed that my skills weren't as prim and tight. We were far enough away that Chance couldn't see my eyes welling up with discontent feeling defeated and worthless.

The naturally empathic Chance, already having the confidence of a more seasoned player, picked up on my poor body language and wavering form. He ceased throwing and yelled out at me, "Caleb! You are a GOOD player! Stop being so hard yourself. Just relax and play." His emotional intelligence was far beyond his years, contrasting wildly with my labile sensitivities yet to be matured. From fifty to sixty yards away, his kind words hit me like a ton of bricks. No one had outright told me I was ever good at anything before outside of my mom. Affirmation from a fellow teammate and peer was revolutionary in gaining a foothold in self-confidence with one simple exchange.

I would continue to hold a deep reverence for Chance despite not being the best of friends. His orbit was very hard to oscillate within and became more difficult as my passions took me towards soccer and away from America's pastime. My move to the next county over only set to increase the distance but the respect and love from that childhood friendship never wilted.

Our dormant kinship would spring alive when tragedy struck Chance. He and I were both playing college ball; Stetson University and University of Georgia, soccer and baseball, respectively. At UGA, they give all athletes mopeds so they can get around campus easily to attend their many obligations throughout the day. Make no mistake; being a student-athlete is a full-time job. Leaving a study group one evening on a whiny moped still invigorated by a homer that he smashed over the fence at his last at-bat, a credulous driver carelessly pulled out directly in front of Chance's, forcing him to lay down the scooter irreversibly injuring his lower back and spinal cord in the process.

His childhood dreams germinating from the makeshift *'Field of Dreams'* and matriculating to college ball and beyond quickly evaporated in one fell swoop. The injury occurred at the thoracic level of the 8th and 10th vertebra (*around the area of the belly button*); he lost all sensory and motor function distal or below the lesion. Effectually, Chance lost his ability to walk, but moreover, the injury would rob him of bladder and bowel control.

Laid up in a hospital bed with many friends and family herded into and out of the Shepherd Center for Brain and Spinal Cord Injury in Atlanta, Chance was puzzled and heartbroken of why such an accident would happen to him? He had never committed an act so reprehensible adjudicating a sentence such as this! He fell blank in recalling any sins of the past that may have elicited such severe recompense. Certainly, nothing to steal his ability to walk! Anger and resentment soon filtered in. He had worked and toiled all his entire life in pursuit of his childhood dream, keeping away from bad influences and remaining an inspiration to everyone he encountered. And this is what he got for it? People would repeatedly say to him, "Everything happens for a reason."

As he wheeled around the white halls of the Shepherd Center, he boiled over with a deep discontent with that common adage. "Everything happens for a reason." "Does it really?" he would ask himself. He could elucidate no instance of why his dreams were ripped from him. He would begin festering in a mixture of heartbreak and anger: heartbreak from losing his one true passion in this world, anger towards God or whatever nebulous entity that was to blame. A fellow teammate would later collide with another in fielding a ball hit outfield. In another sick twist of fate, one of the players suffered an injury resulting in paralysis from the upper chest down. "What was the *reason* for all this suffering!?"

Chance would wrestle with this question for many years. He would continue with school at UGA quite successfully. Still, the life of a former college star athlete with an electric personality at one of the most renowned party schools in the nation did not mix well or mixed entirely too well. Partying and personal relationships do not lend themselves to happy cohabitation, especially when you throw in existential angst. I certainly can empathize. He would lose his high school sweetheart in all the calamity and confusion. I imagine it would not be any stretch of the imagination that he hadn't considered a life of pure nihilism henceforth.

However, he remained steadfast in supporting his brothers on the baseball team in the characteristic Veazey fashion. He could have folded from the pain of not being able to participate and withdrawn completely. But that's not Chance. Even though it must have been nigh impossible to sit in his wheelchair and gaze upon the luscious green grass fresh with dew and the freshly raked Japanese rock garden of an infield wanting nothing more than to carve up those raked lines with all his skill and prowess at 2nd base. Interminable, gentle torture, I am sure it was. *A feeling I would be soon acquainted in coming years.*

Five years after the accident, he would encounter an article by John Pavlovitz, an American pastor and author, which demonstrably changed his outlook, as well as mine. In Pavlovitz's article, *"Why Everything Does Not Happen For A Reason,"* he explores the faults in the common adage, "Everything happens for a reason." His critique predominantly holds the contention that the saying gives far too much power to the tragedy itself. Instead, he poses that things happen for no reason at all, but it is in our faith in God that comforts us throughout trying times.[43]

Pavlovitz goes on, "Instead, I prefer to understand God as One who bleeds along with us; who sits with us in our agony and weeps, not causing our distress but providing a steady, holy presence in it."[43] In other words, grace within suffering. We can choose to meet that suffering with peace and calm. Or, as Pavlovitz states, and Chance reportedly most revered, "Be encouraged as you suffer and *choose*."[43]

Powerful words, no doubt. Indeed, life is suffering. Since God gave us the power of reason, we have been doomed to contemplate the nature of the cosmos and the human condition. The fact that we are sentient beings with the awareness of our own existence comes with the self-acknowledgment of our own suffering. We walk around knowingly, ignoring the sheer fact that we will all die one day and pass into oblivion. The teachings of Jesus Christ allow us to opt for willful acceptance of our universal suffering. Whether you meet that challenge with a smile on your face or a frown is your choice.

Chance would find these words incredibly encouraging. His charisma and positivity far outweighed anything that would attempt to deter him, anyways. He would go on to graduate from UGA and take over a local State Farm Insurance agency until he started his own in January of 2021. He was reunited with Molly, his high school sweetheart; it wouldn't be long before they were married. She works in a neighboring county with special needs children.

His competitive spirit is still alive and well. He funneled his unbounded energy and love of life into bow hunting, where he has traveled as far as British Columbia to hunt big game like deer and elk. I asked him when I interviewed him about his experience, "What do you most wish you had back from before the accident?" And to my surprise, it wasn't walking. He replied, "I wish I had control over my bowel and bladder." And that struck me more than anything else, as you don't appreciate what's under the surface. Something as simple as relieving oneself on a daily basis has become a daily challenge. He is an amazing and inspiring example of human resiliency and triumph over tragedy. Chance continues to meet every hardship with the charming 'enveisié' his name so encapsulates.

Chance and I would learn this harsh fact of life. Both of us would want nothing more than to have never had to have learned it, at least not in the nature that we have. I differ from Chance in one fundamental way: *I do think that things happen for a reason, even tragedy.* Even though I, too, have been compelled to opine the contrary at times. I have settled on the fact that there is a degree of predestination in our lives; however, I think it is not immediately evident to us. Realize the Supreme Being exists outside of time and space, and what is not immediately apparent to us may come together as the universe is unfolded before you. It is only through the celestial cookie crumbs that we get a taste of what is actually taking place. Little do we know.

151

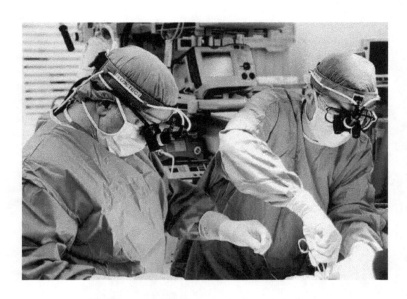

Dr. Daniel Beckman (left), Me (right)

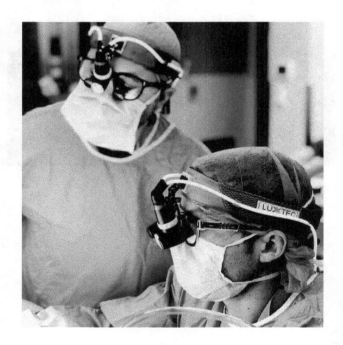

Dr. Gurion Lantz (left), Me (right)

(From right to left) Gurion Lantz MD, (top) Mark Mankins MD, (chief) Panos Vardas MD, (co-chief) Kashif Saleem MD, (photo) David Blitzer MD, (bottom) Yogesh Patel MD, Kevin Graham MD, Amanda Stram MD, Michael Kasten MD, (ME). Cardiothoracic surgery residents at Indiana University, 2017-18

Fellow Residents at IU, '20. (right to left) Mohammad Yahya Zaidi MD, Dan O'Brian MD,

Sam Rheinhardt MD, Josh Manghelli MD, Lucas McDuffie MD, ME, Neal Ramchandani MD

Sam, an excellent chef, cooked a magnificent meal as most of us were soon to be off to other institutions to continue training, beginning careers, or, in my case, continuing treatment

Dr. Everett, ME

Angelique and I following the white coat ceremony at University of Florida, '13-14

Michael and I the night before I received my change in diagnosis chowing down at a local Italian restaurant in New York City

ME, Michael Murralles, Kai Eckenrode, Jonathan Mendoza, Luis Ocejo My teammates and lifelong friends at Stetson University

My Mom and I at my brother Josh's wedding.
(Note the dark sleeve: I had just received shoulder radiation for a
metastasis that left me with severe frozen shoulder on my right side)

Josh, Mom, and ME

Josh and I overlooking Bryce Canyon during our trip out west
Mother (stepmom), ME, Teal, Father at the white coat ceremony

Mother and Dad at our home in Nashville, Georgia

159

Mother and Dad at our home in Nashville, Georgia

ME and Tealbug (sister)

David Goggins was a constant source of motivation. While Josh and I were exploring out west, he dropped in to lend some encouragement

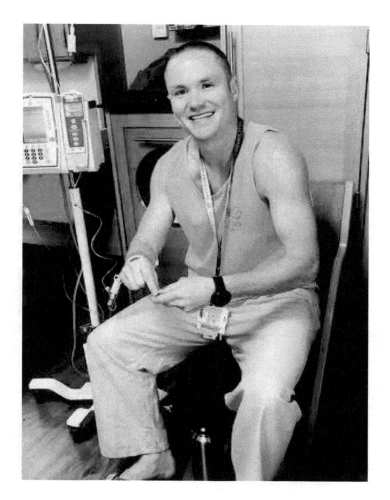

First day of chemotherapy

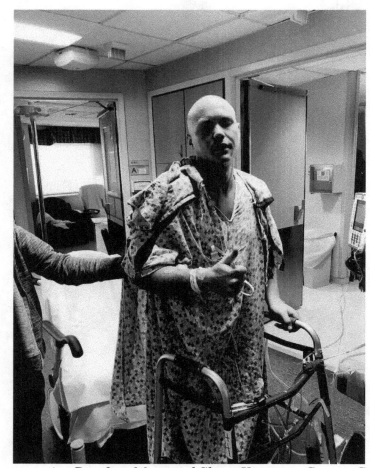

Postoperative Day 2 at Memorial Sloan Kettering Cancer Center

Saying goodbye to my favorite nurses at MSKCC

First Postoperative pull-ups. Note the scars from the bilateral thoracotomies and my right thigh from compartment syndrome

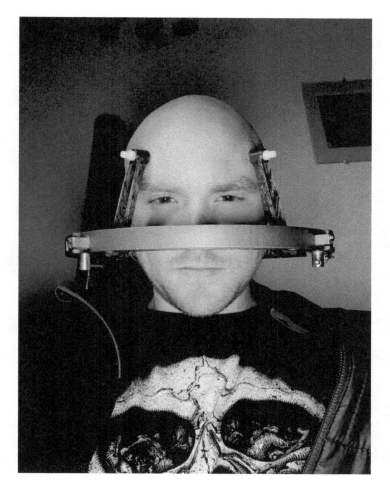

The Halo to keep my head fixed while receiving brain radiosurgery

Motion analysis in attempts to improve on my gait following brain surgery

Radiation Revenge

1. De Ruysscher, D., et al., *Eligibility for concurrent chemotherapy and radiotherapy of locally advanced lung cancer patients: a prospective, population-based study.* Ann Oncol, 2009. **20**(1): p. 98-102.

2. Rekhtman, N., *Neuroendocrine tumors of the lung: an update.* Arch Pathol Lab Med, 2010. **134**(11): p. 1628-38.

3. Herbst, R.S., D. Morgensztern, and C. Boshoff, *The biology and management of non-small cell lung cancer.* Nature, 2018. **553**(7689): p. 446-454.

4. Foster, N.R., et al., *Prognostic factors differ by tumor stage for small cell lung cancer: a pooled analysis of North Central Cancer Treatment Group trials.* Cancer, 2009. **115**(12): p. 2721-31.

5. Byers, L.A. and C.M. Rudin, *Small cell lung cancer: where do we go from here?* Cancer, 2015. **121**(5): p. 664-72.

6. Wang, S., et al., *Current Diagnosis and Management of Small-Cell Lung Cancer.* Mayo Clin Proc, 2019. **94**(8): p. 1599-1622.

7. Bernhardt, E.B. and S.I. Jalal, *Small Cell Lung Cancer.* Cancer Treat Res, 2016. **170**: p. 301-22.

8. Goldstraw, P., et al., *The IASLC Lung Cancer Staging Project: Proposals for Revision of the TNM Stage Groupings in the Forthcoming (Eighth) Edition of the TNM Classification for Lung Cancer.* J Thorac Oncol, 2016. **11**(1): p. 39-51.

9. Wheat, L.J., et al., *Histoplasmosis.* Infect Dis Clin North Am, 2016. **30**(1): p. 207-27.

10. Kochanowsky, J.A. and A.A. Koshy, *Toxoplasma gondii.* Curr Biol, 2018. **28**(14): p. R770-r771.

11. de Vries, L.S., *Viral Infections and the Neonatal Brain.* Semin Pediatr Neurol, 2019. **32**: p. 100769.

12. Carruthers, V.B. and Y. Suzuki, *Effects of Toxoplasma gondii infection on the brain.* Schizophr Bull, 2007. **33**(3): p. 745-51.

13. Koppenol, W.H., P.L. Bounds, and C.V. Dang, *Otto Warburg's contributions to current concepts of cancer metabolism.* Nat Rev Cancer, 2011. **11**(5): p. 325-37.

14. Seyfried, T.N. and L.C. Huysentruyt, *On the origin of cancer metastasis.* Crit Rev Oncog, 2013. **18**(1-2): p. 43-73.

15. Helin, K., et al., *Loss of the retinoblastoma protein-related p130 protein in small cell lung carcinoma.* Proc Natl Acad Sci U S A, 1997. **94**(13): p. 6933-8.

16. Kaye, F.J., *RB and cyclin dependent kinase pathways: defining a distinction between RB and p16 loss in lung cancer.* Oncogene, 2002. **21**(45): p. 6908-14.

17. Toufektchan, E. and F. Toledo, *The Guardian of the Genome Revisited: p53 Downregulates Genes Required for Telomere Maintenance, DNA Repair, and Centromere Structure.* Cancers (Basel), 2018. **10**(5).

18. Li, F.P. and J.F. Fraumeni, Jr., *Soft-tissue sarcomas, breast cancer, and other neoplasms. A familial syndrome?* Ann Intern Med, 1969. **71**(4): p. 747-52.

19. Crick, F., *Central dogma of molecular biology.* Nature, 1970. **227**(5258): p. 561-3.

20. Daniel, V.C., et al., *A primary xenograft model of small-cell lung cancer reveals irreversible changes in gene expression imposed by culture in vitro.* Cancer Res, 2009. **69**(8): p. 3364-73.

21. Ancona-Lezama, D., L.A. Dalvin, and C.L. Shields, *Modern treatment of retinoblastoma: A 2020 review.* Indian J Ophthalmol, 2020. **68**(11): p. 2356-2365.

22. Rendtorff, N.D., et al., *Analysis of 65 tuberous sclerosis complex (TSC) patients by TSC2 DGGE, TSC1/TSC2 MLPA, and TSC1 long-range PCR sequencing, and report of 28 novel mutations.* Hum Mutat, 2005. **26**(4): p. 374-83.

23. Noguchi, M., K.T. Furukawa, and M. Morimoto, *Pulmonary neuroendocrine cells: physiology, tissue homeostasis and disease.* Dis Model Mech, 2020. **13**(12).

24. Travaglini, K.J., et al., *A molecular cell atlas of the human lung from single-cell RNA sequencing.* Nature, 2020. **587**(7835): p. 619-625.

25. Yesner, R., *Small cell tumors of the lung.* Am J Surg Pathol, 1983. **7**(8): p. 775-85.

26. Seute, T., et al., *Detection of brain metastases from small cell lung cancer: consequences of changing imaging techniques (CT versus MRI).* Cancer, 2008. **112**(8): p. 1827-34.

27. Chute, J.P., et al., *Twenty years of phase III trials for patients with extensive-stage small-cell lung cancer: perceptible progress.* J Clin Oncol, 1999. **17**(6): p. 1794-801.

28. Institute, N.C. *Recalcitrant Cancer Research Act of 2012, P.L. 112-239 (S. Amdt. 3180 to S. 3254/H.R. 4310, 112th Congress).*

2021 November 8th, 2021; Available from:
https://www.cancer.gov/about-nci/legislative/recent-public-laws#recalcitrant-cancer-research-act-of-2012-pl-112-239-s-amdt-3180-to-s-3254hr-4310-112th-congress.

29.   Moyer, V.A., *Screening for lung cancer: U.S. Preventive Services Task Force recommendation statement.* Ann Intern Med, 2014. **160**(5): p. 330-8.

30.   Thomas, A., et al., *Clinical and Genomic Characteristics of Small Cell Lung Cancer in Never Smokers: Results From a Retrospective Multicenter Cohort Study.* Chest, 2020. **158**(4): p. 1723-1733.

31.   McGuigan, A., et al., *Pancreatic cancer: A review of clinical diagnosis, epidemiology, treatment and outcomes.* World J Gastroenterol, 2018. **24**(43): p. 4846-4861.

32.   Spiegel, D., *Mind matters in cancer survival.* Psychooncology, 2012. **21**(6): p. 588-93.

33.   Matthews, C.R. and P.J. Hess, *Thirty-three, zero, nine.* J Thorac Cardiovasc Surg, 2020. **160**(3): p. 871-875.

34.   Andersen, B.L., et al., *Psychologic intervention improves survival for breast cancer patients: a randomized clinical trial.* Cancer, 2008. **113**(12): p. 3450-8.

35.   Andersen, B.L., et al., *Biobehavioral, immune, and health benefits following recurrence for psychological intervention participants.* Clin Cancer Res, 2010. **16**(12): p. 3270-8.

36.   Faller, H., et al., *[Do psychological factors modify survival of cancer patients? II: Results of an empirical study with bronchial carcinoma patients].* Psychother Psychosom Med Psychol, 1997. **47**(6): p. 206-18.

37.   Reiche, E.M., S.O. Nunes, and H.K. Morimoto, *Stress, depression, the immune system, and cancer.* Lancet Oncol, 2004. **5**(10): p. 617-25.

38.   Sapolsky, R.M. and T.M. Donnelly, *Vulnerability to stress-induced tumor growth increases with age in rats: role of glucocorticoids.* Endocrinology, 1985. **117**(2): p. 662-6.

39.   Sood, A.K. and S.K. Lutgendorf, *Stress influences on anoikis.* Cancer Prev Res (Phila), 2011. **4**(4): p. 481-5.

40.   Consoli, S.M., S. Cordier, and P. Ducimetière, *[Validation of a personality questionnaire designed for defining sub-groups at risk*

for ischemic cardiopathy or cancer in the Gazel cohort]. Rev Epidemiol Sante Publique, 1993. **41**(4): p. 315-26.

41. Goggins, D., *Can't Hurt Me: Master Your Mind and Defy the Odds.* 2018: Lioncrest Publishing.

42. Sof, E., *Operation Red Wings: The darkest day in history of Navy SEALs*, in *Spec Ops Magazine*. 2017, Spec Ops Magazine.

43. Pavlovitz, J. *Why Everything Does Not Happen For A Reason.* 2015 May 29, 2015 [cited 2021; Available from: https://johnpavlovitz.com/2015/05/29/why-everything-does-not-happen-for-a-reason/.

8

Misdiagnosis

The best elixir is a friend.
William Somerville, The Hip

"Get a second opinion!" Michael said to me definitively over the phone in response to what he thought was an outrageous proposition. "That makes NO sense," he stated matter-of-factly. "What do they think you are? An 80-year-old chain smoker?" Dumbfounded, my medical school roommate from our time at the University of Florida was in my disbelief. I reassured him that we had biopsy proof after the bronchoscopy, and tissue doesn't lie. Unlikely as it was, the results were in: it was small cell lung cancer (SCLC). Moreover, I was prepared to entrust my life in the same hands that I had placed my future in training as a cardiothoracic surgeon. I would've considered myself a hypocrite seeking healthcare anywhere else.

After six months in Gainesville, Michael became my roommate throughout all medical school. We were paired for practicing chest compressions for basic life support (BLS) on a mannequin, and we never stopped hanging out for the next decade and counting. As an avid Florida Gator fan, Michael made sure I would fall in line. I had nowhere near the tireless school pride as he. Waking up on game days, he would yell at the top of his lungs, "Game Day!" at 7 a.m. Bloodshot eyes from his constant allergies or from having a few drinks the night before, more likely a combination of both, he'd attempt to coax me into that same enthusiasm for football.

I commend his efforts to compel me to hop on the bandwagon, but I preferred the solace found in study. Spending all day in imbibement didn't seem to be a very good use of time when we had so much to learn in so little time. *I'm a dumb country boy, so things took a little longer for me to digest.* Therefore, during game days, while the campus would come alive with die-hard Gators adorned in their favorite combination of orange and blue, you would more likely find me studying in our apartment downtown while the rest of the town would head to midtown for the game.

In my four years in Gainesville, Fl, I went to the stadium once for an actual organized game. Otherwise, I'd only go there to run the towering stadiums, what we call Gator Mountains, which is an all-out sprint to the precipice of stadium steps. The steps were so steep and plentiful that I could only complete eight to ten reps. Desperate to reach the pinnacle, I would be sucking down the steamy oxygen rising from the field after just having been watered in complete exasperation and desperation, hoping not to pass out. The Swamp had gotten its name for a reason.

He had every reason to bleed blue and orange. I never found the appeal of intense school pride, likely from having done my undergraduate studies at a small private college, Stetson University. Although my father had a similar experience at the University of Georgia, he never went to a game at his alma mater. He preferred rock climbing on the weekends. *The apple doesn't fall far...*

Michael, on the other hand, had completed his undergraduate studies and master's degree in Biomedical Engineering at UF prior to going to medical school. As the eldest of three, his younger sister would attend UF along with his middle brother, who was a member of the football team. Italian in heritage and son of devout Catholics, his parents worked most if not their entire careers at NASA. As a result, one could correctly assume that, along with being a brilliant individual, his principal dietary intake involved some combination of meat and cheese.

Although he would deny this, Michael had a photogenic memory, barely needing to see something twice before committing it to memory. I was the antithesis of this; I had to beat a subject into submission for me to fully grasp the concept studying twice of much to receive the same marks. We scored within 10 points of each other on the United States Medical Licensing Exam (USMLE). I had my first visceral response after taking an exam. After taking the USLME, a test that evaluates your competitiveness and preparedness prior to graduating medical school, computing a single raw score that is the culmination of all the hard work and thousands of hours of studying, I vomited as soon as we left the testing center. You can ask Michael; he was there. No single test has more of a weight on physicians' future than the first USMLE. *Yes, there's more than one; three, actually.*

After big exams, we would strike out to Gainesville downtown to let out some steam, gathering our best friends at our apartment located only a short walk away from the local watering hole. Michael and I were masters of self-deprecating jokes as we would entertain whoever would listen to our brainless diatribes and spirit-infused dialogue. Mike's blue-gulls (*eyes*) and Sicilian features contrasted greatly with my pale, freckled complexion and auburn hair (*ok, it's red*). Our physical characteristics differed just as much as our temperaments: him, the Italian stallion with the calm, playful sarcasm

176

initially puzzling to the less acquainted yet alluring within the azure of his irises; me, the talkative Scotch-Irish-Welsh Georgian quick to alliteration and grandiosity. He was the blue; I was the red. I relinquish no shame in boasting that we were quite the spectacle during our evenings out and about in medical school.

An egg of one hour old, bread of one day, a goat of one month, wine of six months, flesh of a year, fish of ten years, a wife of twenty years, a friend among a hundred, are best of all number.
Wodroephe, Spared Houres, p. 253. (1623)

"Dude, come to New York. I will ask around to see who the experts are here in New York City." Michael had gotten accepted to Columbia University for residency. I was as surprised as everyone else in my graduating medical school class that he would have chosen NYC, of all places to call home for the next four years. He had been accepted into their anesthesia program. Like me, he's a country boy, albeit a Florida country boy, which differs slightly from those in Georgia, probably the saltwater. The prospect that he would be walking around Washington Heights in NYC in boots and scrubs was laughable to me; however, that's probably exactly what that city needs.

"I'll think about it," I replied. "Okay, just don't do anything major yet." Michael implored. At this time, I had already been started on the standard-of-care (SOC) chemotherapy for small cell lung cancer (SCLC). My oncologist and company were generous in their evaluation of the extent of my disease. Recall the minute lesions in my brain, all less than half a centimeter, were too small to biopsy, which left my cancer at stage 3 and some change. We were hopeful the brain findings were evidence of a resolved infection, perhaps from childhood or exposure to an endemic area ripe for a fungal infection, toxoplasmosis or histoplasmosis, respectively.

Each wasn't much of a stretch. One-third of the world's population is estimated to be effected by the intracellular parasitic infection, Toxoplasmosis.[1] But remember, if these brain lesions proved NOT to be infectious in origin and instead malignant, I had stage 4 disease. Practically, regarding the subsequent treatment of small cell lung cancer (SCLC), I had two options: for stage 3 disease, I would receive both radiation to my chest and chemotherapy versus chemotherapy alone for stage 4 disease.[2]

In either case, the chemotherapeutic regimen of choice would be a platinum-based therapy, namely cisplatin (*there are others)* which damages cancer cells (*and all other cells, for that matter*) by cross-linking strands of DNA at several points interfering with normal cellular turnover or replication. [3-5] Cancer cells turnover at higher rates than normal cells. So, the idea is to give enough poison to kill the cancer, but not so much that you kill the person. Indeed, a tightrope to walk, one can imagine how many bodies have piled up trying to answer that question. I can only appreciate and pay homage to every cancer patient who came before me, providing current safety data we now enjoy. Moreover, respects must be paid to all unsuspecting medical breakthroughs which resulted from the World Wars taking place during the early 20th century. Tragedy and luck would partner to provide hope for the masses.

Realize, the first chemotherapy wasn't chemotherapy at all but an agent of war. Chemical warfare has been used as far back as the Athenians in 600 BCE when they used poisonous herbs to taint the water sources of enemies.

During the Civil War between 1861 and 1865, Union and Confederate forces suggested poison gas projectiles in battle. Despite international treaties discouraging their utilization, they would reenter the battlefield during the World Wars of the early 20th century. By the end of World War I in 1918, 1.3 million casualties were claimed by chemical weapons, and the Geneva Protocol endorsed by the League of Nations forbade the proliferation of chemical weapons in 1925. However, the Axis powers of World War II, both Germany and Italy, are cited using gaseous agents like tabun, or nerve gas, mustard gas, and Cyclone B. The latter was the agent complicit in the mass murdering of Jews in the Nazi concentration camps.[6, 7]

On December 2nd, 1943, during World War II, at the port of Bari overlooking the Adriatic Sea at the boot heel of Italy and home to nearly 200,000 people, thirty allied ships along with nine merchant ships carrying everything from medical supplies and food to heavy munitions and artillery suffered a surprise bombing from the German Luftwaffe. The heavily populated harbor included an oil tanker which set the entire port into flames: 17 allied ships were sunk, and over 1,000 British and American soldiers died in the fiery horror. Some who lived swam through the flaming waters, suffering ranging degrees of burns only to escape to a worse death waiting on shore.[7-9] Reports from the media dubbed the bombing "a little Pearl Harbor."

Unfortunately, as history has proved in the previous World War, the Axis powers had chemical warfare capabilities. Still, surprisingly enough, Adolf Hitler had been exposed to poison gas as a soldier in WW1, so he abstained from using these agents on soldiers of either side. However, he had no problem using it in gas chambers in secret concentration camps for the extermination of Jews.[6, 7] Even though the second World War was not marked by abundant use of poison gas as a military weapon, both sides, Axis and Allies, maintained the potential.

The Allies, British and Americans specifically, had secretly stored that *potential* in the harbor of Bari in a large stockpile on an American ship, the John Harvey, one of the 17 ships to be destroyed. Along with the breached oil tanker from the German attack, the contents of John Harvey's vessel were added to the noxious milieux that percolated through the flames: one hundred tons of nitrogen mustard gas solution.[9] Despite the Geneva Protocol,[10] the Allies wanted the ability to respond promptly to a potential chemical attack in kind; history taught us to come prepared. Unfortunately, before the John Harvey could leave port to reach a safer destination, Bari suffered a low-flying attack.[6, 7]

As the surviving troops arrived on shore covered in oil and, unknowingly, dissolved mustard gas, they began complaining of unquenchable thirst followed by scattered red-tinged blisters, nausea, and vomiting. Few aboard the John Harvey knew of the actual contents of the ship's cargo.[9] Thus, soldiers were left to marinate in their poison, drenched uniforms for hours without receiving medical attention amongst the ensuing chaos. Even more concerning was the ensuing cardiovascular collapse from the intimate toxic exposure resulting in low blood pressure and weak thready heart rates. Healthcare workers were perplexed; rumors began to circulate as to the use of biochemical weapons at the hands of the

Germans.[6, 7] Logically, this made perfect sense: if B follows A, A must have caused B. The Allied administration would have ridden that temporal fallacy until the tracks were worn and dismantled.

General Dwight D. Eisenhower and Prime Minister Winston Churchill certainly would have as well, as they were ultimately responsible for the top-secret mission. If the cat got out of the bag, the consequences would be to the order of magnitude I fear to postulate. Even the captain of the John Harvey, Captain Elwin F. Knowles, was not *supposed* to know. Publicly, President Franklin D. Roosevelt had recently condemned their use as if the Geneva Protocol of 1925 didn't already.[9, 10] If the Axis powers were aware of the spillage, retaliation was almost a guarantee as they would interpret the spill as a future intent to use. If this information drifted beyond the confines of Bari bay, chemical warfare would undoubtedly be unleashed, changing the landscape of the entire war, perhaps its entire outcome.[7]

Lieutenant Colonel Stewart F. Alexander was charged with investigating the strange myriad of symptoms taking soldiers' lives long after the inciting event. Appearances must be upheld despite the high likelihood that higher-level administration fully knew what was stored on the John Harvey. The further the unsuspecting Alexander dug, the more he realized that there was no way that the exposure came from the Germans' attack. The gaseous form of mustard gas had not been used, which must've been required by the aerial assault. Instead, it appeared its liquid form was the only culprit in producing this constellation of symptoms. Reporting on his findings to his superiors, Alexander's outstanding work was instantly buried and classified. Churchill vehemently denied any allegations of the Allies meddling in chemical warfare; Eisenhower followed suit with inaction.[7]

The 628 mustard gas casualties did not die in vain, however.[9] Nitrogen mustard gas was noted to produce some interesting effects. The affected soldiers' blood, bone marrow, and lymphoid tissue were nearly completely void of white blood cells, your body's defense cells.[8, 11] Stateside Colonel Cornelius P. "Dusty" Rhoads, chief of the Medical Division of the Chemical Warfare Service, in civilian life, worked at New York's Memorial Hospital for the Treatment of Cancer and Allied Diseases, or present-day Memorial Sloan Kettering Cancer Center. Early, he recognized the therapeutic potential of Stewart's discovery even though the details thereof would be shrouded in mystery for three decades preventing commendation of his hard work.

Thus, a serendipitous unearthing born of malice and conflict led to hope for many. After August 6th, 1945, the atom bomb, Little Boy, was dropped on Hiroshima in Japan, and another, Fat Man, on August 9[th,] signaling the end of WWII. Quickly thereafter, plans were made to break ground on a new cancer center in NYC devoted solely to the war on cancer. Subsequently, the Memorial Sloan Kettering (MSK) Institute for Cancer Research was born officially opening in 1948. [7, 12]

"Woke up today and decided to kill my ego, It ain't ever done me no good no how Gonna break through and blast off to the Bardo In them flowers of light far away from here and now."
John Sturgill Simpson, Metamodern Sounds in Country Music, "Just Let Go"

As mentioned, the agent to wage my own personal war against cancer would be platinum-based Cisplatin which impairs cancer's normal replicative processes. [3-5]   What and how are other tissues or cells affected?   Those that are more rapidly dividing than others: oral and gastrointestinal mucosa causing dry mouth or diarrhea, hair follicles causing hair loss or secondary alopecia, anemia or lower red blood cell count, and a litany of other effects reaching about 40 side effects.[13]   Specifically, Cisplatin can cause nephrotoxicity [14] (*Oh my poor kidneys!*) and ototoxicity (*"What was that? I'm hard of hearing."*).[15] Not to mention, Cisplatin is one of the emetogenic agents in an oncologist's armamentarium, eliciting dizziness, nausea, and vomiting requiring its intravenous infusion to be coupled with high-dose steroids.[13] However, it didn't stop me from going out for a run after an entire day cooped up in an infusion chair.

What's notable about Cisplatin is that it was the first of its kind, a platinum-based chemotherapeutic agent.[16] It has been used in a myriad of solid organ malignancies, from head and neck to bladder cancer. Notably, Lawrence Einhorn MD at, you guessed it, Indiana University, used a combination of cisplatin, vinblastine, and bleomycin (PVB regimen) to drastically curb the rate of cure for testicular cancer from 10% to 80%.[17] Of popular note, Lance Armstrong received his care at the Simon Cancer Center in Indianapolis, where stationary bikes remain at the entrance of some wards.

To reiterate, I was considered to have stage 3, or *limited* disease, and was scheduled for mediastinal chest radiation as a central portion of my treatment plan. If I were to be considered *extensive* stage, this step would have been omitted. I would have continued with the frontline therapy, for which nearly 70% respond appreciably well. [5, 18] Follow that with some radiation to a localized area, and we got this thing licked...*this is my positivity talking.*

There's a catch to this plan, however. The so-called '*limited*' disease was, in fact, very *extensive,* testing the very limits of what one would call *limited* disease. Barely had it fit within the boundaries of a single radiation portal. *Let's follow the proposed path of the cancer.*

Most likely, the primary cancer had originated in the superior segment of my *left* lower lobe of my *left* lung, probably 2 to 3 centimeters from the hilum, almost invading the division between the upper and lower lobes or *fissure.* Cancer cells would hitch a ride through the lymphatic system infecting the associated nodes along the way. The lymph node at my carina, the bifurcation of the trachea into the left and right main bronchi, or airways, would take the brunt of the insult growing almost as large as the primary foci of cancer. (*Probably why I had a dry cough for months leading up to the diagnosis.*) More importantly, the cancer had crossed my body's midline, from *left* to *right,* tainting lymphatic channels in its path. Ultimately, the trail of lymph nodes would terminate at one of my most superior lymph nodes in my chest. (*For those interested, it reached my 2R lymph node*). Thus, it was highly likely that it would, or had, traveled to the brain given its current radiologically confirmed position.

What I am getting at is that it was a long way to travel! Subsequently, a large area to radiate! Even with the tissue sparing methods devised over

184

the years, there are still considerable toxicities, especially at higher radiation dosages.[19, 20] If you are unfamiliar with anatomy, the crucial real estate we are concerned with here is the heart![21] Say adios to the hope of avoiding coronary artery disease if I am to survive that is. Other potential cardiac injuries include: myocarditis (*inflammation of the heart muscle*), conduction anomalies (*electrical wiring is damaged communicating how the heart should properly function),* valvular damage, a range of cardiomyopathies, and even heart failure.

In fact, the leading cause of non-cancer-related deaths in cancer survivors is cardiovascular disease. [22] Cardiovascular disease is the leading cause of death in people without cancer, too [23], but still. Several side effects stem from chest irradiation, i.e., the injury to the lung, possibly resulting in pulmonary fibrosis, a thickening of the lung which reduces the capacity for oxygen to be absorbed and carbon dioxide to be respired.[20] What does this mean? Basically, you are slowly suffocating over many years as the disease progresses. However, neither you nor your doctors are paying much mind to the *downstream effects* of a particular therapy when you're met with a diagnosis like SCLC. They are worried about saving your life and damn the consequences. We will cross that bridge when we get there if we get there.

And let's imagine that I tolerate mediastinal radiation in the short term. Could I then become a surgical candidate while the cancer is handicapped by the radiation? *You bet.* That is assuming that my cancer is radiosensitive, which SCLC certainly is, most of the time.[18] But would obliging to the preoperative radiation increase my surgical risk, so much so that I wouldn't make it off the operating room table even if I responded well to radiotherapy? *That's a good question to have.* Ostensibly, would the cure kill me?

Radiation can affect wound healing following surgery and make it challenging to navigate normally well-defined surgical planes enabling safe dissection around critical anatomical landmarks.[24] With more minor pulmonary resections, i.e., a lobectomy where they remove a smaller anatomic section of your lung, it doesn't appear that the data would support an increase in surgical risk following radiation.[25] However, depending on the degree of my response to the radiation, an entire pneumonectomy may be indicated, i.e. my whole left lung would be taken out.

As you can imagine, taking someone's entire lung out is a significant perturbation in your normal physiology, whereby the entirety of pulmonary blood flow comes from one set of pulmonary vessels. Pulmonary arteries (*carrying deoxygenated blood to the lungs*) and pulmonary veins (*carrying oxygenated blood from the lungs*) are the major vessels directing blood flow to and from the heart, respectively. Pneumonectomy, removing an entire lung, leaves one set of pulmonary vessels to do all the work and remains one of the most moribund operations we do in thoracic surgery.[26, 27]

It's worth repeating. Imagine the blood flow. After receiving venous blood returning from a trip from peripheral tissues, the blood enters your right heart and travels through the pulmonary arteries to the lungs. The lungs oxygenate the blood emptying into pulmonary veins from either lung. Then the left heart pumps blood through the aorta and back to the peripheral tissues.

Think of the two main pulmonary veins, the vessels receiving oxygenated blood from the lungs, as highways as they coalesce to meet and direct blood to the left-sided heart. A pneumonectomy, the removal of an entire lung, is akin to a ten-car pileup with a semi-truck impeding the normal traffic flow, in this case, blood. People aren't happy with the obstruction, undoubtedly causing downstream traffic damage, within the existing lung. However, this traffic jam is permanent, yet there is still the same number of cars on the road. The circulatory system is a closed system, but the traffic needs to move all the same. Cars have to adjust to a new traffic flow. Blood that initially traveled to two lungs is now going to one.

Sometimes, traffic patterns do not readjust quickly enough resulting in a treacherous condition known as postpneumonectomy pulmonary edema, or PPE.[28] In other words, it is major congestion of the lung. Those at risk are commonly those whose fluids are mismanaged in the early postoperative period. The patient's body is not quite accustomed to large fluid shifts so soon following an operation of that magnitude. I have first-hand experience with residents not understanding the proper role of fluid mechanics in post-pneumonectomy patients. An innocent bag of saline can quickly turn into a nail in a coffin if you are not careful and judicious. *Know your fluid mechanics! It will help you in any specialty! You can save a life.*

If there is any chance of me receiving mediastinal chest radiation and a follow-up major thoracic operation, it certainly would behoove me to know the risk thereof?

A comprehensive, multicenter retrospective review was conducted by Brunelli et al. analyzing the European Society of Thoracic Surgeons (ESTS) database. They aimed to characterize the morbidity and 30-day mortality after *lobectomy* AND *pneumonectomy (PN)* in over 50,000 major lung resections *after* receiving *induction* therapy. *Induction* therapy included chemotherapy alone or chemoradiation in one group. *Simply put, they compared a more minor lung resection, a lobectomy, and a more extensive lung resection, a pneumonectomy, and sought to analyze the differences in outcomes AFTER treated with induction therapy or not.* Their conclusion read, "neoadjuvant therapy [*induction* therapy] is not associated with an increase in perioperative risk after either lobectomy or pneumonectomy, warranting a more liberal use for patients with locally advanced operable lung cancer."[25] *It would seem that there is no increased risk from having preoperative or induction therapy, and moving forward with an operation following radiation would present no problem.*

Not so fast. Even if that is true, it wasn't true in my case. Let's take a closer look within the lens of my problem. In this study, of the 46,395 *lobectomies*, 3827 received *induction* treatment, with only 932 patients receiving chemoradiotherapy. The mortality rate with and without *induction* therapy among the *lobectomies*, in general, was within a 0.2% difference, i.e., virtually none at all. However, comparing the complication rates (*or morbidity rates*) between chemotherapy alone and chemoradiation in a head-to-head comparison excluding other participants, a clear difference surfaces: 16% versus 19%, which was statistically significant. *In other words, the addition of radiation significantly raises the complication risk of my operation, but not death if limited to a lobectomy. A cursory read through the abstract would not reveal that conclusion.* Remember, this is true for *lobectomies*, where you remove much less lung parenchyma.[25] Causing a traffic jam on one of the smaller state highways.

In this study, let's turn to pneumonectomies (PNs) or the highway pileup. There were 6587 PNs; 1316 (20%) receiving *induction* therapy, again the combination of preoperative chemotherapy or chemoradiation. Only 218 had chemoradiation. The 30-day mortality for the *induction* group was 5.2%. However, if you look through the *induction* group and compare chemotherapy alone versus chemoradiation, one notes double the risk of 30-day mortality. Following PN, the addition of radiation to chemotherapy was 8.9% versus 4.5% (p = 0.007).

Thus one could conclude that preoperative radiation, in all probability, drives up the risk of pneumonectomy, as others have shown.[25, 29, 30] There's also a milieu of other reasons not to get a PN, and the pros and cons thereof are argued tirelessly in the thoracic surgery community.[27, 31] In my case, it's hard to reach that conclusion by simply glossing over the abstract. Moreover, my main concern was quality of life thereafter, how limited would my functional capacity be? [32]

In summation post-chemoradiation, lobectomy fine. Pneumonectomy, not so fine. The risk is dependent on the extent of lung resected. There would be an almost 10% mortality if I had a pneumonectomy. Chilling, no doubt. But it may be worth the increased risks if it frees one of cancer![33] However, if the chemoradiation down-staged me or I responded well to induction therapy, I could have had a smaller resection saving my lung, but there was NO guarantee. I was already on chemotherapy; do I continue with radiation in hopes of downsizing the cancer despite the risks? What would you do? Much to think about for someone approaching their 28th birthday.

"Taking a 49 divine day vacation From reality and all else in between
Gonna transmigrate to my destination Far beyond time in eternal dream"
John Sturgill Simpson, Metamodern Sounds in Country Music, "Just Let Go"

Michael was referring to this when he said not to do anything major. Chest radiation and a radical, but perhaps indicated, operation. What Michael didn't know from our conversation over the phone was that I had already been weighed and measured for chest radiation; schematics had been drawn to deliver a whopping dose of radiation.

A week before we spoke, my oncologist consulted one of our radiation oncologists at my home institution. Any imaging and radiation-based therapies are typically done in the basement for safety. If the imaging machines are buried, there's more chance to squash any infinitesimal amount of radiation that may escape and harm an innocent bystander— making any risk approach nil or nonexistent. Therefore, I descended into the basement of the Simon Cancer Center at Indiana University. An overwhelming sense of uneasiness came over me.

The radiation oncologist who, by no fault of his own, was less than personable. His mouse-like features, avoidance of eye contact, and crass greeting were off-putting even though there was no maleficence at its root. Poor bedside manner would be the best way to say it. When I inquired about the degree of symptomatology and potential side effects, I was met with blunt and short responses. I quickly realized why this doc preferred his subterranean workplace and why his colleagues didn't mind him nesting there.

After my abbreviated visit with the radiation oncologist, the radiation nurse walked me to a Goliath of a scanner complete with an affixed camera facing directly below where a supine patient would lie. The camera would rotate around what seemed like unlimited axes pointing in any and all directions. However, this wasn't any camera; this was a linear accelerator. Linear accelerators produce high-energy radiation waves destroying cancer cells in their wake. [34, 35]   However, there's always a tradeoff in treatment; the indiscriminate nature of radiation damages normal healthy cells as well.

Lying back on the hard, cold table as this robot twisted and turned around me, fear slowly crept into the scanner, provoking tears down my face.   This was only a mock run for the planning of the mediastinal radiation, yet the fear was ever present and became deeply entrenched. Forced to remain immobile while computing the schematics, I realized my sudden powerlessness. There was no number of miles I could run to escape my fate. Staring at the monstrosity of this miracle of modern medicine, there was no distracting me from the fact that soon an invisible force would bake my entrails. The product of which may not be apparent for years to come.[35]

Solemnly, I returned home directly wanting to hide from the world. My only wish was to collapse atop my lofted bed, hoping to fall into a deep sleep and disappear. Trudging up the stairs to my condo, something possessed me not to proceed inside. Instead, I sat in the chair positioned at the entryway at the top of the stairs in a cozy nook looking out over Alabama street. Spring had dug her heels in, standing on the precipice of summer in 2019. Upon that perch, an overwhelming sense of calm washed over me. A steady willful wind blew through the chimes of the unit below my roost and further through the hardwood leaves, enjoying their newfound freedom. Blight had taken hold the season before, necessitating the affected trees' thinning.

Overlooking the street, a delipidated house with an empty pool and overgrown brush stood next to the complex in protest of Old Northside's active gentrification. You wouldn't think when you looked at it, but this house had inhabitants. The occupant was an aloof lawyer who refused to improve the structural integrity of his home or yard despite the entire neighborhood embracing revitalization. Further down the street sat Jim Jones's house or previous commune, I should say. A quaint park sat askew from me. When there wasn't a homeless guy sleeping or children playing, I found solace in embracing my studies about all things cardiothoracic on my weekends off from work, not unlike those GameDay weekends in Gainesville, Fl, at the University of Florida. The weight of the pages of Sabiston's surgical textbook would maintain firm adhesion countering the intermittent gusts of wind.

Each flurry of wind and glittering dance of sunlight through the tree leaves rewarmed my spirit; my fear evaded and was replaced by a sense of triviality and insignificance. A warm tingling through my body met every breath I took. Breathing became indistinguishable from wind. As I closed my eyes in a trance-like state, my body swayed back and forth in tempo. I felt a keen synchronicity resonating between the midwestern winds, where I was, and the southeastern waves of the Atlantic, or home: pushing and pulling, pushing and pulling.

Pushing and pulling. Pushing and pulling.

Like a Sufi Whirling Dervish, I had fallen into this harmony that I had never experienced before and haven't since. I felt linked like there was something ancient I tapped into approaching the prospect that my end was nigh approaching. And I was okay with it. Whatever my fate was, at that moment, I was at peace. With all my aspirations in life, my ego began dissolving, washing away into the endless pushing and pulling of the ocean's tides. It occurred to me; I am insignificant. I am nothing. What did my suffering with cancer really matter among the eternity and mystery of our existence? One can remark upon these things in a religious studies class in college, but I had FELT it. The feeling became real. Is this what death feels like? A complete dissolution of self, coupled with complete rest? If so, people should have nothing to fear. It was so beautiful; I didn't want to return to the daily tide. Quite rightly, I look forward to meeting it again.

The prodigious English writer Karen Armstrong, my favorite religious scholar, and former nun writes extensively about this idea of *ekstasis* in her many works. *Ekstasis* is the feeling or sensation of being outside of oneself, with an almost complete and total suspension of the ego. *Ekstasis* is the Greek word for ecstasy, but, used in the former way, there's more of a religious connotation attached. All religions have some flavor of this practice to reach a state of otherworldliness. Christians: fasting and praying.

Sufis (Islam): dancing in circles for hours (e.g., Whirling Dervish). Hindu: Yoga. All these practices are executed for long periods of time to attain the desired trance-like state. Attached are a few recommended books by Armstrong.[36-38]

Whatever had seized my consciousness that day, I wish I could share with you. Maybe after all the craziness and hustling done in the early weeks after my diagnosis, I finally had the opportunity for calm and self-reflection. I opened myself to the universe in those few moments and tapped into something ethereal and ineffable. Whatever God had in store for me, I was encouraged that I was ready.

I called Michael back, "It's time for a second opinion." He had already emailed his contacts in New York City and arranged a clinic appointment with one of the leading experts in SCLC research. Time for a trip.

"Am I dreaming? Am I dying? Either way I don't mind at all Oh, it feels so good you can't help by crying Oh, you have to let go so the soul may fall." *John Sturgill Simpson, Metamodern Sounds in Country Music, "Just Let Go"*

"I am not entirely convinced that you have small cell," said the thoracic oncologist at Memorial Sloan Kettering Cancer Center (MSKCC) in New York City. "You simply don't look like a small cell patient." Charles Rudin MD was his name. He had an almost unshakable disposition about him. Seemingly, nothing could rattle his cages. He spoke softly and unpressured as someone accustomed to walking a tight rope in conversation. This skill was likely well-developed, delivering bad news to patients regularly. Being sure not to suggest too much hope in the prognostication of illness but also not crushing a patient's spirits in the process, indeed, an invaluable skill to develop as an oncologist.

I had postponed my radiation treatment and promptly took the next flight to NYC with planning stickers still arranged on my person, signaling the radiation oncologist where to position the linear accelerator. This particular flight is when Mr. Goggins had phoned me imparting words of encouragement in the classic Goggins fashion, "Stay Hard." The cement landscape stood in stark contrast to the vast expanse surrounding Indianapolis. You could walk for miles without touching or seeing a blade of grass. Moreover, the putrid smells from whatever foulness lurking below the busy streets reluctantly enticed one to ponder what amalgam of human and rodent excrement could produce such stench. Eek! Having watched Morgan Spurlock's *Rats* not a couple of years before didn't settle my stomach much. Only in Central Park could one get a nice breath of fresh air.

Don't get me wrong! NYC is magnificent, an incredible feat of human innovation and progress. Stretching for miles, the impressive panorama marked by right angles and sharp edges about the Hudson and further across the horizon is unforgettably awe-inspiring. In this environment, the best and worst of man were evident. Greed, innovation. Poverty, Wealth. This multicultural macrocosm was both cesspool and Fountain of Youth. The Statue of Liberty stood as a beacon of freedom, towering over the thousands who have been systematically oppressed, from the African Americans to the Irish. And so many people! It is nearly discombobulating for a country boy who wasn't surprised to have a tractor holding up traffic instead of a Mercedes Benz. My head was spinning with the overstimulation.

Moreover, the stale subways were only aggravating the cough I had grown increasingly cognizant of.   The hustle and bustle of the city antagonized my growing headaches. After about four days, I needed to get out of there. But it wouldn't be before I'd touch base with one of my mentors, Dr. Jefferey Everett, cardiac surgeon at Indiana University, who was serendipitously in NYC. One of his daughters lived there, and he and his wife would occasionally visit.

Dr. Everett was the quintessential cardiac surgeon. Tall, handsome, athletic. His pearly white teeth and cutting jaw gave him the look of Woody from Toy Story. (*Ha, he'll get a kick out of that!*) He was as quick-tempered as he was skillful and fast. And boy was he fast! Every movement was streamlined for efficiency. This is what every cardiac surgeon desires. For it is long known and since proved in multiple studies longer your time on the cardiopulmonary bypass machine (CPB), the worse your outcomes postoperatively.[39] Being on CPB alone is a great insult to your body. You are in a race against the clock after you stop someone's heart to perform open-heart operations. Your goal is to get in and get out.

An exemplary teacher, he was never quick-tempered with training residents. I promise I tested his resolve on multiple occasions. His patience probably stemmed from having three children of his own, three remarkable women who would provide outstanding moral support for the trying times ahead. Their inextricable good nature was derived from the matriarch of the family, Dr. Everett's wife, Jackie, who was endearing as she was welcoming. Regretfully, I had to beat Dr. Everett at a game of HORSE at our last resident get-together, which he will deny. However, bragging rights remain mine!

I hitched my wagon to him because I wanted to emulate his operating style. Not to mention we had a pretty good time together, sharing more than a few hops from time to time. That's the wonderful and timeless aspect of surgical tradition.

You are bestowed the gifts of your predecessors, a craft thousands of years old.[40] Being molded by time and the thirst to ameliorate human suffering through the dexterity of the human hand. What better occupation is there to devote your life to? After you are dead and gone, you live through this age-old craft, and your style and expression thereof reverberates through time immemorial. It may change and morph throughout time, but your imprint remains.

"Oh my God, It's so beautiful Everything a part of me It's so hard looking through all the lies made of wool But if you close your eyes it becomes so easy to see" *John Sturgill Simpson, Metamodern Sounds in Country Music, "Just Let Go"*

The morning after I had flown into JFK from Indianapolis, Michael and I had a large pasta dinner at his favorite Italian restaurant on New York City's west side the night before the clinic appointment. Bald already from chemotherapy, I must've resembled a big red egg slurping up a pile of noodles. The large bolus of carbs from our glutinous behavior left us awakening with swollen bellies. We desperately needed a long walk for waistline deflation. A trip from Columbia University on 168th street, where Michael worked and lived, to Memorial Sloan Kettering Cancer Center

(MSKCC) on 53rd street, would provide much-needed steps to burn away the excess calories, not to mention the shame.

Trudging our way through the underground arteries of New York's subway system, we maintained a rapid pace. Impressed at the clip, we maintained, in a couple of years, this Florida country boy had adapted to the high-paced ambulation of NYC. Struggling from wafting noxious fumes emanating from the subway, undoubtedly tickling the large lymph node positioned at my carina, exacerbating my dry cough, I was happy to emerge from that subterranean gutter. After thirty minutes of high-paced ambulation, we arrived at MSKCC. Just as the Germans unleashed their fiery assault upon the port city of Bari, Italy, in WWII in the previous century, Dr. Rudin would soon unleash a bombshell of his own. Just as Lieutenant Colonel Alexander was skeptical about the origin of the mustard gas that spilled into the Adriatic a century before, Dr. Rudin questioned my assumed diagnosis, "Things just don't add up. I mean, look at you! You don't look like your typical small cell [SCLC] patient despite the pathology report."

Looking at Dr. Rudin, I couldn't help but be reminded of J.K. Simmons, a famous actor featured in *Whiplash, Spider-Man*, and *The Accountant*, to name a few. He, too, was bald, or at least on the trajectory thereof. Maintaining his calm temperament, "Unfortunately, we don't have all your pathology from Indiana; I cannot say with certainty. Once we attain all your records, we will double-check your pathology [*the samples of the cancer retrieved from the biopsies from the bronchoscopy at Indiana*]. In fact, this sort of thing is *not uncommon*." When doctors speak with double negatives,

198

it means that they don't want to inspire too much hope. It is as if not committing too much certainty in their language will lower the expectations in the patients' view. It seems to have that effect, anyways. "I suspect that it is much more likely that you have something called carcinoid cancer." Remember, as Dr. Rudin would tell me, "You really have to earn the diagnosis of small cell [SCLC]."

"…this sort of thing is not uncommon," rang in my ears. Well, how common is it to misdiagnose someone setting them out on an entirely different treatment plan!? In other words, *how common is it to make a crucial diagnostic error that results in serious harm?*

Newman-Toker et al. at Johns Hopkins School of Medicine, Brigham and Women's Hospital, and Harvard Medical School had similar inquiries into patient safety in a retrospective study of national insurers between 2006 to 2015. Their aim was to report on the degree of, so aptly stated in the title of the study, "Serious misdiagnosis-related harms in malpractice claims: The "Big Three" – *vascular events* [like heart attacks and stroke], *infections, and cancers.*"[41] They reviewed claims identified from the Controlled Risk Insurance Company's (CRICO) databank representing almost 30% of the United States' resolved malpractice suits. [42] The study was published in 2019.[41]

The study gathered over 55,000 closed claims culminating in 11,592 diagnostic error cases. These claims were reviewed by experienced medical personnel with years of training in their fields, mostly registered nurses. They then subdivided the "Big Three," vascular events, infections, and cancers, into 15 categories, five in each. They scaled the degree of harm in each case on a 9-point system with a score of 6-9, indicating highest severity of error. High severity is defined as resulting in *serious and permanent disability*, or of course, the worst outcome: *death*.[41]

Of the "Big Three," 7,397 cases met the high severity category distinction, with 53% related to death. To emphasize, *death attributed to being misdiagnosed*. 85.7% of cases in the high severity group were due to lapses in *clinical judgment* defined as: (1) "failure or delay in ordering a diagnostic test," (2) "narrow diagnostic focus with failure to establish a differential diagnosis," (3) "failure to appreciate and reconcile relevant symptoms, signs or test results," (4) "failure or delay in obtaining consultation or referral," and (5) *"misinterpretation of diagnostic studies, i.e., imaging, pathology, etc.)."* [41]

Focusing only on cancer, the study revealed that compared to other cancers like breast, colon, and prostate, an error in lung cancer diagnostics results in the highest degree of death, not to mention disability, by an appreciable margin. Rates of severe harm in breast and colorectal cancer are 17% and 16%, respectively, while errors in lung cancer diagnoses are 38%. More than twice the *severe harm*! Observing the data from another angle, among ALL cancer groups investigated, disability alone was 1.4-fold more likely than death. However, with lung cancer cases, specifically, death was 1.7 fold more likely.[41] Of course, this is related to the inherent lethality of lung cancer, underlining the need to ensure you get it right the first time![43]

To reemphasize, this sample of cancer patients in Newman-Toker et al.'s study was selected after being carefully evaluated by healthcare

200

professionals scoring each patient on a scale of 0 – 9; 6 – 9 being the highest severity. This higher tier experienced the greatest consequence of *misdiagnosis*: death or permanent disability. Within that higher risk group, a disproportionate sample of patients were those with *lung cancer*, accounting for more than twice the percentage of deaths and disability than other cancers like breast, colon, and prostate.[41]

Newman-Toker's study represents only over a quarter (28.7%) of malpractice claims in the United States.[41] This entire study may be subject to selection bias as they are, in fact, malpractice claims at the highest tier of consequence. The true rate of misdiagnosis is not likely to be that high in the general population, right? In the outpatient setting where most cancer care is conducted, Singh et al. in 2014 reported that diagnostic-related errors occurred at a rate of 1 out of every 20 adults, or 5%, seemingly reassuring. However, in the lung cancer arm of the study, the diagnostic error rate was 21.6% (127 errors in 587 lung cancer cases reviewed), more consistent with Newman-Toker et al.'s observations.[44, 45] Nonetheless, Singh et al.'s primary goal was an extrapolated analysis of the primary care setting along with errors in colorectal and lung cancer diagnoses in toto; the combined diagnostic error estimate among adults was ~5%.[45]

Although the departed would beg to differ, published in Journal of the American Medical Association (JAMA), a systematic review of autopsy data from 1966 to 2002 revealed a median misdiagnosis rate of 23.5%.[46] The sample size was 53 patients and spanned thirty-six years in review; therefore, the practicality and reproducibility of such a study would be in question. Undoubtedly, the dead will keep their secrets, not without dropping us a hint that our failures may be more frequent than we assume.

Moreover, the burden on our healthcare system is no small penny. Using claims data from the National Practitioner Data Bank, Saber et al. found total payout to claims was a resounding 38.8 billion dollars between 1986 and 2010. [42] Additionally, within Newman-Toker's review in 2019, total claims payout was $104,937,298 for 472 lung cases within a ten-year window. Altogether including all cancer cases featuring 3470 claims, $776,251,670 was paid, with each claim averaging over 200,000 dollars.[41] It is safe to say, diagnostic errors cause considerable harm to the patient and our pocketbook as a society.

In Newman-Toker's study of malpractice claims, the authors admit to an inherent bias in cancer cases due to the longevity for which events unfold and the outpatient nature of cancer care. In other words, the ability to scrutinize an assumed negligence from a "medicolegal perspective" is perhaps more feasible. Ostensibly, a discerning eye has more time to gaze through a magnifying glass. The long-term unfolding of cancer cases differs remarkably from the acuity of vascular events (i.e., heart attacks, aortic dissection, stroke), for instance.[41] Moreover, most of cancer care is provided outpatient requiring travel, punctuality, and willful compliance. There is ample opportunity for that communication loop between doctor and patient to unravel.

Therefore, scrutiny of cancer cases should be approached with pause. Due to the study's design and the inherent differences amongst the "Big Three," pathophysiology dictates treatment infrastructure, i.e., outpatient versus inpatient setting or cancer versus vascular events, respectively. Comparisons within the cancer group alone are telling of the intragroup differences, with lung cancer being orders above in its severity versus other common cancers, i.e., breast, colon, and prostate—each with their own suite of challenges in treatment.

The bottom line: To Err is Human.[47] No one goes through four years of undergraduate studies, four years of medical school, and three to six years of residency only to harm their fellow man. To improve, we must be honest with ourselves without indictment. And let's not downplay the role of patient responsibility in their own healthcare either. Noncompliance to treatment recommendations is rampant. Compliance is low even for general medications that address osteoporosis and hyperlipidemia [48]. Surprisingly, medication non-adherence rates are as high as 50%, even with vital drugs like anticoagulants to prevent stroke, which stem from arrhythmias like atrial fibrillation. [49]

Nonetheless, to answer my own question regarding lung cancer, the data indicate mistakes in diagnosis occur more than we'd like to admit. An error in lung cancer diagnostics is met with a higher chance of dire consequences. Thankfully, my medical school roommate would be the one to completely transform the trajectory of my life. A Florida boy with the blue-gills, who decided to do his residency in NYC, the most unlikely place to seek his post-graduate training, would prove to be my saving grace. That all started with doing chest compressions on a mannequin at UF.

Exiting MSKCC, stunned by the prospect of a massive change in my life's forecast, Michael says, "See, man! I told you to get a second opinion! That made no sense. All we have to do is wait!"

A faithful friend is the medicine of life.
Apocrypha: Ecclesiasticus, vi, 16.

Waiting. Waiting. Waiting on news. Waiting on results of scans. Waiting on lab results. Every cancer patient shares in the torture of waiting, keenly aware of the feeling of being caught in a purgatory of angst and anticipation. You're present, but you aren't really. You're a meat vessel and a bag of pumping blood acting on the day's normal activities. You, yourself, are somewhere else entirely. A constant cloud lingers over even your happiest days while you search for that silver lining that you can't quite envision yet. Sure, chemotherapy, radiation, and surgeries are bummers; physical pain will come and go. The psychological game is something you constantly battle; an aspect of cancer I was becoming well-acquainted. The only certainty was continuous uncertainty, a lesson for which I was receiving a crash course.

Michael needed to go to work; my next year would be devoted to kicking cancer and conducting clinical research. I linked up with Dr. Everett and Mrs. Jackie while they were still in NYC. They took me to a nice steak dinner where I had my first Tomahawk steak. Their eldest daughter, Allison, was in attendance but unable to share in the celebratory libations as she was with child. We cheered for the potential change in diagnosis, not to mention the health of the yet-to-be-born, Charly. Although the future was cloudier than ever, at least it wasn't pitch black.

Dr. Everett and I struck out for a tour around all the notable NYC tourist attractions. Well acquainted with the area, he had our itinerary well mapped and easily orchestrated. From Columbus Circle to the Rockefeller, we trotted at the same pace that he operated: quick and efficient. Of course, I was up for the challenge; we maintained a good tempo hitting some notable landmarks. He had a knack for photography; I had a high-dollar camera I hadn't spent learning how to work. Between residency, maintaining a semblance of a physique, and studies, residency didn't leave much room for hobbies. But as we toured around the city, I received a small introduction to what I considered an alternative trade when my fingers tied their last surgical knot. His catalog is impressive; you can find him on Instagram: @jeverettphotos; website: Jeffrey-Everett.com.

After a surprising visit to NYC, I returned to Indianapolis only to wait more. I'd venture out on long runs during the interim as if to run off the malignancy like a bad cold I couldn't get over. My girlfriend, Jen, now ex-fiancé, was an ICU nurse at Indiana University. She still lived at home; therefore, I had much contact with her endearing family, who eventually morphed into my extended family. They provided a home away from home and a much-needed reprieve from the real world and all the questions that came with it. "How are you?" "How are you feeling?" "What's the latest?" Suddenly, I couldn't find the answer to those questions anymore. Am I honest, or do I unload a dump truck of fear upon them? Jen provided a safe haven that bequeathed an almost enchanted existence free from worry and badgering questions from those who, in all reality, meant well.

Coming from a home steeped in Catholic values focusing on a tight-knit family, she and her family were the nuclear family I had always imagined. They welcomed me with open arms. Jen being the oldest of three; she has a middle sister and a younger brother. Living on a cul-de-sac, they had two dogs with a pool in the backyard. Neighbors would trickle in and out to share a nightcap or to watch the latest game on television. Depending on the season, the neighbors were constantly sharing gifts and holiday traditions. A lively cul-de-sac it was, to an extent of which I had never seen. I thought this only existed in the movies.

Admittedly, I had only ever focused on self-improvement despite the undesirable character attributes that would follow. I'd always ask myself, "What was the next step?" in my career or otherwise instead of living and being happy. Being balanced was never my forte. I was convinced that if I were to be a skilled cardiothoracic surgeon, there were going to be things I would have to sacrifice. I was happy to do it. Jen and her family illustrated precisely what I needed to perhaps seriously reconsider. The more I fell in love with her and her family, the more I thought of another way of living. I have Jen and God to thank for showing me that, *revealing what I would soon lament.*

News had reached my closest friends in medical school who had continued to all different parts of the country to their respective postgraduate training programs. Despite their busy schedules, nearly thirteen or more of my dearest friends traveled to Indianapolis in an illustrious display of support for a friend in need. Packed like sardines in a nearby Airbnb, we celebrated life and being together just as it were during those rapid four years of graduate studies. We were ionically bonded by the trials and stress of medical school, and our relationships were molten together as we celebrated each steppingstone throughout the journey until we matriculated.

Sitting around my favorite Poke' restaurant, refueling after a long, steamy walk-through downtown Indianapolis passing the signature canal adjacent to the NCAA headquarters, we had just placed our orders. Inhaling the sweet aromas of sushi rice and tuna topped with soy sauce and spicy mayo, we sat down in great anticipation as if this was a Last Supper of sorts. Before I could devour one of my favorite meals, my phone rang. It read Charles Rudin MD, my thoracic oncologist at MSKCC.

I bolted away to escape the chatter and the nearby street creating excess noise that always made talking on the phone impossible to discern. I needed to fully comprehend the conversation to follow. "Hello! Dr. Rudin," thankful I didn't already have a mouthful of sushi rice. He responded instantly, "It looks like our suspicions were correct. Our pathologists all agree. It's Atypical Carcinoid."

I don't think anyone has ever celebrated a cancer diagnosis, but that day we sure did! Although I was gassed from the platinum-based therapy from the past two months, I did my best to enjoy this momentous news with the people I had grown to love dearly. And what were the chances that they would all be there? Residency is probably the busiest time in a physician's training, with hardly a weekend to spare. Yet, somehow schedules aligned like constellations, and the seas parted to allow this momentous news to be delivered on this day! The best part was that we were to experience it. I was one week away from receiving mediastinal chest irradiation, which might have inextricably and incalculably transformed my entire treatment outcome. One. Week. Away.

Thankfully, I had people in my life that gave me the courage to question.

Now back to the Big Apple!

1. Desmettre, T., *Toxoplasmosis and behavioural changes.* J Fr Ophtalmol, 2020. **43**(3): p. e89-e93.
2. Wang, S., et al., *Current Diagnosis and Management of Small-Cell Lung Cancer.* Mayo Clin Proc, 2019. **94**(8): p. 1599-1622.
3. Poklar, N., et al., *Influence of cisplatin intrastrand crosslinking on the conformation, thermal stability, and energetics of a 20-mer DNA duplex.* Proc Natl Acad Sci U S A, 1996. **93**(15): p. 7606-11.
4. Amini, A., et al., *Progress in the management of limited-stage small cell lung cancer.* Cancer, 2014. **120**(6): p. 790-8.
5. Byers, L.A. and C.M. Rudin, *Small cell lung cancer: where do we go from here?* Cancer, 2015. **121**(5): p. 664-72.
6. Everts, S. *A Brief History of Chemical War.* 2015; For more than 2000 years human ingenuity has turned natural and synthetic poisons into weapons of war.]. Available from: https://www.sciencehistory.org/distillations/a-brief-history-of-chemical-war.
7. Conant, J. *The Bombing and the Breakthrough: How a chemical weapons disaster in World War II led to a U.S. cover-up—and a new cancer treatment.* 2020.
8. MS, T.C., *Tripping Over The Truth: How the Metabolic Theory of Cancer Is Overturnnig One of Medicine's Most Entrenched Paradigms.* 2017, White River Junction, Vermont London, United Kingdom: Chelsea Green Publishing. 3.
9. Staff, H. *World War II: German Raid on Bari.* 2006; Available from: https://www.historynet.com/world-war-ii-german-raid-on-bari/.
10. *Geneva protocol at last.* Nature, 1970. **227**(5261): p. 884.
11. Tracy Wyant, D., RN-BC, AOCN, CHPN, EBP-C, CPPS, Senior Director American Cancer Society medical and editorial content team: . *History of Cancer Treatments: Chemotherapy.* 2014 June 12, 2014 December 3rd, 2021]; Available from: https://www.cancer.org/content/dam/CRC/PDF/Public/6055.00.pdf .
12. Center, M.S.K.C. *History.* 2022; Available from: https://www.mskcc.org/research/ski/about/history.
13. Oun, R., Y.E. Moussa, and N.J. Wheate, *The side effects of platinum-based chemotherapy drugs: a review for chemists.* Dalton Trans, 2018. **47**(19): p. 6645-6653.

14. Manohar, S. and N. Leung, *Cisplatin nephrotoxicity: a review of the literature.* J Nephrol, 2018. **31**(1): p. 15-25.

15. Milosavljevic, N., et al., *Nongenomic effects of cisplatin: acute inhibition of mechanosensitive transporters and channels without actin remodeling.* Cancer Res, 2010. **70**(19): p. 7514-22.

16. Ghosh, S., *Cisplatin: The first metal based anticancer drug.* Bioorg Chem, 2019. **88**: p. 102925.

17. Einhorn, L.H., *Treatment of testicular cancer: a new and improved model.* J Clin Oncol, 1990. **8**(11): p. 1777-81.

18. Simon, M., A. Argiris, and J.R. Murren, *Progress in the therapy of small cell lung cancer.* Crit Rev Oncol Hematol, 2004. **49**(2): p. 119-33.

19. Oskan, F., G. Becker, and M. Bleif, *Specific toxicity after stereotactic body radiation therapy to the central chest : A comprehensive review.* Strahlenther Onkol, 2017. **193**(3): p. 173-184.

20. Hanania, A.N., et al., *Radiation-Induced Lung Injury: Assessment and Management.* Chest, 2019. **156**(1): p. 150-162.

21. Ping, Z., et al., *Oxidative Stress in Radiation-Induced Cardiotoxicity.* Oxid Med Cell Longev, 2020. **2020**: p. 3579143.

22. Armanious, M.A., et al., *Cardiovascular effects of radiation therapy.* Curr Probl Cancer, 2018. **42**(4): p. 433-442.

23. Xu, J., et al., *Mortality in the United States, 2018.* NCHS Data Brief, 2020(355): p. 1-8.

24. Gu, Q., et al., *Effects of radiation on wound healing.* J Environ Pathol Toxicol Oncol, 1998. **17**(2): p. 117-23.

25. Brunelli, A., et al., *Morbidity and mortality of lobectomy or pneumonectomy after neoadjuvant treatment: an analysis from the ESTS database.* Eur J Cardiothorac Surg, 2020. **57**(4): p. 740-746.

26. Algar, F.J., et al., *Predicting pulmonary complications after pneumonectomy for lung cancer.* Eur J Cardiothorac Surg, 2003. **23**(2): p. 201-8.

27. Alloubi, I., et al., *Early complications after pneumonectomy: retrospective study of 168 patients.* Interact Cardiovasc Thorac Surg, 2010. **11**(2): p. 162-5.

28. Parquin, F., et al., *Post-pneumonectomy pulmonary edema: analysis and risk factors.* Eur J Cardiothorac Surg, 1996. **10**(11): p. 929-32; discussion 933.

29. Cerfolio, R.J., et al., *Pulmonary resection after high-dose and low-dose chest irradiation.* Ann Thorac Surg, 2005. **80**(4): p. 1224-30; discussion 1230.

30. Krasna, M.J., *COUNTERPOINT: Pneumonectomy after chemoradiation: the risks of trimodality therapy.* J Thorac Cardiovasc Surg, 2009. **138**(2): p. 295-9.

31. Shapiro, M., et al., *Predictors of major morbidity and mortality after pneumonectomy utilizing the Society for Thoracic Surgeons General Thoracic Surgery Database.* Ann Thorac Surg, 2010. **90**(3): p. 927-34; discussion 934-5.

32. Leo, F., et al., *Impaired quality of life after pneumonectomy: who is at risk?* J Thorac Cardiovasc Surg, 2010. **139**(1): p. 49-52.

33. Daly, B.D., et al., *Pneumonectomy after high-dose radiation and concurrent chemotherapy for nonsmall cell lung cancer.* Ann Thorac Surg, 2006. **82**(1): p. 227-31.

34. De Ruysscher, D., et al., *Radiotherapy toxicity.* Nat Rev Dis Primers, 2019. **5**(1): p. 13.

35. FitzGerald, T.J., et al., *Treatment Toxicity: Radiation.* Hematol Oncol Clin North Am, 2019. **33**(6): p. 1027-1039.

36. Armstrong, K., *A History of God: The 4,000 Year Quest of Judaism, Christianity and Islam.* 1993, Random House Publishing Group: Ballantine Books.

37. Armstrong, K., *The Bible.* 2007, 841 Broadway, New York, NY 10003: Grove Press.

38. Armstrong, K., *The Lost Art of Scripture: Rescuing the Sacred Texts.* 2019, New York: Anchor Books: A Division of Penguin Random House LLC.

39. Madhavan, S., et al., *Cardiopulmonary bypass time: every minute counts.* J Cardiovasc Surg (Torino), 2018. **59**(2): p. 274-281.

40. *Prehistoric Surgery.* Jama, 2019. **321**(1): p. 110.

41. Newman-Toker, D.E., et al., *Serious misdiagnosis-related harms in malpractice claims: The "Big Three" - vascular events, infections, and cancers.* Diagnosis (Berl), 2019. **6**(3): p. 227-240.

42. Saber Tehrani, A.S., et al., *25-Year summary of US malpractice claims for diagnostic errors 1986-2010: an analysis from the National Practitioner Data Bank.* BMJ Qual Saf, 2013. **22**(8): p. 672-80.

43. Malhotra, J., et al., *Risk factors for lung cancer worldwide.* Eur Respir J, 2016. **48**(3): p. 889-902.
44. Singh, H., et al., *Characteristics and predictors of missed opportunities in lung cancer diagnosis: an electronic health record-based study.* J Clin Oncol, 2010. **28**(20): p. 3307-15.
45. Singh, H., A.N. Meyer, and E.J. Thomas, *The frequency of diagnostic errors in outpatient care: estimations from three large observational studies involving US adult populations.* BMJ Qual Saf, 2014. **23**(9): p. 727-31.
46. Shojania, K.G., et al., *Changes in rates of autopsy-detected diagnostic errors over time: a systematic review.* Jama, 2003. **289**(21): p. 2849-56.
47. Institute of Medicine Committee on Quality of Health Care in, A., in *To Err is Human: Building a Safer Health System*, L.T. Kohn, J.M. Corrigan, and M.S. Donaldson, Editors. 2000, National Academies Press (US)
Copyright 2000 by the National Academy of Sciences. All rights reserved.: Washington (DC).
48. Cheen, M.H.H., et al., *Prevalence of and factors associated with primary medication non-adherence in chronic disease: A systematic review and meta-analysis.* Int J Clin Pract, 2019. **73**(6): p. e13350.
49. Brízido, C., et al., *Medication adherence to direct anticoagulants in patients with non-valvular atrial fibrillation - A real world analysis.* Rev Port Cardiol (Engl Ed), 2021. **40**(9): p. 669-675.
50. Levinsky, N.C., et al., *Outcome of delayed versus timely esophagectomy after chemoradiation for esophageal adenocarcinoma.* J Thorac Cardiovasc Surg, 2020. **159**(6): p. 2555-2566.
51. Chang, A.S., et al., *Cardiac surgery after mediastinal radiation: extent of exposure influences outcome.* J Thorac Cardiovasc Surg, 2007. **133**(2): p. 404-13.
52. Albain, K.S., et al., *Radiotherapy plus chemotherapy with or without surgical resection for stage III non-small-cell lung cancer: a phase III randomised controlled trial.* Lancet, 2009. **374**(9687): p. 379-86.

53. Algar, F.J., et al., *Prediction of early bronchopleural fistula after pneumonectomy: a multivariate analysis.* Ann Thorac Surg, 2001. **72**(5): p. 1662-7.

54. Blanc, K., et al., *Early acute respiratory distress syndrome after pneumonectomy: Presentation, management, and short- and long-term outcomes.* J Thorac Cardiovasc Surg, 2018. **156**(4): p. 1706-1714.e5.

55. Boffa, D., et al., *Surgically Managed Clinical Stage IIIA-Clinical N2 Lung Cancer in The Society of Thoracic Surgeons Database.* Ann Thorac Surg, 2017. **104**(2): p. 395-403.

56. Couñago, F., et al., *Neoadjuvant treatment followed by surgery versus definitive chemoradiation in stage IIIA-N2 non-small-cell lung cancer: A multi-institutional study by the oncologic group for the study of lung cancer (Spanish Radiation Oncology Society).* Lung Cancer, 2018. **118**: p. 119-127.

9

The Big Apple

But to have the power to forgive, Is empire and prerogative:
And 'tis in crowns a nobler gem To grant a pardon than condemn.
Butler, A Heroical Epistle of Hudibras to His Lady, 1. 135.

The clinical suspicion surrounding the misdiagnosis was finally vindicated. According to the pathologists at Memorial Sloan Kettering Cancer Center (MSKCC) in New York City, I did not, in fact, have small cell lung cancer (SCLC). What, or who stood to blame for this error? Upon review of my surgical pathology, what made MSKCC reconsider other than due diligence? What exactly is carcinoid cancer, and how could someone miss this crucial diagnosis? In the last chapter, we reviewed the consequences of lapses in clinical judgment, especially concerning a *misdiagnosis* in lung cancer and subsequent *harm*.

The answer to the first question is easy: no one. Differentiating between carcinoid tumor and SCLC is not easy, as will see. The pathologists at my home institution acted without any ill will. They didn't give me cancer; what would be the motivation? Incompetence, maybe, but maleficence? Hardly. Did that shield me from any frustration in being treated with chemotherapy that might not have been indicated? *No, it did not.*

What is carcinoid tumor? As its name implies, carcinoid tumor was not always thought to be cancer (*-oid* means *like*, so cancer-like). Gut carcin*oid* was first described in 1867. The gut, or the intestines and associated structures, is the largest neuroendocrine organ in the body, giving rise to 60-70% of all neuroendocrine tumors or NETs.[1] *From here on, consider*

214

carcinoid and neuroendocrine tumor (NET) to be used interchangeably. Nomenclature can be a pain, I realize!

In the bronchopulmonary system or lungs, pulmonary neuroendocrine cells, or bronchial *Kulchitsky* cells, are responsible for 20-25% of neuroendocrine cancers, including small cell lung cancer, SCLC.[2-4] However, in 1937, carcinoid tumors of the lung were referred to as bronchial adenomas, or benign growths, with no malignant connotation.[1, 5] As we learned more, we realized that they have the capacity for uncontrolled growth, one of the hallmarks of cancer, and as such, were deemed *malignant,* joining the ranks of its distant cousin, twice removed, SCLC.

Remember that neuroendocrine cells are nearly everywhere and have normal functions like secreting certain hormones and biogenic amines.[6] Some of these hormones, when produced in excess, can cause intractable diarrhea, flushing, and heart disease, all combining in a condition called carcinoid syndrome, often associated with systemic or stage 4 carcinoid cancer. Luckily for me, that is mainly seen with gut carcinoid and not in the lung or pulmonary carcinoid.[7] Moreover, a 50-year analysis of 13,715 carcinoids, irrespective of tissue of origin, including rectum, lung, pancreas, whatever, the overall 5-year survival after diagnosis is 67.2%. Five-year survival after diagnosis of lung carcinoid is 73.5%.[5] These figures were far more appealing than the abyssal prognosis of SCLC. *Wait for it; yes, there's a catch.*

Jumping back into nomenclature, lung carcinoid and SCLC find shelter under the same umbrella, both being designated pulmonary *neuroendocrine* tumors, or PNETs. More commonly, the spectrum of PNETS is described in increasing order of severity due to their invasiveness and survivorships: typical carcinoid (TC), atypical carcinoid (AC), large-cell neuroendocrine cancer (LCNEC), and small cell lung cancer (SCLC). A multitude more exist; let's keep it simple.[8] PNETs are divided into these subclassifications by the degree to which they are *differentiated* or how alike they are to a normal cell.

A very primitive neuroendocrine stem cell that becomes mutated early in its development produces a *poorly differentiated* or high grade (Grade 3), PNET. SCLC and LCNEC are examples. Some cells get further down along the line of cellular differentiation before a perturbation in the maturation process, again a mutation further down the assembly line, and are thus termed *well or intermediately differentiated* PNETs, Grade 1 or 2. *These cells had more time in the maturation process to gain normal features, but they could have been left in the oven for ten more minutes.* Typical (TC) and atypical carcinoid (AC) are examples.[6] That is the prevailing theory anyways. To reiterate, on the pulmonary neuroendocrine spectrum from most differentiated, or most alike a normal cell, to the poorest differentiated cell; they are arranged as follows: Typical Carcinoid (TC), Atypical Carcinoid (AC), Large Cell Neuroendocrine Cancer (LCNEC), Small Cell Lung Cancer (SCLC).

Typical carcinoid (TC) is most like a normal cell and the least threatening, as reflected in the survival rates following diagnosis. The 5-year survival rate from TC, AC, LCNEC, and SCLC are 96.2%, 77.8%, 40.3%, and 35.7%, respectively.[9] *Do we see the trend?* TC and AC account for just 2 and 1% of all lung malignancies.[10] Of course, these rates vary slightly depending on where you get your information; however, the general trend for neuroendocrine cancers of the lung (PNETs) is steadfast.

We have established that SCLC and carcinoids come from the same family, so to speak. But I don't find this meager description captures how different they are, however. Picture a baseball field. The catcher at home plate is typical carcinoid (TC), the most like a normal cell. In the outfield playing with butterflies is atypical carcinoid (AC). Outside the stadium in the parking lot and probably even the next county are SCLC and LCNEC, as far as their likeness to a normal *differentiated* cell. In other words, they are entirely off the reservation.

If these cells are like comparing apples and oranges, how could they have been so incorrect? At my home institution, no less! You would think they would at least double-check their work before giving me irreversible chest irradiation?! As surgical residents, we have many review books studying for board examinations so we can become *certified* cardiothoracic surgeons. Even one of my review books, *TSRA Clinical Scenarios in Cardiothoracic Surgery: 2nd Edition,* states matter-of-factly in one of the patient vignettes following a biopsy for SCLC, "The pathology should be re-reviewed. The workup should proceed if SCLC is confirmed by a second review from a different pathologist."[11] Moreover and more unsettling in my eyes, another surgical resident was misdiagnosed with a different cancer; he was a couple of years above me in training.

Every man of any education would rather be called a rascal than accused of deficiency in the graces.

Samuel Johnson. (Boswell, Life, iii, 54.)

Well, it turns out that pathohistology, the study of what is wrong with cells on the microscopic level, isn't so easy. I'd like to preface my statement with the admission that I am no cytopathologist, but I do know how to read *good. Although I was slow learning growing up; I like to run, not read.* Dr. William D. Travis, director of thoracic pathology at the MSKCC in New York City, in 2012 remarked upon the difficulty in differentiating between SCLC and non-small cell cancer (NSCLC) alone in his publication in *Modern Pathology*, "Update on small cell carcinoma [SCLC] and its differentiation from squamous cell carcinoma and other non-small cell carcinomas."[12]   To make matters even more complicated, there are combined phenotypes; or cancers where you have elements of both SCLC and NSCLC.

With light microscopy, SCLC resembles polygonal oat cells; a description first coined by Kreyburg in 1962.[13] imagine a bowl of oatmeal as you peer under the microscope; each oat is a cancer cell. As Travis continues, the SCLC cells consist of "diffuse sheets of small malignant cells [with] extensive necrosis present," or cell death. Most of a normal cell is cytoplasm, with the nucleus housing all the genetic material. But, with SCLC, there is "scant cytoplasm," and as far as the elements of the nucleus, such as the chromatin and nucleoli,[14, 15], which maintain the integrity and stability of the genome become "finely granular, […]" with "frequent mitoses," or cellular divisions, and those nucleoli are "inconspicuous or absent."[12] *In summary, the cells of SCLC cells are marked by much cell death and loss of typical structures.*

You can think of a normal cell as being happy as a clam in a bathtub filled to the brim with healthy cytoplasm, water, and associated machinery; scrub brushes, shampoo, and may I suggest Irish Spring body wash! However, the deranged DNA faucet squeaks on replacing healthy cellular contents, like the nucleoli whose function is to maintain normal protein synthesis,[14] with some misshapen and maligned form of itself. No more room for clean bathwater and soap for immersion, transforming a once clean, healthy cell into one that is unrecognizable and appears half feral. The contents of the bathtub become replaced with a fat mutate oat spilling out on all sides.

Travis proceeds in his description and review of neuroendocrine cancers of the lung in 2012, and please appreciate the fact that I am purposely adding the year of publication, 2012. Unlike SCLC, "both TC and AC are characterized histologically by a uniform population of tumor cells growing in an organoid pattern and having moderate eosinophilic, finely granular cytoplasm nuclear chromatin." Mitosis rates, or those cellular divisions, are several folds *lower*. The same can be said for the amount of cellular necrosis.[12] *Therefore, notably: between SCLC and TC & AC, there is more evidence of cell death for SCLC and more evidence of uniformity on the side of TC & AC, not to mention that the degree of mitosis is much lower with TC and AC, not dividing as fast, or not as invasive.*

Between SCLC and carcinoid, there are indeed notable differences. What have those pathologists done to properly scale the difference between and within a specimen to characterize neuroendocrine cancer of the lung? They count. They simply count the number of *mitotic figures* per *high power field* (HPF), or per microscopic field of vision, also referred to as *mitotic count*. How many times are those cancer cells dividing per unit area? The higher-grade, G3 or SCLC and LCNECs, would have a higher density of *mitotic figures* per HPF, [16], or simply more mitotic figures. There are other aspects of description, including the degree of cellular pleomorphism and architectural irregularities, each just as subjective as the next.[17, 18]

Travis's study of 200 neuroendocrine cancers in 1998 showed that *mitotic figures, or mitotic count,* are an independent predictor of mortality; the risk thereof increases as you meander the neuroendocrine spectrum from TC and AC to LCNEC and SCLC, or home plate to the next county.[16] This paper, published in 1998, used a value cutoff between TC and AC as $0 - 2$ and $2 - 10$ mitoses per 2 mm^2 of viable tumor (at 10 to HPF), with LCNEC and SCLC being anything above. *Thus, they have used mitotic counts as a central tool in distinguishing neuroendocrine cancer between typical carcinoid and small cell lung cancer.*[16]

These numerical cutoffs would be expanded in 2015 by the World Health Organization classification of lung tumors led by Travis and further supported by the European Neuroendocrine Society. They are now $2 - 20$ mitoses per 2 mm^2 (10 HPF), AC inhabiting the space between; however some still maintain the $2 - 10$ mitoses per 2 mm^2 (10 HPF) distinction.[4, 8, 19] As I am writing this, they are probably coming out with another update with new recommendations. Counting mitotic figures remains a dominant way in which we describe and grade tumors in their harmfulness and prognosis for patients.

Standardization in the laboratory technique in *how we count* these figures was introduced in 2001.[18] In other words, different institutions may have had different protocols for processing a pathological sample making cross-talk difficult, especially in the language of cytopathology. There is no pathology police that I know of, so it is doubtful that a single paper would change practice. But Thunnisen, in the journal *Histopathology* (Histo- = cell) in 2001, remarked upon many considerations to be made when using the *mitotic count.* We have used staining and counting as a primary means of assessing a tumor's proliferative potential as it is most convenient and cheap. Staining is a way to process the sample tissue to analyze the intracellular contents, the contents of the bathtub. Otherwise, everything would be translucent under microscopy.

Thunnissen and colleagues bring up some important points in their critique of this mode of microscopic analysis, counting. Tumors within themselves have heterogeneity in the degree and stage of mitosis they occupy. It all depends demonstrably on where you make the slice on the tumor specimen. Imagine an apple being cut down its core where you can see the star-shaped seeds versus on the side where you can only appreciate the red skin and white meat. Moreover, consider if you have more than one tumor in the same body; there may be differences between them: intratumoral differences versus intertumoral differences. There are many other variables, including but not limited to: histological slide quality, observer variance, and counting procedures and standards.[18] Indeed, microscopic analysis, including *counting* and *other processing procedures,* seem largely at the whim of *interobserver variance*, not to mention *tumor section variability*.

Another level of complexity can also be appreciated. In 2020, Sung highlighted that the diagnosis can be influenced by the tissue you are sampling. Is it the primary tumor or the lymph node serving as a home for cancer cells being sampled? [20] Often, the primary cancer is far out of reach from the many less invasive means to receive a biopsy, like a bronchoscope. Instead, you must settle for taking a sample of a lymph node that is draining the cancer. *No problem, right?* Sung writes, "the distinction between SC[L]C and incidental lymphocytes/germinal center cells within a reactive lymph node can be challenging, as both are comprised of many small-to-medium round blue cells and are subject to *crush artifact* and (pseudo)molding, especially in instances of suboptimal smear preparation."[20] Remember, my initial diagnosis was based on a small bronchoscopy sample of a lymph node, NOT from the primary tumor. *Lymphoid cells look a lot like SCLC cells*!

Moreover, what if you are dealing with a cancer that is prone to something called *crush artifact,* complicating the specimen's processing even more? Noted in 1986, artifact in lung cancer tissue have many causes, and painstaking care during sample procurement and fixation can prevent mischaracterizations. [21] *Crush artifact* is just as the name implies. Placing a cancer specimen on a thin slide between two fine pieces of glass smashes the cellular contents, producing a *crush artifact* and creating yet another problem for the pathologist. The crushing effect is obscuring, almost as if you were taking a picture of someone running or a racecar going at maximum speed. It has been well documented that this is an issue for carcinoid and SCLC.[22] In 1990, researchers posed that *crush artifact* was unique to SCLC, [23] but within the neuroendocrine spectrum, it only

222

makes things more confusing as BOTH carcinoid and SCLC are subject to this phenomenon.[22]

When I had my bronchoscopy, where they, under anesthesia, stuck a tube down my airway to take samples of lymph nodes laden with cancer cells, they were limited in the amount of tissue they could take. There are tremendous bleeding risks, especially when dealing with a highly vascular tumor like carcinoid, although they didn't know what it was at the time.[3, 11] Therefore, they wisely sampled only what they needed. We are talking millimeters; the average fiberoptic bronchoscope specimens in one study were between 0.1 to 0.4 cm. Contrast this to 0.5 to 4.3 cm in most surgically removed biopsies.[10] Usually, a small sample is adequate in making a definitive diagnosis for certain cancers, but for my case and many others, more tissue may be necessary. *Inadequate sample size* could have played a role in misdiagnosis.

In review, a pathologic sample is thus held at the mercy of a plethora of variables, including and certainly not limited to the *mitotic count* (how we count it, who does the counting, and where we count), *intra- and intertumoral variance, [18], intra- and inter- observer variance* [18, 24], *sample origin* (primary tumor vs. lymph node) [20], presence of *crush artifact* [22], and *inadequate sample size* [10, 25]. This is hardly a complete list but is nauseating, nonetheless. Many of these factors are subject, in large part, to *human error*. Is there any way to minimize the role of human processing error?

The more we know, the better we forgive; Whoe'er feels deeply, feels for all who live.
Madame De Stael, no source discovered.

It's called immunohistochemistry (IHC).[26] With IHC, we can tag certain proteins, or antigens, with manufactured antibodies within a cell with a highlighter yellow jacket (*green, actually*) or fluorescence.[27] We can make almost whatever antibody we desire, and we can *quantify* the intensity of the signal that a particular tissue or cell is emitting. The applications for IHC are endless. Can we use this technology to identify rapidly dividing cells like cancer? Yes. Is there a nuclear antigen that is overly expressed rapidly dividing cancer cells? Yes.

Among other NE markers,[22] Ki-67 is a nuclear protein identified as early as the 1980s. Interestingly, it is only expressed in dividing cells, not quiescent cells. Recall, that cancer cells are rapidly dividing. Depending on how fast the cells are dividing, they express this nuclear antigen, Ki-67, to a greater degree. With IHC, Ki-67's expression can be determined by an image analyzer with computer software, removing the subjectivity of something like mitotic counting. The intensity of a Ki-67's fluorescence, or *how green the sample,* can be reported in a percentage value. Not only does it serve as a tumor proliferation marker, but also a diagnostic tool and prognostic indicator.[28] Therefore, a more intense green would indicate a higher grade NET, like SCLC and LCNEC, and less indicative of lower grade carcinoid like TC and AC. *For our clever readers, I did not receive any chemotherapy or radiation prior that might have affected my Ki-67 levels.*

Ki-67, being seen as a marker for tumor proliferative fraction (TPF), was appreciated as early as 1991 [29, 30] and has been validated for use in evaluating human lung tumors.[31] In 1995, it was suggested to aid in the decision making in adjuvant, or additional, treatment after surgery for carcinoid. [32] In 2005, Pelosi reported on 220 surgically resected neuroendocrine tumors of the lung; the "median value of Ki67 was 2.3% in 100 TCs, 9% in 36 ACs, 47.5% in 52 LCNECs, 64.5% in 32 SCLC's,"[10] showing a clear grading in intensity. Also, in 2005, Aslan reported a Ki67 of less than 25% virtually *excluded* the diagnosis of SCLC. [22] As time passed, evidence for Ki-67's utility continued to mount. In 2010, Rekhtman and others appreciated a similar pattern: Ki67 percentages were 2% or less for TC and less than 20% for AC. SCLC samples were much higher: 60 – 100%.[33] Similar figures were reported by Grimaldi a year later in 2011.[24]

Travis, the same researcher as previously mentioned, remarked upon Ki67 in not only making the distinction between low grade (G1-2) NE tumors, like TC and AC, from high grade (G3) tumors, like LCNEC and SCLC, in 2012, [34] but also in 2015 when he was the lead author on the WHO's classification of Lung Tumors in a *State of the Art: Concise Review.*[8] Liu states in 2014 that most if not all SCLCs have Ki67's greater than 50%, and eliminating the interobserver variability is paramount. [25, 35-37] The evidence continues to boil over for the use of Ki-67 from 2015 through to 2020, even as a potential therapeutic target, not just a marker of cellular division helping to classify cancers and elucidate proper treatment. [3, 19, 20, 28, 38] Also, it revealed itself to be a powerful prognostic tool. [19] Time and cost may be concerns, but so are the consequences of *misdiagnosis.* As noted in the previous chapter, hundreds of millions of dollars are spent in healthcare dollars. Of note, I was born in 1991, and diagnosed in 2019. *Medical advance moves at a snail's pace.*

What about the confusion that *crush artifact* brings to the table in differentiating carcinoid and higher-grade neuroendocrine cancers like LCNEC and SCLC? It is eliminated. Reactivity for Ki-67 is highly conserved despite *crush artifact*. Aslan states in the American Journal of Clinical Pathology in 2005, "The diagnosis of SCLC should be questioned if fewer than 25% of cells show reactivity [stain] for Ki-67."[22] According to the folks at MSKCC, my Ki-67 was 10 to 15%. You guys should be experts by now; that is not a proliferative fraction of SCLC but approaching levels of *atypical carcinoid* (AC).

Between typical and atypical carcinoid, Ki-67 of 4 to 5% marks the cutoff. TC being below, AC being above.[12, 19, 32] As previously mentioned, anything below 25% Ki-67 virtually excludes the diagnosis of SCLC. My atypical carcinoid had a Ki-67 index of 10 – 15%. Unfortunately, it has a higher tendency of lymph node involvement and distant spread or metastasis [33, 34, 39], but I'll take it!

My good buddy and fellow resident would probably say that Ki67 is "tried and true!" Samuel was a dear friend to who I had entrusted a stack of goodbye letters to friends and family following my demise. Sam was equally as obsessed as me in discussing for hours different operating techniques as learning residents and diving into the rich history of surgery. All while enjoying a few frosties when we could. I remember my pen dodging the teardrops while writing brief but painful letters. Luckily, they have remained tightly bound by two rubber bands with pre-purchased stamps. God willing, those bands will never need to be broken.

Despite the evidence to support Ki-67's use in highly ambiguous cases, like deciding between SCLC and atypical carcinoid, there's no evidence of its use during my initial biopsy despite its utility being cited in the medical literature for over thirty years now.[8] Why wasn't it initially done? Sure, Ki-67 is not universally used in all pathology labs or institutions. Nonetheless, if it weren't for this single test, I would've kicked off on a treatment pathway that would have undoubtedly caused considerable *harm*. *Harm* from using less sophisticated counting methods instead of superior tools like immunohistochemistry. Ultimately, this would have resulted in a terrible misclassification or *misdiagnosis*. The implications of which we highlighted with Newman-Toker et al.'s study of malpractice claim data in 2019.[40]

Why were my friends and I so elated, not just to be gorging ourselves on Poke bowls for which mine had grown mildly spoiled by my overindulgent soy sauce application, after receiving such "good" news? I still had cancer, after all! TC and AC are typically not subject to radiation or chemotherapy. Bummer, right?

Making up only 0.5 – 2.0% of all lung cancers,[5, 10] TC and AC are considered a *surgical disease* having a much more agreeable prognosis! In other words, the two are susceptible to surgery alone, obviating the need for chemoradiotherapy![33] Neoadjuvant therapy in the form of chemotherapy has been used in some cases,[41] but not necessary. *Recall, I had already invertedly received neoadjuvant chemotherapy in the form of cisplatin, or platinum-based therapy, when we were under the assumption that I had small cell lung cancer (SCLC) not atypical carcinoid (AC). In all reality, those two rounds probably helped even though it was not 100% indicated.[41]* In essence, no harm, no foul, even though we were operating under false assumptions. Lucky me!

Appreciate the results of a 2016 study published in the Journal of Cardiothoracic Surgery. Reporting on 96 patients with TC and 25 patients with AC at intervals of 5 and 10 years after surgical therapy, survival was between 96% and 88%; 87% and 69%, respectively. At 5 and 10 years, well over 50% survival! *Now we are talking!* Not so fast... In the same study, 85% of the patients studied were *stage 1.* There were no stage 4 patients. [42] And rightly so, being deemed stage 4 would have contraindicated me for surgery. Remember that the findings in the brain were still too small to be properly staged. I remained classified as a lower stage 3. We would soon view this mischaracterization or *misdiagnosis* as a blessing.

Father, forgive them; for they do not knowthey do.
New Testament: Luke, xxiii, 34.

"Who the HELL dropped me on my leg!?" This was the first thing I said after I awoke from surgery. Or I should say, this was the first thing I remember saying following my surgery. Completely discombobulated and uninhibited, I am sure I slipped a few more expletives following what turned out to be a *thirteen-hour* operation. It was 4 a.m. the next day. As my eyes creaked open, my right leg was screaming in pain. I was convinced that someone had dropped me on the floor while transferring me from the operating room table to the bed.

Now that we had confirmed the pathology, I had agreed to the surgical removal of the atypical carcinoid, which had taken seat in my left lower lobe of my left lung. Along with removing the primary tumor via a left thoracotomy, a small portion of my left upper lobe, the lingula, was also removed. Then, in an effort to achieve a resection with no residual cancer, a so-called R0 resection, an additional thoracotomy on my right side was needed to reach all cancerous lymph nodes. As a result, I was fileted on either side of my chest with four chest tubes draining the intrathoracic space (around the lung, not within the lung) to prevent infection and pneumothorax.

Reportedly and anecdotally, thoracotomy is one of the most painful surgical incisions.[43] I had two! Moreover, each of your ribs is lined with very sensitive nerves that wrap around your rib cage, spine to sternum, at each level of the 12 nerve roots levels bilaterally. Once you crack, literally crack, open Pandora's box, you are in for a world of pain. I will say these words multiple times throughout this book, "It is hard to describe the amount of pain that I was in. Indescribable." This clam wasn't meant to be hinged upon but was necessary for the surgeon to gain proper visualization for a safe operation. "Oh well, Caleb, it's only around the time of the operation," you might say, "The pain improves." A percentage of patients still have pain years later, a condition called post-thoracotomy pain syndrome.[44] *I am one of those people, x2. You learn to live with it.*

As mentioned previously, carcinoid is a highly vascular tumor.[3] I expect that my surgeon, Dr. David Jones, Professor and Chief at MSK with over 23 years of experience in thoracic surgery, a southern boy from West Virginia, had his work cut out for him. A highly vascular tumor would mean much bleeding; meticulous dissection would be required. A certain resolve and determination would be required for me to leave the operating room with an R0 resection, and he was the man for the job under the circumstances. Given the extent of my lung cancer, this undertaking was no easy task.

Before my operation, I had expressed to Dr. Jones that I wanted to save as much lung parenchyma as we could. As farfetched and delusional as it may be, I still aspired to run marathons, albeit at a fraction of the time. Following the operation, I knew I would lose around 30% of my total lung capacity. Nonetheless, I had convinced myself that any subsequent long-distance running would only be a matter of proper conditioning and hard work. *Pssh.* Minimally invasive surgery thoracic surgery is a keen interest of Dr. Jones. Therefore, he was happy to accept the challenge.[45, 46]

Although the operation would call for two thoracotomies, he was on board with taking only what he must. I had consulted other surgeons; most informed me that I was in all probability going to end up with a pneumonectomy. That just seemed untenable to me; a part of me would rather die. However, if it were essential, I told Dr. Jones to take the whole left lung for an R0 resection or surgical margins free of cancer. So be it.

I had elected not to have operation at my home institution. Sure, I was sour about the misdiagnosis; but as we have reviewed, the differentiation between AC and SCLC is not an easy distinction to make. Moreover, the surgical department had not much to do with the pathology department. Surgeons, if so inclined or if they have a particular knack for pathology, do venture into the path department from time to time, reviewing the cytopathology for themselves. Indeed, this is not necessary.

Nonetheless, the harm from a *misdiagnosis* was averted. As a soccer player and budding surgeon, it's crucial to have a short memory and not dwell on the past. *I recall tireless Erol V. Belli, MD, fellow cardiothoracic surgeon at the University of Florida while I attended medical school, currently at Tampa General Hospital. He always operated with a smile on his face despite all obstacles. Recall, he too was a soccer player but at the University of South Florida.*

As much as it pained me, separating myself from my home institution was best. Moreover, I cannot imagine the pressure it might have placed on the operating surgeon. Every decision would be scrutinized and dissected not only concerning surgical technique but in the backdrop of intradepartmental politics, which extended to battles that far outreached my case. For objectivity's sake, I decided to sink that ship before the increasing knots made steering the vessel unmanageable. Ultimately, I abandoned ship and sank to ol' Davy Jones' Locker.

After my clinic visit with ol' Davy Jones MD, it was clear that he would make every effort for me to ascend safely from the depths of the operating theater. If I died on the table, I was comfortable with my decision. Dr. Jones MD stood tall and slender with hair grayed by experience, an insatiable work ethic, and probably his currently venerated position in the thoracic community. You would never know it by speaking casually with him; he was soft-spoken and kind despite his clinical designation. His stoic and placid presence in the room gave patients a feeling of relief, much like Dr. Rudin, my medical oncologist at MSKCC. Perhaps, that's what made them such a good treatment team. Also, the only reason he hadn't come see

231

me during one of my postoperative weeks was because he was visiting his daughter at university. Despite his title and immense responsibility outside the operating room, he still had time for family. *Yup, that's my surgeon!*

At the end of the operation, my mom commented on how exasperated Dr. Jones was, evidenced by the sweat on his brow and scrubs. Surgeons don't typically take coffee or bathroom breaks while a patient is on the table. I suspect ol' Davy Jones abstained as well. It was around 10 pm when he informed family and friends that they were closing incision.

Besides the unrelenting pain in my right thigh, the first thing I remember was two nurse practitioners (NPs) deliberating on how to handle the situation. With the two NPs, the overnight doctors shared in their bewilderment as to the cause of my unforgiving pain. After all, I had lung surgery; the right thigh is a hop and skip away from the lungs.

The best way to operate on either side of the chest is to place the patient on their side with a pillow between their legs and plenty of cushion with the arms supported to prevent a brachial plexus injury, which is a collection of nerves extending from your spinal cord winding either arm. There are a few other tricks in positioning to optimize exposure. Ultimately, you place the patient in the right lateral decubitus position with the left facing up if you are operating on the left lung. You place the patient in the left lateral decubitus position with the right facing up if you are operating on the right side. Makes sense?

A note for aspiring surgeons, you must start from the ground up. Before you even scrub in, help pick up trash around the OR before and after the operation. Always walk back with the patient to the post-anesthesia unit.

Introduce yourself to the patient prior to the operation. Make the lives of those around you easier. Be considerate to everyone. Remember, you must earn your spot in that world. Going to medical school is just a small piece of the puzzle. If you're not already, work on being a good, respectful person. You are owed nothing. The current climate would like to abolish hierarchies; the powers that be fail to appreciate the value of structure and discipline.

At the time of my operation in the summer of May of 2019, I was 170 pounds with less than 10% body fat with no fat on my legs from a whole life of training on the soccer pitch. They began the operation on my left lateral decubitus position, right side up, devoting around five hours of dissection on the right side. Then I was flipped to address the side of the primary cancer, the left side. Thus, I was turned to the right lateral decubitus position, left side up, for the resection of my left lower lobe and lingulectomy with lymphadenectomy. This required eight hours on my right side. In toto, the operation was thirteen hours, a marathon.

When your lower body is predominantly muscle from playing nothing but soccer for well over twenty years, your lower body is lean meat and connective tissue void of fatty cushion. When you are uncomfortable while sitting or lying down, you subconsciously or consciously change your position to adjust your body position to allow blood flow to those compressed areas. You might recognize this as your arm or leg "falling asleep," and you naturally fidget to reestablish blood flow. That prickling sensation signals all that blood rushing back into the area. When you are actively under anesthesia, this protective mechanism is paralyzed. Indeed, it would be challenging if I was trying to kick Dr. Jones's scalpel from his palm after every incision. Although that would be entertaining to watch, like a live version of the vintage game *Operation.*

Intricate sheaths of connective tissue infiltrating and surrounding muscles house the nerves, veins, and arteries, branching in search of their target tissues. That connective tissue, or fascia, surrounding the muscle is an exceptionally durable compartment, especially as those tissue fibers reach the tendonous connection to bone.[47] Blood flow can cease if the pressure becomes too great within that compartment. Human tissue tends to die after 6 hours of muscle ischemia or being starved of oxygen. The pathophysiologic mechanism of this *compartment syndrome* (CS) is complicated and can be caused by many traumatic events: a long severe long bone fracture, crush injuries, severe burns, casts, or even strenuous exercise.[48, 49]

In my case, CS was caused by the unsuspecting reason of prolonged immobility, e.g., a thirteen-hour surgery combined with reperfusion injury. Reperfusion injury refers to a prolonged period of little to no blood flow, or ischemia, then a rapid reestablishment of adequate perfusion to an affected area, i.e., my right thigh—the injury results in activating a series of damaging pathophysiology ultimately resulting in cell death.[50] As the products of cellular decay build, they cause inflammation and swelling. Inflammation begets inflammation. Swelling begets swelling. The pressure mounted to such an extent that meaningful blood flow could not be reestablished. Commence the clock ticking on the viability of my leg.

CS, for any reason, is a surgical emergency. If you reestablish blood flow or reperfuse, within 6 hours, you have almost a 100% chance of saving the affected limb.[48, 51] Between 6 and 12 hours, you're looking at 68% limb salvage with normal function. After 12 hours, less than 10% have normal function.[52] If you recall, they began the operation in the left lateral decubitus position, right side up. I remained there for three to four hours. I was then flipped to the right lateral decubitus position, left side up, for the remainder of the operation, about eight hours. The right-side thigh would suffer the injury. I recall the fellow remarking upon how painstaking the operation was, "Everything was just stuck. We didn't have any issues with bleeding, but everything was very stuck." *Perhaps the preoperative chemotherapy did have an effect after all.*

There is no way to predict when the limb-threatening ischemia began to pose a severe threat to my right thigh. Also, there is no way to know how much my lean habitus or the five-mile run, my last run with full lung capacity, through NYC's Upper East Side the night prior played a role in the CS, either. *I know, foolish.* Nonetheless, it wouldn't be until an entire night and morning of increasingly intensifying right thigh pain until they would conduct fasciotomies at around 3 pm, cutting the strong connective tissue impeding adequate blood flow.

Saving a limb is a concern, but they're more scary things to consider. We exist because of electrochemical gradients within our cells that are constantly creating energy for our normal bodily processes. Two essential ions are potassium and sodium. The two are coupled in a multitude of biochemical processes. They accomplish work within our cells because they are compartmentalized: potassium is an intracellular ion, and sodium is an extracellular ion. Both are positively charged; they maintain neutrality between the two of them. The exchange between the two across the compartment, or cell, allows the two to accomplish meaningful *work*.

When you have a significant injury to any tissue, the gradient and separation between sodium and potassium are disrupted or, better said, annihilated. Most importantly, the heavily concentrated intracellular potassium gets released into the bloodstream. Potassium chloride is what they give for lethal injections for those adjudicated the death penalty.[53] Too much potassium in your blood, hyperkalemia, can cause heart arrhythmias and death.[54, 55] This is rare, but so is lung cancer in a 28-year-old.

Moreover, the products of skeletal muscle breakdown, or rhabdomyolysis, are incredibly harmful. Not only is the spillage of potassium into the bloodstream a concern, components of the muscular apparatus that spill into the system are tough on your kidneys. One of the cardinal signs of rhabdomyolysis is myoglobinuria. Myoglobin is what transports oxygen to your muscles. Uria- means urine. In turn, urine becomes dark red, indicating that your kidneys are trying to filter the blood of these broken-down muscle products. As you can imagine, filtering such large molecules harms your kidneys. Sometimes patients have to be placed on dialysis temporarily, sometimes permanently.[49]

Historically, the first mention of rhabdomyolysis was during the Israelites' return from Egypt in the Old Testament of the Bible. During their journey home, they ate the common quail, *Coturnix coturnix,* at such a volume that they reported symptoms of weakness, pain, and dark-colored urine. In the spring, quail overeat the hemlock herb, which contains a poisonous compound called Coniine, toxic to humans and livestock. [49, 56]

If I didn't die from a possible arrhythmia from too much potassium, my kidneys could have failed. The clinical signs of CS are classically described by the five P's: pain, pallor, pulselessness, paralysis, and paranesthesia. The pain is usually described as being *"out of proportion."* Meaning that seemingly innocuous movements, even touch, of the affected extremity are met with wails and screams. *Me when I woke up from surgery.* Acute CS is considered a *clinical diagnosis*, which means it can be diagnosed on examination, and no confirmatory laboratory tests or imaging is necessary. [49, 57] Just good ol' fashioned doctoring.

Although when a patient is coming to after being knocked out for thirteen hours, discerning the source of their discomfort can be more challenging than you think, especially after having been carved up like a Thanksgiving Day turkey. Additionally, this turkey was affixed to two chest tubes on either side to drain the intrathoracic cavity, the space between my chest wall and lung, to prevent infection or pneumothoraxes. With each breath, the four chest tubes irritated the intrathoracic nerves previously described as wrapping around the entire chest wall. Incisional pain, musculoskeletal pain, and nerve pain created a wonderful symphony of agony. Absolute and complete agony. As much pain as I was in from the intended operation, I was complaining most right thigh pain! Now you understand the extent of pain CS places you in, *"out of proportion."*

Largely incoherent in a daze of unrelenting pain and narcotics, I was in no shape to adequately describe my pain, complete with a full review of symptoms. These folks needed to rub some brain cells together and start a fire…fast! Was it the pain from receiving bilateral thoracotomies or the pain in the leg? I'd be stroking my beard, too if the chemo hadn't already stolen my hair. If only there were a device to gauge the rising pressure in my thigh so as not to lose a limb after a chest operation?

There is; it is called a Stryker needle. If you have ever smoked a rack of ribs or any type of meat, you must always keep an eye out for the temperature. For hours. Or you risk poisoning your guests. Like a BBQ's temperature gauge, you insert a pressure gauge, a large bore needle, into the tissue of interest. For me, it was my right quadriceps or my right thigh. Wakes you up better than a coffee enema! *No, I never had one.* My pressure reading was, of course, borderline for taking me back to the OR. [48] *Of course it was. Was there anything about me, my case, that would be straightforward and definitive?*

After I cleaned out the stocks of pain medication that Sunday morning at MSK, my compartmental pressures had finally reached a pressure that would irrefutably support my return to the operating room for a fasciotomy of my right thigh. Incising the fascia surrounding my right thigh would relieve the pressure and allow blood flow. The incision required would extend from my right hip to my knee on the lateral side of my thigh. A muscular defect was left behind; the CS claimed a small portion of my thigh which required debridement and resection. *I had two operations for the price of one; what a bargain!?*

As we have established, CS is a surgical emergency. Every second counts. Every second was a dying muscle fiber. Every second was my ability to walk. Every second was unquenchable pain. I was appropriately rushed back to the OR while scrub techs and nurses were scuffling about the room to prepare the urgent case. Even though it was deemed urgent, this was still every day for the workers and staff. It WAS every day for me! They were chatting away like this was business as usual. What they failed to realize is that I had been in severe pain since 4 am; it was 3 in the afternoon when I arrived in the operating suite.

Chest tubes dangling and pinching the spaces in between my ribs coupled with fresh thoracotomies spreading my clipped angel's wings upon each shoulder; I was transferred from the mobile bed to the operating room table. When I planted on the table, the pain experienced was immeasurable. So much so that a simple inspiration was no longer tenable. I peered up at the bright operating room lights, breathless for fear of moving any single rib or any portion of my throbbing leg, which was actively turning to cement as the thigh compartment progressively tightened like a boa constrictor wrapping around each heartbeat. Whatever evil had dreamed up this terrible vice of pain had gotten the attention of a scrub nurse as he looked down at my purpling face. I wanted to die. *To reiterate, I had one of the most painful incisions known to surgery, the thoracotomy x 2 accompanied by one of the most painful clinical phenomena known, compartment syndrome.*

Without breath, you can't produce sound. My face was paralyzed by pain; I released a single tear from my left cheek. I don't know why I remember which one. I attempted to recall that sunny day out on my perch in Indy before my change in diagnosis, where I had experienced a brief moment of *ekstasis*. The *pushing* and *pulling*. *Pushing* and *pulling*. In search of peace and serenity far away from this Hell, every memory of the soothing wind, waves, and sun that once saved me on my day of existential angst evaded me. Instead, I was betrayed by a heavy, gnawing thump of blood that reverberated through my eardrums to my right leg and back in its own sinister tidal waves—pain, *pushing and pulling*. I wanted tempo and harmony; I received it.

I did not know if I'd ever breathe again. A seasoned nurse must have noticed my dropping oxygen saturations or the tear streaming down my face. He looked up at everyone helping in positioning and the anesthesiologist and said in his NYC accent, "We gotta go!"

Light's out. "Be still and know that I am God.
Be still and know that I am.
Be still and know.
Be still.
Be."
St. Patrick

I had the opportunity to thank that nurse for kicking everyone into gear after that day. I had seven opportunities, in fact. The large incision down the lateral aspect of my right leg needed to be washed out and cleaned every few days so an infection would take root. A vacuumed dressing was placed to promote wound healing and reduce swelling, not to mention discourage infection. I would be back in the OR seven more times for a wound vac change and further debridement before I left NYC. It would be two months before the last stitch from my leg was removed.

Bald. 4 chest tubes draining out of my chest. Tube draining my right leg. And a thumbs up. But we are just getting started.

A systemic issue I experienced as a patient was the inherent delays produced by the computer systems, or the electronic medical record (EMR), from changing locations within the hospital. Within the system, in order to activate orders within a particular encounter, you must select the encounter indicating your precise location, whether that be in a patient room, radiological suite, or operating room. There's much utility in these systems, as painstaking as they are. When you change locations, pre-existing orders must be reactivated, at least in this particular system. I was changing locations constantly for repeat washouts, CT scans, X-rays, etc. With each location change, orders in the system needed to be redone.

Not everyone knew to renew orders with the change in location. Therefore, the delivery of pain medication was often delayed or forgotten. Now with a mile-long incision on my person, tubes hanging out on either side with four chest tube atriums, wound vacuum leeching fluid from an edematous thigh, and not to mention cracked ribs, this was no time to miss a dose of pain control. Paramount was pain control; this was a recurrent issue for the first week. Pain begets pain, especially in my case.

On my 2nd day postoperatively from the primary operation, and 1st day postoperatively from the second, a pain crisis was declared. Its standard procedure to get patients up into a chair; early mobilization is key to recovery. *An object in motion will stay in motion.* However, there remained an issue. Three, actually. 1. The analgesia ordered for me was only delivered via an epidural, providing only localized pain control only to the thoracotomies, not the leg. 2. Leading to the second fact: I had no systemic pain control ordered after my 2nd operation as the orders existed from the operating room encounter but were not reordered for the inpatient room encounter. 3. I could not receive a medication that dealt with post-thoracotomy pain with the most efficacy: Toradol.

Let's tackle the latter issue first. Ketorolac, or Toradol, is a powerful non-steroid anti-inflammatory drug (NSAID) that squashes musculoskeletal pain, especially those associated with thoracotomies. I would take Toradol any day over the most powerful opiate. That stuff is magic. What was the problem with me receiving this medication? It can be nephrotoxic, potentially very damaging to your kidneys. [58] With all those harmful products of muscle breakdown, the rhabdomyolysis, floating around in my system, I risked causing irreversible kidney damage. Thus, Toradol was contraindicated until my kidneys cleared out the junk from the damaged muscle.

The ramifications of the 1st and 2nd issues were slowly building in intensity just when the nurse decided to break off for shift change. Sitting in a chair, chest tubes on either side, I attempted to cough to clear the expectorant from the past two days of immobilization. Nauseating pain crashed down around my chest, extending further to my leg. The call button was just out of reach. Suffocated, again, with anguish, I somehow managed to yell. *I realize you cannot yell if you are suffocating.*

A gang of hospital personnel came flooding into the room. A particular nurse, young but clearly seasoned charge nurse for the day, took charge of the room, ordering the new fellows who had just joined the MSK ranks on precisely the medicine I needed. She was magnificent; she had dark hair and a Jersey accent, and ultimately commandeered the room. Rightfully, she was immensely displeased that this happened on her watch. She made that fact known to the newcomers. I had my operation during August, where there is a large change in personnel, i.e., residents and fellows, each year. These newcomers are still getting used to the new computer systems and all the other ins and outs of working at a new hospital. If you must have surgery, it's best to do it outside the months of July and August. [59] There are fewer mistakes outside of those months.

Finally, relief was infused, and I felt like I could breathe again. The first week was littered with lapses in proper pain control, but thereafter we got on a good schedule. For 2 to 3 weeks, I remained in the hospital receiving a plethora of pain medications; morphine, Toradol, Tylenol, fentanyl drip, gabapentin, and more, I am sure. These medications were essential; however, I began building a considerable dependency to pain medication. I loathe what they do to me behaviorally, making me a less than desirable person to be around. Constant pain can transform people. Towards the end of my stay in NYC, a total of 4 weeks spent, I quit cold turkey. Not an easy endeavor, to say the least, the shakes and sweats did not make for an enjoyable lunch, especially with a side of fresh thoracotomies.

Before that comedown turkey sandwich of physical drug dependency, I would be comically disinhibited at times from all the fun drugs. I'd call up some of my bosses at all hours of the night during my hospitalization to update them on the goings on. It didn't matter if it was 4 in the morning. I don't know how many times I have apologized. But at the time, I'd rationalize, "Eh, they're surgeons. They're probably up."

After spending my birthday in the hospital, I was raring to get out. Although despite my disposition, I loved the doctors, nurses, and staff at MSK. I convinced one of the nurses to take me outside to get some sunshine despite the stale NYC musk. Don't tell ol' Jones! On my birthday, the unit brought me all sorts of treats and goodies for me to enjoy during the remainder of my stay. They even helped arrange a special birthday dinner when Jen, at that time my girlfriend, now ex-fiancé', came for a visit. Just like we overlooked Eskenazi Hospital's parking lot in Indianapolis when I was first suspected of having lung cancer, we were now overlooking the busy NYC streets.

"I pray to God to give me the perseverance to deign that I be a faithful witness to Him to the end of my life for my God."
Saint Patrick, The Confession of Saint Patrick: With the Tripartite Life, and Epistle of the Soldiers of Coroticus

Throughout my recovery, I remained on prophylactic antibiotics due to having an open wound on my right thigh protected and kept clean by a wound vac dressing. The dressing seemed to have a mind of its own, breaking its seal at random points throughout the day, leaving me with soiled shorts in inconvenient places, like the main room of Athletica. Even though I had no evidence of infection, having an open wound would undoubtedly put me at risk for one. I would remain on antibiotics for four weeks until the leg was completely closed.

Antibiotics are one of the greatest discoveries of the 20th century, [60]; however, they are terrible for your gut microbiome. [61] Much of proper digestion depends upon the function and balance of an entire community of microbiota. Antibiotics hurl a grenade into that delicate balance. What I am trying to say is that I experienced the most frightening diarrhea; everything went directly through me. Do not pass Go. Do not collect 200 dollars. Go directly to jail. And pick up no vital nutrients as you make your way through. I weighed approximately 170 pounds before the surgery; I had lost 20 pounds by the month's end. Albeit, the immense stress of the operation played its role as well.

I returned home to Indianapolis to enjoy some leisure time, conduct some clinical research for the surgical department, and attempt to regain my strength with tireless rehabilitation. My long-running treks were out of the question, but I could sprint short distances for cardio despite the right leg. My form and function remained intact for the time being. I figured my lung capacity could be improved with yoga and rigorous high-intensity workouts, which I was fairly used to from twenty years of soccer. With enough time and patience, I wouldn't even notice my deconditioned state. *Walking the line of hope and delusion, yet again, maybe. What's the use in making the distinction if it casts limits on your potential?*

Between research obligations and the occasional organ procurement for hearts and/or lungs for donation, Jen and I would spend our free afternoons at the pool before the summer was out. We both maintained a sense of realism but never would speak of the cancer returning. As we awaited my following scan, we enjoyed the fall of 2019 as best we could.

As I was slowly gaining strength and endurance, I would sneak back into the operating rooms to help in any way I could, eager to get back in rotation. Perhaps I could use this time to hone my surgical skills; I'd roam the operating rooms picking and choosing cases as I saw fit, as long as I held up my research productivity. When next year comes around, I might come back more skillful than when I left! What a blessing! So what if it cost me a generous portion of my lung!? If I became a better cardiothoracic surgeon, I didn't give a hoot. Here I thought the last case that I would ever scrub would be with Dr. Daniel Beckman before I left for MSKCC in NYC. I was wrong!

However, the reality of the thoracotomies came to light when I stood adjacent to Dr. Joel Corvera on one of his long thoracoabdominal aortic operations. Depending on the degree of aortic resection and/or additional components of the operation, e.g., valve replacement, coronary bypass, or what have you, he could be in the operating room for half to the entire day and anywhere in between. He was the epitome of endurance. Dr. Corvera must've seen me fidgeting in discomfort; he kindly suggested I break and get lunch. His assumption was correct; I had been in pain for hours during the case. Surgical mask guising my tears; I came back for closure. I had always prided myself on endurance. Now, I could barely stand upright. *Now commence the slow degradation of ego and self-identity.*

Following the four to five months of a welcome reprieve spending time with Jen, family, and friends, I returned to NYC for follow-up scans to check on the status of disease. Back at Michael's apartment near Columbia University, we anxiously waited for the following day, where my scan results were waiting back at MSKCC. Despite my back pain from the thoracotomies, Michael and I braved a ten-mile run south adjacent to the

Hudson. Instead of 7-minute miles, I could only maintain a 9 – 10-minute mile pace. In medical school, I had to coax Michael to run with me. Now, he was constantly circling around to ask if I was all right. "No. But if you ask me that one more time, I will drown you in the river."

The following day I arrived at Dr. Rudin's clinic to review the scans. By then, I had learned the general scheme of the city and could navigate my way downtown. Michael had to work; I'd be on my own in the big city. Arriving in the waiting room amongst all the other cancer patients afflicted with lung cancer, I stuck out like a healthy thumb. Most patients were just as the books describe. They were well into their 60s and 70s, with a faint hint of cigarettes emanating across about floor. A few oxygen tanks were scattered at people's hips.

Hopeful as to the status of my brain and full body scan, I entered the clinic patient room where Dr. Rudin would see me momentarily. Recall that if brain lesions had been ruled cancer before the operation, thus stage 4, my operation would not have been indicated or allowable by insurance. In other words, it would have been contraindicated. Thankfully the minute lesions had been too small for a definitive ruling. But upon review of the scans with Dr. Rudin, despite our high hopes, the '*lesions*' had grown demonstrably, numbering at least 10 to 13 metastases. My brain was littered with cancer. I was stage 4 all along.

Limping away from the clinic that day, completely deflated by this devastating news, I couldn't return to Michael's apartment. Not for lack of want, I could barely stand from my trembling legs. I wandered aimlessly to finally rest my legs at St. Patrick's Cathedral south of MSKCC. Upon those gray steps, I observed the people rich in their youth and prosperity busy on their phones and chatting with friends and colleagues. All at the pinnacle of their profession or at least in the beginnings thereof. There, in the most populated area in the United States, I sat alone with only my tears to keep me company. After I entered the church, I tiptoed through the pews stopping to pray for deliverance and forgiveness.

Before I left NYC, we would do a lumbar puncture (LP). This minor procedure involves inserting a large bore needle in the small of your back between vertebra to withdraw cerebrospinal fluid (CSF), searching for pathogens or cancer cells, and ruling in or out other possibilities. Basically, a hail Mary.

The brain and spinal cord are suspended in CSF and kept at a regulated pressure and level. If you poke a hole in that CSF container and it doesn't close, you cause a leak. Subsequently, the brain sags in your skull because there is not enough CSF in suspension, so the brain floats freely. How does this present? Answer: In one of the most debilitating headaches one can experience.

This is called a post-LP headache. Caution to the reader: never get an LP from an inexperienced healthcare worker who requires multiple sticks for an adequate sample and, subsequently, rush to catch a bumpy flight from JFK to Indianapolis. You just may become bedridden for several days, unable to stand without inciting one of the worst headaches of your life. Be prepared to receive multiple blood patches in attempts to close the hole leaking CSF.

1. J, H., *Uber gutartige Bronchialtumoren (Cynlindrome and Carcinoide)*. Virchows Archiv fur pathologische Anatomie, 1937. **300**(46).
2. Yesner, R., *Small cell tumors of the lung.* Am J Surg Pathol, 1983. **7**(8): p. 775-85.
3. Dincer, H.E., E. Podgaetz, and R.S. Andrade, *Pulmonary Neuroendocrine Tumors: Part I. Spectrum and Characteristics of Tumors.* J Bronchology Interv Pulmonol, 2015. **22**(3): p. 267-73.
4. Caplin, M.E., et al., *Pulmonary neuroendocrine (carcinoid) tumors: European Neuroendocrine Tumor Society expert consensus and recommendations for best practice for typical and atypical pulmonary carcinoids.* Ann Oncol, 2015. **26**(8): p. 1604-20.
5. Modlin, I.M., K.D. Lye, and M. Kidd, *A 5-decade analysis of 13,715 carcinoid tumors.* Cancer, 2003. **97**(4): p. 934-59.
6. Klöppel, G., *Neuroendocrine Neoplasms: Dichotomy, Origin and Classifications.* Visc Med, 2017. **33**(5): p. 324-330.
7. Gade, A.K., E. Olariu, and N.T. Douthit, *Carcinoid Syndrome: A Review.* Cureus, 2020. **12**(3): p. e7186.
8. Travis, W.D., et al., *The 2015 World Health Organization Classification of Lung Tumors: Impact of Genetic, Clinical and Radiologic Advances Since the 2004 Classification.* J Thorac Oncol, 2015. **10**(9): p. 1243-1260.
9. Asamura, H., et al., *Neuroendocrine neoplasms of the lung: a prognostic spectrum.* J Clin Oncol, 2006. **24**(1): p. 70-6.
10. Pelosi, G., et al., *Typical and atypical pulmonary carcinoid tumor overdiagnosed as small-cell carcinoma on biopsy specimens: a major pitfall in the management of lung cancer patients.* Am J Surg Pathol, 2005. **29**(2): p. 179-87.
11. Louis, J.W.a.C., *Thoracic Surgery Residents Association (TSRA): Clinical Scenarios in Cardiothoracic Surgery 2nd Edition*, ed. J.W.a.C. Louis. 2020.
12. Travis, W.D., *Update on small cell carcinoma and its differentiation from squamous cell carcinoma and other non-small cell carcinomas.* Mod Pathol, 2012. **25 Suppl 1**: p. S18-30.
13. Kreyberg, L., *Histological lung cancer types. A morphological and biological correlation.* Acta Pathol Microbiol Scand Suppl, 1962. **Suppl 157**: p. 1-92.

14. Hacot, S., et al., *Isolation of nucleoli.* Curr Protoc Cell Biol, 2010. **Chapter 3**: p. Unit3.36.
15. Miller, T.C. and A. Costa, *The architecture and function of the chromatin replication machinery.* Curr Opin Struct Biol, 2017. **47**: p. 9-16.
16. Travis, W.D., et al., *Survival analysis of 200 pulmonary neuroendocrine tumors with clarification of criteria for atypical carcinoid and its separation from typical carcinoid.* Am J Surg Pathol, 1998. **22**(8): p. 934-44.
17. Ellis, P.S. and R. Whitehead, *Mitosis counting--a need for reappraisal.* Hum Pathol, 1981. **12**(1): p. 3-4.
18. Thunnissen, F.B., et al., *Mitotic counting in surgical pathology: sampling bias, heterogeneity and statistical uncertainty.* Histopathology, 2001. **39**(1): p. 1-8.
19. Dermawan, J.K.T. and C.F. Farver, *The Role of Histologic Grading and Ki-67 Index in Predicting Outcomes in Pulmonary Carcinoid Tumors.* Am J Surg Pathol, 2020. **44**(2): p. 224-231.
20. Sung, S., et al., *Pulmonary small cell carcinoma: Review, common and uncommon differentials, genomics and management.* Diagn Cytopathol, 2020. **48**(8): p. 790-803.
21. Kim, K., C. Mah, and J. Dominquez, *Carcinoid tumors of the lung: cytologic differential diagnosis in fine-needle aspirates.* Diagn Cytopathol, 1986. **2**(4): p. 343-6.
22. Aslan, D.L., et al., *Ki-67 immunoreactivity in the differential diagnosis of pulmonary neuroendocrine neoplasms in specimens with extensive crush artifact.* Am J Clin Pathol, 2005. **123**(6): p. 874-8.
23. Davenport, R.D., *Diagnostic value of crush artifact in cytologic specimens. Occurrence in small cell carcinoma of the lung.* Acta Cytol, 1990. **34**(4): p. 502-4.
24. Grimaldi, F., et al., *Partitioning of bronchopulmonary carcinoids in two different prognostic categories by ki-67 score.* Front Endocrinol (Lausanne), 2011. **2**: p. 20.
25. Liu, S.Z., et al., *Automated quantification of Ki-67 proliferative index of excised neuroendocrine tumors of the lung.* Diagn Pathol, 2014. **9**: p. 174.
26. Duerr, J.S., *Immunohistochemistry.* WormBook, 2006: p. 1-61.

250

27. Bondarenko, G., et al., *Semiquantitative Methods for GFP Immunohistochemistry and In Situ Hybridization to Evaluate AAV Transduction of Mouse Retinal Cells Following Subretinal Injection.* Toxicol Pathol, 2021. **49**(3): p. 537-543.

28. Li, L.T., et al., *Ki67 is a promising molecular target in the diagnosis of cancer (review).* Mol Med Rep, 2015. **11**(3): p. 1566-72.

29. Hitchcock, C.L., *Ki-67 staining as a means to simplify analysis of tumor cell proliferation.* Am J Clin Pathol, 1991. **96**(4): p. 444-6.

30. Sahin, A.A., et al., *Tumor proliferative fraction in solid malignant neoplasms. A comparative study of Ki-67 immunostaining and flow cytometric determinations.* Am J Clin Pathol, 1991. **96**(4): p. 512-9.

31. Chalkidou, A., et al., *Correlation between Ki-67 immunohistochemistry and 18F-fluorothymidine uptake in patients with cancer: A systematic review and meta-analysis.* Eur J Cancer, 2012. **48**(18): p. 3499-513.

32. Costes, V., et al., *Typical and atypical bronchopulmonary carcinoid tumors: a clinicopathologic and KI-67-labeling study.* Hum Pathol, 1995. **26**(7): p. 740-5.

33. Rekhtman, N., *Neuroendocrine tumors of the lung: an update.* Arch Pathol Lab Med, 2010. **134**(11): p. 1628-38.

34. Scott, W.J., *Surgical treatment of other bronchial tumors.* Chest Surg Clin N Am, 2003. **13**(1): p. 111-28.

35. Lin, O., et al., *Immunohistochemical staining of cytologic smears with MIB-1 helps distinguish low-grade from high-grade neuroendocrine neoplasms.* Am J Clin Pathol, 2003. **120**(2): p. 209-16.

36. Zheng, G., D.S. Ettinger, and Z. Maleki, *Utility of the quantitative Ki-67 proliferation index and CD56 together in the cytologic diagnosis of small cell lung carcinoma and other lung neuroendocrine tumors.* Acta Cytol, 2013. **57**(3): p. 281-90.

37. Pelosi, G., et al., *Ki-67 antigen in lung neuroendocrine tumors: unraveling a role in clinical practice.* J Thorac Oncol, 2014. **9**(3): p. 273-84.

38. Chirieac, L.R., *Ki-67 expression in pulmonary tumors.* Transl Lung Cancer Res, 2016. **5**(5): p. 547-551.

39. Fink, G., et al., *Pulmonary carcinoid: presentation, diagnosis, and outcome in 142 cases in Israel and review of 640 cases from the literature.* Chest, 2001. **119**(6): p. 1647-51.

40. Newman-Toker, D.E., et al., *Serious misdiagnosis-related harms in malpractice claims: The "Big Three" - vascular events, infections, and cancers.* Diagnosis (Berl), 2019. **6**(3): p. 227-240.

41. Angelousi, A., et al., *Chemotherapy in NETs: When and how.* Rev Endocr Metab Disord, 2017. **18**(4): p. 485-497.

42. Okereke, I.C., et al., *Outcomes after surgical resection of pulmonary carcinoid tumors.* J Cardiothorac Surg, 2016. **11**: p. 35.

43. Bendixen, M., et al., *Postoperative pain and quality of life after lobectomy via video-assisted thoracoscopic surgery or anterolateral thoracotomy for early stage lung cancer: a randomised controlled trial.* Lancet Oncol, 2016. **17**(6): p. 836-844.

44. Gupta, R., T. Van de Ven, and S. Pyati, *Post-Thoracotomy Pain: Current Strategies for Prevention and Treatment.* Drugs, 2020. **80**(16): p. 1677-1684.

45. Yang, H.X., et al., *Long-term Survival Based on the Surgical Approach to Lobectomy For Clinical Stage I Nonsmall Cell Lung Cancer: Comparison of Robotic, Video-assisted Thoracic Surgery, and Thoracotomy Lobectomy.* Ann Surg, 2017. **265**(2): p. 431-437.

46. Hristov, B., et al., *Minimally Invasive Lobectomy Is Associated With Lower Noncancer-specific Mortality in Elderly Patients: A Propensity Score Matched Competing Risks Analysis.* Ann Surg, 2019. **270**(6): p. 1161-1169.

47. Flores, D.V., et al., *MR Imaging of Muscle Trauma: Anatomy, Biomechanics, Pathophysiology, and Imaging Appearance.* Radiographics, 2018. **38**(1): p. 124-148.

48. Donaldson, J., B. Haddad, and W.S. Khan, *The pathophysiology, diagnosis and current management of acute compartment syndrome.* Open Orthop J, 2014. **8**: p. 185-93.

49. Stanley, M., et al., *Rhabdomyolysis*, in *StatPearls*. 2022, StatPearls Publishing
Copyright © 2022, StatPearls Publishing LLC.: Treasure Island (FL).

50. Wu, M.Y., et al., *Current Mechanistic Concepts in Ischemia and Reperfusion Injury.* Cell Physiol Biochem, 2018. **46**(4): p. 1650-1667.

51. Rorabeck, C.H. and I. Macnab, *The pathophysiology of the anterior tibial compartmental syndrome.* Clin Orthop Relat Res, 1975(113): p. 52-7.

52. Sheridan, G.W. and F.A. Matsen, 3rd, *Fasciotomy in the treatment of the acute compartment syndrome.* J Bone Joint Surg Am, 1976. **58**(1): p. 112-5.

53. Romanelli, F., T. Whisman, and J.L. Fink, *Issues surrounding lethal injection as a means of capital punishment.* Pharmacotherapy, 2008. **28**(12): p. 1429-36.

54. Medford-Davis, L. and Z. Rafique, *Derangements of potassium.* Emerg Med Clin North Am, 2014. **32**(2): p. 329-47.

55. Campese, V.M. and G. Adenuga, *Electrophysiological and clinical consequences of hyperkalemia.* Kidney Int Suppl (2011), 2016. **6**(1): p. 16-19.

56. James L. Tullis, M. *Don't Eat the Quails.* . 2017 [cited 2022 January 15, 2022]; Available from: https://www.massmed.org/about/mms-leadership/history/don-t-eat-the-quails/.

57. Mabee, J.R. and T.L. Bostwick, *Pathophysiology and mechanisms of compartment syndrome.* Orthop Rev, 1993. **22**(2): p. 175-81.

58. Haragsim, L., et al., *Ketorolac-induced acute renal failure and hyperkalemia: report of three cases.* Am J Kidney Dis, 1994. **24**(4): p. 578-80.

59. Phillips, D.P. and G.E. Barker, *A July spike in fatal medication errors: a possible effect of new medical residents.* J Gen Intern Med, 2010. **25**(8): p. 774-9.

60. Hutchings, M.I., A.W. Truman, and B. Wilkinson, *Antibiotics: past, present and future.* Curr Opin Microbiol, 2019. **51**: p. 72-80.

61. Lange, K., et al., *Effects of Antibiotics on Gut Microbiota.* Dig Dis, 2016. **34**(3): p. 260-8.

__10__

Fried Egg

He manned himself with dauntless air, Returned the Chief his haughty stare, This back against a rock he bore, And firmly placed his foot before: ---"Come one, come all! This rock shall fly From its firm base as soon as I" *Scott, The lady of the Lake. Canto v. st. 10*

Late in November 2019, I was forced to remain recumbent on my couch since I arrived from New York City. It was nothing short of a miracle that the contents of my cranium didn't spill out onto the tarmac as we landed in Indianapolis. Each roar of the airplane's engine intensified the growing global headache since receiving the lumbar punction (LP). I needed another few hours to lay down before venturing through stop-and-go NYC traffic and rushing to catch my flight back. However, my tickets were purchased and bags packed to return to the comfort of my condo. After the past week and the news I had received, I wanted to go home to lick my wounds.

Despite lying recumbent for the minimum recommended time post LP, the levees guarding from free-flowing cerebrospinal fluid (CSF) were no match for the multiple misplaced sticks to the small of my back, sending electric shocks down to my toes with each insertion. During the flight, as my headache grew, I fought to contort my body into a more horizontal orientation, attempting to lie my head even with the armchair. A good Samaritan saw me tossing and turning, offering me a couple of Tylenol during the flight, which was a lifesaver.

The frigid air that filled my nostrils provided some relief as I made it through the airport parking lot, and I quickly drove back to Old Northside, my neighborhood in downtown Indy. Head spinning, throwing my bags to the corner of my condo, after almost 6 to 7 hours of travel with the weight of my brain pulling like sled dogs barking down the base of my skull; I finally laid down to instant relief. I quickly fell asleep with my shoes on the couch, where I would hope to wake up with a head clean and clear.

The next morning and the morning thereafter, there were no signs of this debilitating headache dissipating. I have to say; it was impressive and predictable. The positional headache was so severe that within five minutes of sitting erect, I'd have to lay completely back down until the pressure faded. Intermittently, I would have to do things around the house in allotted spurts of energy and relief before the headache would return with a vengeance. Then I would have to rest and re-equilibrate.

Clearly, this was not sustainable. I could only watch so much Netflix. Around six in the afternoon, three days after receiving the LP, I managed to make that short trek from my one-room palace to the Methodist Hospital (MH), where I was greeted by ED staff who instantly recognized me and the miserable state I was in. As they were hooking up monitors and lying me back, an all too familiar voice emanated from behind the curtain, "Ohh...Caleb. What have you gotten yourself into?"

The concerned voice belonged to Dr. Daniel Beckman, beloved cardiothoracic surgeon at Indiana University, having spent his entire career at IU, including medical school and residency. An indispensable cornerstone to the institution, as much a part of the Indiana University as the paint on the walls, his powerful declaration of presence almost made me forget about the barking Siberian huskies hitched to my occipital lobe trampling down my brain's Iditarod Trial. Many of my colleagues would agree that he was more of our 'cardiac godfather' ushering us into the real world of operating, always available to mentor or guide.

Dr. Beckman's dedication and passion for cardiac surgery were unmatched and infectious. Frequently arriving even prior to worn and torn residents, his energy, in and out of the OR, is seemingly endless, perpetually maintaining a positive attitude. He knew and greeted everyone, from the janitor to the hospital's CEO, treating them all the same. His glowing reputation couldn't be more deserved. More than publications and academic distinctions, for which he had plenty, his character and personality have inspired countless generations of surgeons and medical doctors.

Training under Dr. Beckman allowed one to graduate from mind-numbing intern duties to at last feeling a little like a cardiac surgeon. He would walk you through the fundamentals of getting on and off the cardiopulmonary bypass machine (CPB), which allows you to operate on the heart in a near bloodless field. Understanding every nook and cranny of this revolutionary technology is mandatory to learn and manipulate if one has a prayer of being a heart surgeon. And, in OR 29, Dr. Beckman's OR is where this knowledge is bequeathed; where we would discover our "*bona fides,*" as he would proclaim. If Dr. Beckman couldn't teach how to do heart surgery, you should probably consider another profession.

Adorning an old track jacket with the insignia, Indiana University Cardiothoracic Surgery, with underlying blue scrubs, Dr. Beckman is foundational to IU's medical education, not just surgical education. As an encyclopedia of knowledge, he taught with conviction, care, and affection.

His tutelage was seamless with operating; knowledge was unleashed like a tanker spill, and us residents would fight in vain to save all those surgical pearls before they sank into oblivion. You're listening, but you are also focusing on his timeless technique. Dr. Beckman was left-handed; therefore, residents often struggled to position around the operative field, navigating the limited space between heavy headlamps and loupes guiding a narrowed field of vision within the chest cavity. One never wanted to miss a beat. His style of operating, indeed, was *style*, not to mention a sprinkle of grace, only earned from countless hours of practice.

Speaking and teaching with a declarative resolve, having mastered the rule of "3" to encourage maximum retention, the lessons learned became etched in stone deep within your memory's caverns. And he always drove home the message that you should read each day, even if it's only thirty minutes, no matter how tired you were, to continue building upon knowledge that will edify your practice. Before rounds, early in the morning, we would have discussions about new things we had learned. Secretly and playfully, I would attempt to stump him on medical knowledge. Unsurprisingly, that never happened. As far as I know, he still has his daily scholarly time where he gets that 30 minutes in. Indeed, he was the epitome of lifelong learning.

They say that if you want to know the impact of a man's life had on other people, just go to their funeral. I imagine, when the time comes, you will have to buy tickets in order to go to Dr. Beckman's.

I used to joke with him, "The only thing worse than death was not being a cardiac surgeon." *How I eat my words now!* He would laugh me off, but

I was serious; I had read three cardiac surgical textbooks before leaving medical school and entering residency. All my education was geared towards this one goal, and I had made it there, having the time of my life with the most remarkable people. Someone asked me, "If you couldn't be a cardiac surgeon, what else would you be in medicine?" I would reply, "I wouldn't. I'd be a farmer." This was my life.

Indeed, I was a pitiful sight when Dr. Beckman saw me in the ED. As much as I never wanted him to see me so weak, helpless, and in such a state, I was glad he was there. "If anyone can beat this thing, it is you." Of course, he was talking about the cancer, not the post-LP headache. He got one of the cardiac anesthesiologists, not a learning resident or inexperienced NP, to conduct a blood patch that maintained the seal. Finally, some relief sustained relief. His encouragement would be constant and fervent just as he directed me in the OR. Instead of throwing a stitch at the right angle, Dr. Beckman helped maintain a positive and hopeful mindset.

I limped for a couple of weeks after performing as a human pin cushion. Meanwhile, I needed to see inquire about more treatment options. The time was now to hunker down and "circle the wagons," to speak.

There is no despair so absolute as that which comes with the first moments of our first great sorrow, when we have not yet known what it is to have suffered and be healed, to have despaired and have recovered hope.
George Eliot, Adam Bede. Ch. 31.

The following week I would meet with my oncologist at Indiana University. Distraught and depressed, unable to stand up straight, I limped my way over to my oncologist's office, the clinic where I had spent many afternoons in my first couple of years of residency. Despite the pain, I

258

struggled my way up the stairs refusing to take the elevator. As I opened the 2nd-floor door from the stair entrance, I straightened my gait the best I could manage.

I had to sign in. I never had to sign in, but now I was a patient—a subtle reminder of my change in station. Of course, I could walk straight in, but that would be unfair to the other patients. I had already accepted that, in all probability, the lesions littering my brain were cancer before I even left NYC, despite the hail Mary LP. The confirmation came later when Dr. Rudin called me with the results of the LP: all clean from an infectious cause, meaning that metastatic cancer was the culprit despite our efforts to prove otherwise. Despite the heroic efforts of ol Davey Jones's operation that lasted 13 hours and weeks of having a suctioned drain attached to my leg from compartment syndrome, I still had evidence of cancerous lymph nodes in my chest. Cancer in my chest was knocked back by surgery, but it was not a complete resection. At the same time, the brain cancer raged full steam ahead.

I sat in one of the rooms of the oncology clinic. Inconsolable. After having gone through so much pain for a month or more, seemingly for nothing, what were my options? The oncologist entered the room; I could see the concern written on her face. I had exasperated the standard of care options, chemotherapy, and surgery. What was there now? Of course, I could continue with chemotherapy, but my cancer had proven stubborn, showing no response with the preferred regimen...typical of atypical carcinoid. Going back to remove the remnant nodes with surgery was unfathomable, especially with confirmation of brain metastasis. Remember, stage 4 cancer largely contraindicates surgery unless palliative.

After I marginally calmed down, I would ask if there was anything else out there; what clinical trials were available with open enrollment? Do you know anyone who might have different ideas on how to approach this?

Here's the thing: most clinicians barely have time to run a successful practice and perform their own research for which they receive governmental grants to conduct. They could be fired if they do not fulfill their research and clinical obligations. My cancer and other rare cancers are infrequently investigated due to just that: they are rare! Due to the paucity of data and patients, research on rare cancers is under a stranglehold. What's a clinician to do? The only thing to do is draw on conclusions from prior experience and reach out to other people from other institutions. However, you need a clinician willing to go the extra mile to search for that answer. That is not always the case, as much as a clinician cares. Remember, they have other patients as well. What you end up realizing, after two years of being a cancer patient, no one is going to care about your own life as much as you do. *You are your own best advocate.*

After a year into treatment, I was dismayed to learn about something called: www.clinicaltrials.gov. You could search for your particular cancer and see what options are available to you around the globe. All the information as to the details of the trial is right at your fingertips. Albeit haphazardly updated, the information was still there. The only hurdle is understanding which trials apply to you, and, for someone not involved in healthcare, this can be a daunting task. Especially if you are talking about seeking treatment across state lines or even in another country. And to my point, your oncologist likely doesn't have the bandwidth to sift through all the available trials potentially at your disposal.

After I dried my eyes and my face lost its flush, my oncologist brought up the possibility of immunotherapy. This was the logical next step; there has been increased interest in immunotherapy over the past decade[1], and much of her research was focused on that area. Immunotherapy comes in many flavors, but the central tenet is to condition the immune system, which fights off all invaders, foreign and domestic, from parasites and bacteria to fungus and cancer, to search and destroy any potential threat. Some components of the immune system are passive, like the complement system, [2], and others are more targeted, like B-cells and T-cells, which recognize specific moieties of the intruder and mount a directed and well-orchestrated attack. [3] It's a fascinating system.

Ingenious avenues aimed at manipulating this system to heighten our immune readiness and response include cancer vaccines, checkpoint inhibitors (i.e., ipilimumab, approved in 2011 for treating melanoma), and CAR T cell adoptive therapy, to name a few. [4, 5] Vaccines, especially against lung carcinoid cancer, were a dead end for me. I went to Buffalo, NY, to see about a vaccine against carcinoid; however, their vaccine trial was only approved for gut carcinoid. Bummer.

In my opinion, CAR, or *chimeric antigen receptor,* T cell therapy (T cells are immune cells that patrol searching for specific intruders) is most interesting. Cancer can develop mechanisms to go unnoticed by our immune system. As cancer pulls the wool over our T cells' eyes, clinicians harvest your T cells, modify them to recognize the cancer and infuse them back into you. Think of it as sending your immune cells to boot camp and making them battle-ready! Unfortunately, this therapy has only had success in melanoma and blood cancers like leukemia. [5-8] Despite my phone calls and pleas, none would acquiesce to take a chance; I was outside their treatment '*protocol*' for CAR T cell therapy. I get it. However, it doesn't make anything less frustrating.

When you place a selective pressure on cancer, it devises ways to flow around the obstacles conforming and molding its biology in whatever way it can to ensure its survival. Solid organ cancers can bob and weave your immune system, even changing the microenvironment, for example, decreasing the surrounding pH to make the environment more acidic, causing your immune cells to be less effective or outright evading the immune system. [4, 5, 9] Indeed, early screening with low-dose computed tomography (CT) is the most significant advancement in lung cancer treatment. The National Lung Screening Trial results showed a 20% reduction in lung cancer mortality. The US Preventive Services Task Force (USPSTF) recommends annual screening in patients between 55 and 80 with certain risk factors like smoking. [10] Early screening saves lives. Clearly, I already had cancer, so this advancement in practice was superfluous.

To make an exhaustive and evolving topic brief, however, cancer immunotherapy has had limited efficacy, with some recent marginal improvements. [5, 11] By no means is there a claim of cure. Yang's review of cancer immunotherapy out of Duke University in 2015 states, "[...]

immunotherapy only works in a subset of cancers, and only a fraction of patients with cancer respond to immunotherapy." [5]   And after a gang of molecular and genetic tests done on my carcinoid cancer, which is renowned for its stubbornness, nothing would suggest that it would respond to immunotherapy. *For those interested, it was PD1 negative, [12] tumor mutational burden of 0%, [13] and had no mutations that could be exploited for targeted therapy. [14] Looking at over 400 commonly actionable mutations in all cancers, my cancer had not one.*

Basically, my cancer was guised in normality, being just different enough to support uncontrolled growth but not so different to incite an immune response. Remember the discussion of the baseball field and the spectrum of neuroendocrine tumors, TC and AC only have a few differences from normal cells, at least compared to that of LCNEC and SCLC. The immune evasion was being less like cancer in keeping with its traditional charge, i.e., carci-*noid*.

My oncologist informed me of a trial with immunotherapy in which Indiana University was participating. Two years later, the results of this trial would come to light with some appreciable results as far as the extension of life. [15] Be that as it may, I wasn't interested in an extension of life. I wanted a disease-free life. I had no desire to limp along the rest of my days while suffering the potential toxicity of immunotherapy for which there is a multitude. [16] To be fair, so do chemotherapy, radiation, and surgery.

One of the risks of immunotherapy is something called pneumonitis, inflammation of the lungs, which is rare, but, when it happens, results in death about 35% of the time. I just had about 30% or more of my lung removed, so I was not too enthused about having the rest of it be the cause of my demise. Other than potential death, side effects range from muscle aches and dermatitis to renal and cardiac issues. [16] Moreover, like cancer itself, one can develop resistance to immunotherapy. [17] Needless to say, I ended up declining immunotherapy, and I would leave my home institution's clinic wanting for further treatment options. Between IU and MSKCC, there were no strong recommendations on how to proceed.

Before leaving the clinic appointment and giving her a big hug, my IU oncologist offered a medication to help with my mood with the best of intentions. In other words, she offered an antidepressant. Most people might have been okay with that, and antidepressants can work. [18] I, however, have a personal aversion to those medications. I know they can really help people, but that is not how I like to deal with problems. If I am depressed, it is because something in my life needs to be fixed or changed. I refuse to take something that will dull my natural reaction to shit news. That's not what life's about; you must taste the bitter and the sweet. Give me the full dinner with dessert. In my rebellious South Georgia spirit, let's square dance.

Of all the heavenly gifts what mortal men commend, What trusty treasure in the world can counter-vail a friend?
Nicholas Grimald, Of Friendship

Ultimately no decisions were made at that time. Sullen the next day, I called a dear friend of mine, Angelique. Angelique and I met in medical school, and we were part of the same small group which would meet continuously throughout the four years of medical school under a specific instructor. She and I were like peas and carrots (*forgive the Forrest Gump reference*). We always seem to be on the same page, knowing exactly what each other is thinking and annoyingly finishing each other's sentences. We would attempt to study together, but we just found ourselves laughing and joking instead of learning anything of value.

Angelique is Greek, proudly Greek. Her beautiful olive skin complimented her dark brown eyes, and the eclectic smells constantly emanating from her kitchen. Being a dumb country boy myself, her entire being broadened my worldview with every bite of *spanakopita* (spinach pie) and *moussaka* (eggplant and potato-based dish). She was the push to my pull, always having a quick response to one of my playful taunts. Like me, she wore her emotions on her sleeve; if she were unhappy, you would hear about it. And that's why we love her.

Her culinary skill was only met by her passion for healthcare. She was part of an early admissions program for medical school at the University of Florida, graduating a year earlier because of her excellent marks. During undergrad, however, she spent twice a week with children with cancer in a program called *Footprints,* and it wasn't just to add another line to her resume'. One of the children she was paired with in the program passed away far too soon. She impressed upon me that it was one of the most dreadful and influential events of her life.

Naturally, after her experience, she wanted to be a pediatric oncologist but would find her true passion in treating infectious diseases to which immunosuppressed children are susceptible. She is a prolific worker, always with her computer and Louis Vuitton at her hip, working on God knows what. After her residency in Columbus, OH, where she published countless scientific papers and was awarded lofty research grants, she went to Duke University for a fellowship in pediatric infectious disease, where she continues to make a name for herself as a physician-researcher.

When I was first diagnosed, she took a break from her residency to come from Columbus to Indianapolis to see me. As close as they were, residency gets in the way of staying in touch with friends. However, she is the type of friend to drop everything when needed. And she did, no questions asked. She was and continues to be one of the best friends I'll ever have.

"GO BACK TO UF!" she said. I remember exactly where I was when she told me, right across from Jim Jones's old commune on my way to a coffee shop on a crisp sunny day before the weather turned almost inhospitable to a southerner. "At least talk to them. I will find out exactly who to talk to; I can't quite remember his name. But I will get back to you and send you his email." Between Michael, my medical school roommate, and Angelique, I owe them my life.

My coffee hadn't even cooled down before I was talking to Dr. Frederic Kaye at the University of Florida, professor of medicine and medical director of thoracic oncology. He has a notable pedigree: graduating from the University of Maryland with his medical degree, he proceeded to complete his residency at Mount Sinai Hospital in internal medicine as well as his fellowship in Hematology. He furthered his education at the National Cancer Institute (NCI), completing his postgraduate studies in oncology by 1987. He stayed at the NCI for several years and still serves as an associated editor for the Journal of the National Cancer Institute. He would later travel south to take up his current position at UF as a physician-scientist. By the time of our meeting, he had well over 20 years of experience treating thoracic malignancies.

My first impression of him after I had traveled back down to my Alma Mater, UF, was that this guy was a cowboy. Not in a roping and tying cattle sense, but he was not afraid to push boundaries and go against convention. First, we met in the thoracic oncology clinic; I didn't even have a scheduled appointment. In fact, it wasn't even one of his clinic days. Believe me when I say, it wasn't because I had special treatment for being a doctor. He does this for all patients if urgency is required. Wearing worn pants and a button-down sporting a 1980s-style mustache, he ushered me into a clinic room with another doctor's name. I decided right then and there, this is my guy. This is *my* oncologist.

I am friends with one of his post-doctorates in his lab at UF, and he attested to his iconoclastic attitude in treating cancer. I say iconoclastic, but it is more an older view that is kept alive by few. He accompanied Dr. Kaye to a research meeting where they were discussing some topic on lung cancer where it was stated by the presenter, "At this point, most would agree that curing lung cancer is a far beyond an attainable goal…," or something along those lines. His post-doc reported to me that Dr. Kaye corrected the speaker to say, "Umm, I am trying to cure lung cancer," matter-of-factly. That's the kind of attitude I want my oncologist to have, no matter how farfetched the idea. Most of the major advances in cancer treatment come from people willing to push the envelope, to operate on the margins of possibility. I am willing to walk to the edge, and I want an oncologist to take me there.

Lean, modest in stature and nature, he gave no clue to his high clinical appointment. He spoke with scattered hesitancy as if trying to avoid losing the patient's attention in fear of getting too far into the science of his clinical decision-making. Like every good researcher and clinician, he never allowed uncalculated estimations of what the future might hold. He was methodical and stepwise to a fault, masterful in the way of reigning in my dreary postulations. As you can imagine, my mood swings from my high dose corticosteroids to control brain swelling and current disposition were no an easy hill to climb. He would always have to reel me back in for getting too far ahead of myself.

Dr. Kaye, in a coordinated effort, set up my treatment plan. In an email chain, including all those involved in my care up to this point, Memorial Sloan Kettering, Indiana University, and now University of Florida, he corralled the ideas and helped bring some harmony in the tune of my treatment while investigating trials from surrounding institutions like Moffit Cancer Center in Tampa, Florida. He maintained this open communication throughout the major course of my treatments. Most importantly, he brought in Maryam Rahman MD, Neurosurgeon at UF.

I had met Dr. Rahman in one of our small group activities in medical school. There were 3 different small groups in one class, which wasn't a common occurrence. She stood in a room, probably 5-6 months pregnant and not more than 5'6" – 5'7" tall, about to reveal the magnitude of her intellectual prowess. She went around the room asking us for our names; there must've been 20 of us. After requesting our names, she recited each name as if she had known us for years. I was floored. She wasn't doing this to show off; this was fun for her.

We met in the Subway in between my impromptu appointment with Dr. Kaye. I hadn't seen her since I shadowed her in medical school when I observed her remove some boney outgrowths from a patient's spine. If I hadn't gone into CT surgery, I was planning on doing neurosurgery. Dr. Rahman was the inspiration for that notion. With the smell of fresh cold cuts in the air, "Caleb," she said sternly, "We can treat this! Now is not the time to lose hope. Look at you! You're doing so great!" I might have looked it, but I didn't feel that way.

My headaches were mounting in intensity despite my best attempts of minimizing my symptoms. Outside of IU and MSKCC, I had traveled and sought consultation in Buffalo, NY, for a cancer vaccine which ended up being a bust. I remained in phone and email correspondence with the NIH, Moffit Cancer Center in Florida, Orlando Health, and others. Make no mistake, being sick became a full-time job. Being moderately health literate, I don't know how the average patient manages to juggle the demands of regular everyday life concomitantly with cancer.

Those words brought me to tears, however. "We can treat this!" The conviction in her voice cut right through the weeks of sadness brought on by the dimming light of my future. Who knew the hope I was looking for was right back home at the University of Florida. Crying in the middle of Subway was less than desirable, but I didn't care. After her much-needed consoling, she said she would have me see Dr. Friedman while I was in town, her boss and mentor, brilliant and talented in his own rite.

Dr. William Alan Friedman was born in 1953 in the heart of the country in Dayton, Ohio. He went to medical school at Oberlin College and graduated summa cum laude from Ohio State University College of Medicine. He moved to Gainesville, Florida, in 1976. His merits and achievements are too abundant to count. Since his time at UF, he has authored over 300 articles and book chapters, including his autobiography, "Something Awesome: A Life in Neurosurgery."[19, 20] In a Kirkus book review's description, he "[…] recaps on his 44-year career as a neurosurgeon, including his long tenure as the Chairman of the Department of Neurosurgery at UF …" At the end of the review, the memoir was said to be, "An intimate, insightful meditation on the science, art, and business of healing."[19]

In 1873, the stereotactic method, basically positioning objects on a 3-dimensional axis, was introduced within the realm of neurosurgery in operating on the medulla oblongata in animals by Dittmar. [21] Positioning of your incision is paramount, and stereotactics made possible the precision required. Millimeters can be the difference in either ambulation or irreversibly maiming patients.

In the early 1900s, Horsely and Clarke, two English neurosurgeons, differed greatly in their view of the future of neurosurgery in regards to stereotactical applications. Clarke wanted to expand to humans and Horsley abstaining. [21] One could imagine why: the Horsley-Clark stereotactic device involved the fixation to the external ear canal, hard palate (roof of the mouth), and the infraorbital ridge (bone right under your eyelid housing the infraorbital nerve, you can palpate it yourself). [21, 22] Unsettling and painful. Nonetheless, the triangulation of the device was necessary for the accurate and steady insertion of a probe, or whatever is of interest, in 3-dimensional space, i.e., the brain.

In 1947, Speigel and Wyeis in Philadelphia at Temple University would demonstrate the feasibility of the device when applied to human neurosurgery inspiring other neurosurgeons the world over, notably Lars Leskell of Sweden. Speigel and Wycis, in 1958, using stereotactic principles would decrease the operative mortality of neurosurgical procedures from around 15% to 2% for the amelioration of movement disorders. [23] Up to the 1960s, there was much interest in neuroablative procedures for treatment of chronic pain and movement disorders, but the introduction of L-Dopa, [24] a medicinal therapy for Parkinson's disease [25], decreased academic interest in such operative techniques. [21]

Back across the pond, the Father of Stereotactic surgery, Lars Leskell, applied the stereotactic principles to radiation delivery. In 1947 inspired by his predecessors, Horsley and Clarke, coupled with Spiegel and Wycis, the Swede invented an "...arc-centered stereotactic apparatus for intracerebral surgery." Leskell would use paralleled X-ray beams in the form of high-energy *gamma* rays to create a lesion in the brain, like a surgical knife without the incision. [22] Indeed, Leskell was the first to dub "stereotactic radiosurgery" in 1951.[26] Leskell would treat 762 patients from 1968 to 1982 with the so-called, "Gamma Knife," treating predominantly vascular malformations and benign cancer.[22]

After FDA approval, the Gamma knife would be used at the University of Pittsburgh in 1987 by Lunsford et al. [27], drawing its radiation energy

271

from cobalt-60 gamma rays. Also, in the 1980s, linear accelerators (LINAC) would allow for the application of fixed radiation fields across a central axis, the patient. Later the technology would evolve to include multiple arching radiations providing a more concentrated dose to the lesion of interest and exposing less healthy brain tissue to harm. [22] Stereotactic systems involving LINAC have successfully treated hundreds of patients since its conception. [28] Luckily for me, the pioneers responsible for this new sophisticated way to deliver brain radiation were right at my alma mater, the University of Florida: Dr. Friedman and Dr. Frank Bova.[29, 30]

Dr. Friedman and Bova would make a great pair. From my experience, they truly loved what they do, bringing some semblance of hope to the lives of patients who, like me, were given a death sentence. By 2018, Dr. Friedman stepped down as the neurosurgical chair. By then, he had treated over 5,000 patients with the radiosurgery system. [20] I was diagnosed in 2019; I couldn't have been in better hands.

I walked into Dr. Friedman's clinic wishing I hadn't known so much about him, perhaps I would have been a little less nervous. The nurse seated me in my assigned room with my mom in toe. I imagined him as a mad scientist, hair sticking straight up like Albert Einstein's with poor people skills. To my surprise, he stood in absolute contrast to my presumption. He might have been the most soft-spoken and empathetic doctors I had met. He had a very gentle bedside manner, and as my mom and I looked at the ghastly images of my brain MRI, he walked through my treatment plan.

He said while peering through his black-rimmed spectacles, "There are too many brain metastases to get an accurate count. There are 10 to 12 that are obvious. For example, here, here, and here," indicating with the mouse on the computer. With each 'here,' my stomach sank more, more, and more. I was speechless with the progression my disease acquired in just six months. "Because there are so many, I would recommend whole brain radiation, followed by one or two rounds of stereotactic radiotherapy to treat the bigger spots."

Dr. Friedman was more than aware of how shocking this news was to me. At least 12 brain metastases and counting! The largest of which was approaching 3 centimeters (grape-sized) located right at my arcuate fasciculus, a connection between speech production and reception in the left brain. He left my mom and me in the room for a few moments as he and his team could tell by our shell-shocked expressions that everything said thereafter was white noise. My thoughts went blank; my mind ceased operating. Silence turned to tears.

My mom and I are very alike. We always have to be doing something productive, from working out to planning for the future. Since the cancer began to invade my hopes and dreams, she and I worked tirelessly in some way to turn the tables or get a leg up on the cancer, whether it be finding supplements or researching other treatment options. She didn't have much of a science background, but she had done the best a mother could. Moreover, she moved to Indianapolis for a short stent to be close by in case of an emergency. But this was the first time she and I sat helpless together in that freezing clinic room and cried. Her son's life was threatened, and no amount of juicing or supplementation could change that. We never stopped to appreciate the fact that I might not outlive her or any of my parents.

Again, cancer does not care. Cancer does not care how educated you are, how much money you have, or how fast you can run. Cancer does not love or hate. Cancer is indiscriminate, the great equalizer, treating everyone the same. If you are looking for equality, you'll find it in cancer. (*Not entirely true. Some diseases are more common among certain ethnic groups.*) I often wonder if cancer isn't just a result of a lifestyle of leisure caught in excess, at least in America. What problems do we all *really* have? Too much to eat? How is it possible to have a homeless population and, at the same time, have an obesity problem?[31] Walking down the street, half the people you see are overweight or obese. How far will we lose touch with the land that provides the raw sustenance for survival? More importantly, how long until most forget the skill to harvest and hunt? I wonder how long vegans, or conversely, strict carnivores, will remain picky in their dietary preferences when the local supermarket closes? Indeed, it wouldn't be a stretch to say that our dietary preferences and our morals are largely shaped by how loud our stomach grumbles.

In a world increasingly divided by political party, belief systems, you name it; there is something that always will bring people together: suffering. Suffering is what we all have in common; for example, what all Americans felt on September 11th. Suffering is a universal language; where all people, black, white, and polka dot, can find common ground. Being human, sentient beings entails our self-acknowledgment of our personal and collective suffering. At some point, you will die. In the truest form of empathy, recognition of one's own suffering in another may be the key to a better future and understanding.

My Mom and I could have sat there for millennia hoping that time would stand still, that we could be teleported away from our current suffering, pain, and grief. Dr. Friedman knocked quietly before re-entering the room with his team. We were swimming in a pool of tears and disbelief at the sheer amount of tumor burden in my brain. They arranged an appointment with the radiation oncologist, who would plan, map, and administer the WBR. Following which, I would have two additional rounds of radiation surgery that Dr. Friedman would direct.

For love is blind all day and may not see.
Chaucer, The Marchantes Tale, 1. 354

I traveled back home to my place in Indianapolis before undergoing a suite of radiation treatments. Happy to see my friends, colleagues, and Jen, including her wonderful family, I knew I had months of treatment ahead. Jen and I tried to maintain a semblance of normality in our lives with our intermittent time with each other. We would go out on bike rides along the canal, work out, and spend time at the pool between my treatments and travel and her work as a nurse. I enjoyed hanging out with friends; however, I preferred being with her and her family, whom I began to see as my own.

Through my tragedy, our love grew. Although we didn't talk about it much, she had this quiet disposition and confidence that somehow, I would pull through. Jen has a beautiful way about her; calm, elegant, reserved. Pretty much the exact opposite of me. Her thick brown hair complemented her athletic physique, which despite her healthy workout habits, came naturally. Although she could get all done up with makeup and designer clothes shaming other girls in their efforts, in my opinion, she was most gorgeous in some running shorts, sunglasses, and a T-shirt, with no makeup. Her disposition reminded me of my grandmother, Lillian, the matriarch of our family, having sophisticated tastes and hobbies like painting and an affinity for lavish jewelry.

Although only having been less than a year, I wanted to marry her. She had been present throughout most of my experience with cancer to that point, and we brought so much joy to each other. Returning home from my consultation at UF, I had arranged an engagement party for her and me. Despite my confidence, I was nervous. Her Dad and I, who might've been the coolest father-in-law ever, had dinner to discuss the proposition. He acquiesced with no reservation; clearly, she and I were in love. Despite our rapidly changing situation, I decided to ask for her hand in marriage.

On a frigid morning in Old Northside in Indianapolis, I would coax Jen to join me for a stroll around the neighborhood. It was a poor morning for a walk as the side streets are largely ignored from the nightly salt dispersion making a stroll more of a skate without blades. Although the sun was high in the sky with no inkling of cloud cover for the coming day, the temperature remained frosty enough to make the ice stick formidably. Instead of a couple out for a leisurely amble, we both appeared to be afflicted by extreme vertigo, slipping and sliding until we discovered some stable ground.

Despite Jen's grumblings and pleas to turn around, I had a specific destination in mind. We had suffered through the worst portion of the walk; I only had to convince her to advance a block further to a lovely neighborhood park typically full of blooming flowers but had been replaced by patches of snow. Jen's first observation about the park for which we had passed on several walks prior was, "Oh, this is a park for blind people!" This park was gorgeous, yet I had never bothered to read the plaque at the entrance. Probably, the reason was because half of it was written in braille, marking the Great Oak Commons Sensory Park. The flowers and herbs are particularly aromatic to feed the senses. We laughed as we had never appreciated that fact.

Then, I walked her to the corner of the park and knelt. Neither of us can remember what was said, but at the end of the exchange, we were engaged.

Preemptively, I had invited all her friends to the engagement party that I had planned before popping the question. Bold, I admit. Many had traveled quite the distance to share in the celebration. There were two parties for which she had no knowledge: one at her house and the other at one of our favorite breweries. Indeed, I had planned a full day, but I had planned the morning free to do whatever we wished. Whatever Jen wished. I asked, "What would you like to do? Breakfast? Call a bunch of people?" She replied, "Let's go to the gym!" I was tickled pink as this was further confirmation that I had made the correct decision.

The correct decision had been made, but this is no fairy tale. The odds against our survival were just about the same as my 5-year survival rate for stage 4 lung cancer, almost nil. The obstacles to us being happily together, both physically and emotionally, began to multiply in the coming months. Never had I met anyone so perfect, but at the utmost worse timing. Our love for one another would sustain us for some time, but emotional fatigue, distance, and the fallout from unrelenting cancer treatment would eventually demand their toll.

Our robust foundation would continue to be weathered by a growing divide between us. As I fell deeper into the dark chasm of an emotional and painstaking war with cancer, a cancer of a different kind would affect Jen. A cancer that neither of us had the tools or resources to battle within our current setting. We had wandered into a park for the blind when engaged to be married, and that's precisely what we became. Blind. Both blinded by our ignorance to the severity of my condition. Like reaching for any object of familiarity in a pitch-black living room, a living room that wasn't your own, our unguided navigation was bound for failure despite our love for one another. Me, *still* having love for her.

My flight left the next day following the engagement party(ies) for radiation treatment expedited by the good folks at the University of Florida. Talk about a rough plane ride! Indeed, I was nursing a massive hangover, a painful reminder of the sins of the former evening. Worth it! However, I do not know if I deserved the unsavory character seated next to me who was attempting to drink the plane dry, asking for multiple Jack and Coke's. Every swig of libations was topped with an audible fart; *I am not kidding,* adding to his putrid aroma marked by too many cigarettes and not enough bathing. If I could get through quite possibly the worst plane ride I've ever experienced, how bad could Whole Brain Radiation (WBR) be?

"Mama's got the magic of Clorox"
The Clorox Company, slogan

Meanwhile, a researcher at H. Lee Moffitt Cancer Center and Research Institute in Tampa, Florida, would happen across some encouraging findings in the treatment of lung neuroendocrine cancers (NECs). First published online in 2019 and printed in the journal *The Oncologist* in 2020, Jonathan Strosberg MD and others reported on a treatment for pancreatic neuroendocrine cancers, the CAPTEM regimen, or capecitabine-temozolomide, a combinatorial form of chemotherapy re-purposing it for the treatment of advanced, metastatic lung NECs.[32] My response to chemotherapy up to this point had not been measurable in any sense, perhaps keeping the remnants of cancer at bay. My aforementioned surgery had debulked most of the tumor mass from my chest, but there remained radiological evidence of diseased lymph nodes, particularly at my carina, the bifurcation of the trachea. *In other words, I was in drastic need of effective adjuvant chemotherapy, which could sweep the floor clean systemically of any aberrant cancer cells in my body. Note, systemic treatment does not address the brain held with quarantine by the blood-brain barrier.*

Of the 20 patients featured in Strosberg's study, eight patients, 40%, had a Ki-67 proliferation index between 3 and 20% (*recall that falls within the range of atypical carcinoid or AC*), and most had undergone prior treatments (80%), like me. *Thus, making the results generalizable or applicable to me.* Twenty-five percent were officially designated AC. Of the 19 evaluable patients, 6 (30%) had a partial response, and 11 (55%) had stable disease following treatment. The objective response rate, basically a visual decrease in the size of the cancer mass as evaluated by computed tomography (CT) or magnetic resonance imaging (MRI), [33] was 30%. The toxicity profile was reportedly much improved as well. [32] This *had been the most encouraging numbers to date. This re-purposed chemotherapy might work!*

279

This would not come through my measly attempts at research on available clinical trials, which had been fruitless to date; Dr. Kaye, cowboy thoracic oncologist at UF, was the arbiter. After my travel back to my Alma Mater, I would promptly begin my new regimen of cytotoxic chemotherapy, the CAPTEM regimen. After leaving Dr. Kaye's clinic office, I ventured down to an adjacent building to start the planning process for whole brain radiation (WBR).

Terrified of brain radiation even more than mediastinal chest radiation, Dr. Rahman, neurosurgeon at UF and protégé of Dr. Friedman, reassured me that neuronal cells of the brain were remarkably resilient to the effects of radiation, unlike cancer cells which were more susceptible. [34] Admittedly, I still haven't researched the long-term effects of whole brain radiation for fear of what I might find. Some reverse form of the placebo effect may take hold, convincing myself of cognitive decline where they may be none. Moreover, how would that information serve me? I can guess at the downstream effects: early-onset dementia, cognitive slowing, decreased memory and retention, and hormonal and mood disruptions. The latter of which I had already been experiencing thanks to the high dose steroids to reduce brain inflammation and swelling, producing a perpetual headache. Based on the Monro-Kellie hypothesis, the limited space within my skull and the mass effect from my brain's growing tumor burden increases intracranial pressure, further propagating my symptoms. [35] Ignorance was my friend.

My radiation oncologist, Dr. Robert J. Amdur MD, shared the same contention. Admittedly, I did hint at some of the long-term deficits one may experience after radiation. In other words, would I turn into a walking fried egg drooling over my yolk? A towering man, always dressed in a bowtie and nice slacks, replied, and I am paraphrasing, "You are not NOT going to receive radiation because of some possible side effects, are you?" I found his reply a little off-putting, but I knew the point he was trying to convey. "Let's save your life first, and then we will worry about that."

He said that in the gentlest way he could while maintaining a certain straightforwardness. Pontifications and off-the-cuff predictions don't serve anyone. I noticed one of my defense mechanisms was to over-intellectualize or ask questions loosely relevant to what I knew I couldn't change to maintain some form of power over my situation where I had none. The illusion of control was a hard-won realization and would further mature throughout treatment. A year later, I would re-encounter some schemes and habits that would realistically curb my fate, or at the very least improve my quality of life, but that would not come for another year.

I would spend much time with Dr. Amdur, and as unsettling as our first encounter was, I began to enjoy his odd sense of humor and the eclectic bowties he'd sport. He explained the course of WBR, "It would take an entire month, the rest of December and some of January. Because of the holidays, we can only do four treatments a week for three weeks." Looks like I won't have to decide between my mom and dad as to whom I'd spend Christmas and New Year's, an annoying yearly decision for my brother and me. "We will go ahead and complete the planning and mold for planning and get started next week." To administer the same dose of radiation to each part of the brain consistently, the patient must be in the same position each time, hence the necessity for the mold.

When I was first wheeled into the radiation suite, it appeared like any other CT or MRI suite. But again, it would be another linear accelerator, or LINAC, like the one pointed at my chest for mediastinal radiation just six months earlier. Recall the aforementioned device that would deliver high-energy radiation in such a way as to destabilize and kill the cancer cells but spare normal brain tissue. I laid down on what felt like a bean bag. As it molded around me with the help of the radiation techs, they removed all the air from the bean bag, conforming perfectly with my body contour.

What seemed like a comfortable childhood creature comfort quickly turned into the cradle of mental distress as the mold stiffened around my body, further reinforcing the fact that there was no getting out of this. My anxiety intensified, my heart racing as the LINAC twisted and turned around my person. They would write my name on my personal mold and tossed it among a pile of others, sadly indicating that I was not alone in the fight.

To make the experience less anxiety-provoking, the cheerful radiation technicians kept an upbeat tempo and music playing while conducting their duties. They affixed the mask over my face, which was also securely molded to my profile and the back of the table. Another surge of anxiety pulsed through my extremities as the warm mold slowly cooled and hardened over my face from the tip of my brow to the back of my neck. Between the face mold and the bean bag, we could be confident that I was getting the correct radiation dose to the exact locations for the duration of treatment. *And I was confident of my cold reality.*

Once I began my series of treatments, I would request my favorite band, "Houndmouth," a band from southern Indiana, to be played on Spotify. The familiar tunes, however, did not pacify my emotional state. Like a SciFi scanning device revolving about my crown, the LINAC delivered its computed radiation indiscriminately with each mechanically derived beam, eliciting tears with each rotation.

Although each session took only 15 minutes, I felt like all my years of hard work in training to become a doctor were actively being erased; I would never regain the mental acuity I had worked tirelessly to achieve. Head immovable by a Hellraiser mask and body immobile by the mold, I knew I would never see the inside of an OR again, at least as a surgeon. When the radiation wave reached my olfactory (smell) bulb, I experienced the nauseating smell of bleach, a smell that still elicits chills down my spine, even to this day. I imagined my brain being wiped sterile of any of the hard-won knowledge throughout my arduous years of education. After each session, I skipped all social pleasantries and rushed out of the radiation suite attempting to hide my tears and flushed face. Within a few sessions, I asked the radiation techs to change the music.

Behold, now is the accepted time; behold, now is the day of salvation.
New Testament: 11 Corinthian, vi, 2.

Instead of spending the Christmas holidays with family, I needed to be nearby the hospital due to the almost daily brain radiation treatments. Coincidentally, I was offered refuge with someone who had already been immensely influential in my desire to become a cardiothoracic surgeon, Dr. Tomas Martin (*see Rite of Passage*). Recall that he was the first surgeon who allowed me scrub into the operative room and quizzed me on the rhythm of the beating heart as a medical student. Watching the heart squeeze about its oblique axis smoothly sliding upon surfaces of the surrounding pericardium glistening in the bright operative lights was, for me, like a pirate gazing upon a chest full of gold. Mesmerizing and captivating, I was hooked on cardiac surgery from that day forward.

What I hadn't mentioned in the previous chapter was how important he is to the world of cardiothoracic surgery, and the downstream effects his illustrious career had on my interest in cardiac surgery, not the mention the influence he would inadvertently have on me during my cancer treatment. Dr. Tomas D. Martin is a professor of surgery in the division of Thoracic and Cardiovascular Surgery at UF and the director of the UF Health Aortic Disease Center. He completed his rigorous surgical training in Baylor University in general and vascular surgery in Texas. He would complete a cardiothoracic surgical residency at UF, where he would stay as faculty.

He would train multiple surgeons, many of whom have been absolutely centerfold in my abbreviated professional career. To name a few, Dr. Thomas Beaver, Dr. Philip Hess, Dr. Joel Corvera, Dr. Karen Rieger, and Dr. Omeni Osian. All played a significant role in my early operative training but would provide even more support during my future time of need. Dr. Martin instilled a legacy of goodwill and expertise throughout his surgical career. If not represented by his progeny of trainees far exceeding my brief list, his charitable acts were exemplified around the globe, from the Philippines to Haiti, providing surgical care to underserved populations.

Up to this point, however, Dr. Martin had been somewhat ethereal to me, an inspiration as a young, aspiring heart surgeon. Dr. Philip Hess, who had trained under Dr. Martin, was much of the reason, if not all, for my decision to move to Indianapolis for surgical training. Dr. Hess and I had many things in common, one of them having a taste for fine bourbon and guns. I had not reached the surgical skill to graduate to his operating room yet, but I was looking forward to owning the opportunity in my later years of training.

Dr. Hess, with his auburn brown hair, which he would comb through with his fingertips in times of contemplation, is adored by all the surgical residents. Youthful despite his many years of operating late nights, he maintained an inviting, comforting disposition, enticing residents to openly share their concerns relating to any and everything. He had a natural way of giving you a whole different perspective. One always left his office feeling better than when you walked in; finding his counsel on many issues that plague a surgical resident came naturally while under his wing. I suppose this might've stemmed from him being a father of two beautiful children, a boy and girl.

The oldest, Megan, about to graduate college, would call me to wish me well during my treatments, which came with no coaxing from her father. The apple doesn't fall from the tree. His wife, Pamela, was always excited and welcoming when I'd come over to share in an evening cordial. Dr. Hess and I would discuss anything but heart surgery and made plans to go bird hunting in the Dakotas or fish down in the Florida Keys. As exciting as all this sounded, these plans would be hampered by the events to come.

When I informed Dr. Hess that I would receive radiation treatments at UF during the Christmas holidays, he suggested that Dr. Martin and his wife, Sally, would happily welcome me into their home. They had an adjacent wing of the house that would give me plenty of space while undergoing my weekly broiling. And I would need it once the effects of WBR, coupled with the new chemotherapeutic regimen, CAPTEM, started taking its toll; there were days when I couldn't get out of bed.

A week before Christmas, I arrived at the Martin's home. Dr. Hess would accompany me for a short stent to see his long-time mentor and dear friend. We were met with immense hospitality by Mrs. Sally, a doctor herself, as we parked in the driveway shaded by large coastal Oak trees that call Central Florida their home. *Both Dr. Martin's poked fun at me for always using their official titles, preferring me to call them Tom and Sally, but my southern manners were far too ingrained in my upbringing to dare to address them in any other way.* It was December, but you wouldn't know it. When Dr. Martin arrived at the house from the hospital, he teased Dr. Hess about how dreadful the weather in Indiana was this time of year. Clearly said in jest but attempting to convince Dr. Hess to change his zip code. Shorts could've been worn that entire *winter* in Gainesville.

During my stay with Dr. Martin, as much as I wanted to talk about his experience in heart surgery, he would redirect the conversation to lean toward myself. We did, indeed, talk about his days and his surgical cases for the week; although, I could tell he wasn't too interested in that flavor of conversation. Eventually, as we became more acquainted, I would see him less as an illustrious surgeon and more as a friend.

Sitting out back, enjoying the cover of the Oaks serving to shade the golf course and the Martin's pool in the backyard, we faced westward with the sun just about to retire for the evening. The brain radiation had my hair falling out in clumps, and my perfectly bald head glistened with a faint hint of sweat on my brow, having been untouched by the sun's rays since my birth. Just as the sun was approaching its evening dive into the horizon to rise again the following day, I, too, would experience my reawakening. Unsuspectingly, I was about to be reborn.

Dr. Martin was a devout Christian. Every morning I would find him in the living room, before a busy operative day, reading his bible with coffee. We sat, and as much as I wanted to talk about my plans and possibilities still remaining in pursuit of my dream of being a heart surgeon, he would ask me if I had thought about my relationship with God. He stated calmly with our feet up on the side-by-side pool chairs, "The most important thing in this life is your personal relationship with Lord."

Because I was baptized at a young age, perhaps too young, I hadn't fully appreciated God's active role in my life. Once I reached my college years, I unwittingly continued to fail to recognize Him and His vital role in my success in life until a reawakening through tragedy ten years later. My enormous blessing and talents bequeathed to me, athleticism, intellect, personality, and family, had not been appreciated. I hadn't fully acknowledged the indescribable reality that allowed all this to happen. Blessed beyond measure, I had been caught up in an illusion of my own creation, not paying homage to the one thing that made this possible. Dr. Martin re-kindled something in me on those plastic pool chairs that I had long since forgotten. We owe everything we have to God.

I do not wish to have a theological discussion on the nature of God. Indeed, there are different flavors of belief, much of which are influenced by culture and time. But what I came to appreciate is not what everything religion, Christianity in my case, *isn't*, but *what it is*. It is a formidable guide. It is comfort. Something to inspire hope in difficult times; and something to adulate in the good. It's not entirely historically correct, *it wasn't meant to be*, but the lessons ring true for time immemorial.

I shake my head at the unfair critiques of the Biblical stories; I used to do the same thing. But, my friends, don't miss the point. These truths allow us to live a just and fruitful life with a healthy sense of morality. And I had neglected the power of the Spirit in place of study for endeavors in human knowledge. I had made a false god out of material pursuits, for example, my insatiable desire to be a heart surgeon, forsaking all of which was more important: family and my relationship with the unknowable, ineffable reality, God. *Yes, even though I was entering a profession that would ultimately help people.*

The power of our pool discussion wouldn't hit me until months after I was done getting my egg fried. My family would come to Gainesville to visit the Martins' residence during the holidays; there were days I couldn't peel myself off the skillet after radiation had me laid flat like a fresh pancake. We celebrated Christmas at the end of my first week of WBR. The following week, my little sister, Teal, would visit and watch movies I

288

could never finish. While I was near incapacitated, she and Sally would paint in the garage studio. Teal would have cookies prepared for me when I woke up. Just like our Mother, she'd go on to be a nurse, and, as you can imagine, she is an excellent one. On days I could manage, I'd go to the gym only to collapse in exhaustion when I returned to the Martin's. Many days I wouldn't even see Dr. Martin because I would fall asleep too early.

Serendipitously, it is strange to note how many aspects of our lives are most influenced by the most unsuspecting events that can be distilled down to minute-long interactions. These brief moments have profound and far-reaching effects, for example, growing up alongside my good buddy Chance or attending a simple lecture in medical school by Dr. Beaver. Both led ultimately to a couple of pool chairs and a discussion of the ineffable reality and my potential early encounter with Him. These tiny ripples of conversation on one shore in time become tidal waves on another. Our poolside conversation would help me through dark times ahead.

A wise son maketh a glad father.
Old Testament: Proverbs, x, 1.

At the culmination of my WBR treatments, I was sick of Florida, and the bleach forever imprinted in my olfactory bulb. The sweet, sappy smell of Georgia pines and buzzing gnats below the Fall line was just the medicine I needed to restore my senses to baseline. Memory deficits might be a risk of WBR, but every buzz of the annoying pest at my ear would surely provoke fond memories providing its own form of restoration. Also, my dad and step-mom, Mother we call her, had made every effort to welcome me back home. During the Coronavirus pandemic, visitation remained difficult in any situation. My father has certain risk factors that would preclude him from accompanying me on doctor visits; Mother was the head nurse at a local nursing home where the highest risk population resided. My father had a particular animus and aversion towards doctors and hospitals. Naturally, I'd become one.

My father and I are very much alike, stubborn and headstrong to our core. When we say we will do something, we don't sleep until the job's done. I sorely missed him during treatments, along with Mother. When we finally had the opportunity to be reunited, I knew just how to celebrate my long-awaited reprieve from treatment and return to southeast Georgia.

After the WBR treatments, they allow patients to take home the Hellraiser mask, the plastic mold that keeps your head in the same position throughout radiation treatment. Out at our farm, we have a shooting range and no shortage of weapons, from shotguns to pistols. From around 25 to 30 yards, I unloaded over 100 rounds of ammunition at that mask in a rebellious display of catharsis. Each round unloaded sent bits and pieces of molded plastic flying high. I disposed of what was left of the face mask in the burn pit. As the remnants of the plastic mold melted away, so did some of my frustration of having my dreams and future torn away.

I rode the ATV around the farm, appreciating all the hard work that my father had us do as kids in putting up barbed wire fences or cultivating hay, which felt like every weekend. Each 'ting' of the handheld post hole digger was another small bolster for our character shaping a solid work ethic. It must've been challenging to tolerate our whines and discontentment as we reluctantly toiled over the fence on weekends. I imagine, at times, he would fear losing favor with his boys. Like every good father, he would do what was required to raise strong men.

And he did. Thank you, Dad.

Learn to labor and to wait.
Longfellow, A Psalm of Life

The break wouldn't last for long. The whole brain radiation could deliver a spanning dose of radiation at a lesser intensity in the hope of wiping out anything we couldn't see with a brain MRI. For the 10 to 12 larger metastases, the largest was measured to be around 3 centimeters, unfortunately, positioned within a tract of nerves known as the arcuate fasciculus. It connects speech production and speech reception in the left hemisphere. An intensified, more targeted radiation application approach would be required: stereotactic radiosurgery, SRS.

As previously mentioned, advances in SRS were pioneered at the University of Florida; assuredly, my care was in good hands. However, in my case, we were exceeding the limits of what would be considered susceptible to SRS. Most studies involving SRS for the treatment of intracranial metastases numbered between one and four; data supporting the benefit of SRS for the management of greater than four metastases become progressively scant as the number increases. I had at least twelve. [36] We had ascended from ol' Davy Jones locker only to tread in uncharted waters testing the limits of the brain to withstand radiation. I was always interested in clinical research; however, I never imagined being a data point, an experimental one at that.

After a month of WBR, I felt like death and looked much worse. The extreme level of fatigue one experiences is unrivaled; I felt like I had played two 90-minute soccer matches back-to-back each day in the sweltering Florida sun. The severe exhaustion reminded me of 3-a-days during preseason at Stetson University. Only worse. Unfortunately, to combat the overwhelming fatigue and reduce the impending inflammation from WBR, I was ingesting whopping doses of dexamethasone, the strongest steroid in a physician's arsenal. [37, 38] Being on high-dose steroids has considerable behavioral side-effects; short-tempered and irritability, to name a couple. I was not a pleasant person to be around at times.

Especially when factoring in the sleep disturbances induced by the steroids, my time in bed, in no way, reflected the amount of regenerative sleep I received. Chronically sleep deprived, my mind was constantly teeming with new research ideas and all my plans once I returned to work. Indeed, my mentors were convinced that this poor guy was not only delusional but manic. Most likely, they didn't have the heart to tell me. At baseline, I always bit off more than I could chew, but steroids had allowed me to reach a whole new level.

Once again, I would descend into a subterranean radiation suite in my manic zombie-like state where a gang of other patients was waiting to receive their targeted dose of SRS. Jovial chatters could be heard before I walked into a tight room where all the other baldies huddled at six in the morning, sharing their experience with cancer. I was in NO mood. Having just received a month of WBR, the fluorescent lighting singed my eyes. The laughs and snickers from a select few without any sense of situational awareness fervently annoyed me. Thankfully, Dr. Friedman and Dr. Bova would soon take the stage, introduce themselves, and continue explaining the day's schedule. I hardly listened; like a bat, I was searching for the darkest, most quiet room to hide to find relief from my escalating headache.

The day of SRS would be arranged in the following fashion: our halo fitting, head computed tomography (CT), and, finally, targeted cranial radiation. The halo fitting was much like the original Horsley-Clark stereotactic device but less medieval. The halo mount was affixed to a patient's head with screws splitting the four cardinal directions around your scalp right about your eyebrow level. This established a steady and consistent axis for the radiation treatment to be administered, ensuring the correct orientation when the LINAC would deliver its radiotherapy. Of course, they used lidocaine for the insertion of the screws. Each screw was like a bee sting waking me up better than an Opus cup of coffee. I desperately clung to maintain a moderate amount of wakefulness as we continued the processing. After the halo was mounted, a head CT was performed to confirm its position and finalize a plan of approach. When it was your turn, they would treat the lesions, when *it was your turn, of course.*

They decided the order of treatment: whoever had the least amount of tumor burden would go first. The most would go last. Can you guess where I was in line? Dead last. I had the most tumor burden; thus would take the longest to treat. It was only fair. This was the most streamlined way they could treat a high number of patients.

My mom and I found a quiet abandoned office near the radiation suite out of earshot from the other patients. The circular halo at brow level allowed about an inch of clearance surrounding my head, making it extremely difficult to find a comfortable position to rest my egghead. Every adjustment sounded off a 'ting' or 'tang' with a 'tinge' of pain. So despite my fatigue, there would be no sleeping. Additionally, the rim of the halo was directly at eye level, impeding my ability to distract myself from the discomfort with work. Each attempt at repositioning was met with another tinge of pain and an audible '*ting.*' Somehow I managed to be productive working on scholarly papers for the cardiothoracic surgical department at IU. Despite my current discomfort, I refused to have time wasted.

Exhausted from the month of WBR and sleep deprivation, I would find no rest in that basement, waiting on my turn for SRS. Because I was last in line, I sat for twelve hours typing away, unable to find any semblance of comfort, reaching in vain for a dependable distraction. The only satisfaction I had while patiently waiting my turn was completing two scholarly papers for the surgical department. I refused to have time wasted. And if I was worried about not having enough time for painful solitude, I had another SRS session scheduled for the following month. Guess who was last again?

1. Osmani, L., et al., *Current WHO guidelines and the critical role of immunohistochemical markers in the subclassification of non-small cell lung carcinoma (NSCLC): Moving from targeted therapy to immunotherapy.* Semin Cancer Biol, 2018. **52**(Pt 1): p. 103-109.

2. Ling, M. and M. Murali, *Analysis of the Complement System in the Clinical Immunology Laboratory.* Clin Lab Med, 2019. **39**(4): p. 579-590.

3. Bonilla, F.A. and H.C. Oettgen, *Adaptive immunity.* J Allergy Clin Immunol, 2010. **125**(2 Suppl 2): p. S33-40.

4. Velcheti, V. and K. Schalper, *Basic Overview of Current Immunotherapy Approaches in Cancer.* Am Soc Clin Oncol Educ Book, 2016. **35**: p. 298-308.

5. Yang, Y., *Cancer immunotherapy: harnessing the immune system to battle cancer.* J Clin Invest, 2015. **125**(9): p. 3335-7.

6. Eshhar, Z., et al., *Specific activation and targeting of cytotoxic lymphocytes through chimeric single chains consisting of antibody-binding domains and the gamma or zeta subunits of the immunoglobulin and T-cell receptors.* Proc Natl Acad Sci U S A, 1993. **90**(2): p. 720-4.

7. Brentjens, R.J., et al., *Eradication of systemic B-cell tumors by genetically targeted human T lymphocytes co-stimulated by CD80 and interleukin-15.* Nat Med, 2003. **9**(3): p. 279-86.

8. Weiss, S.A., J.D. Wolchok, and M. Sznol, *Immunotherapy of Melanoma: Facts and Hopes.* Clin Cancer Res, 2019. **25**(17): p. 5191-5201.

9. Hinshaw, D.C. and L.A. Shevde, *The Tumor Microenvironment Innately Modulates Cancer Progression.* Cancer Res, 2019. **79**(18): p. 4557-4566.

10. Alexander, M., S.Y. Kim, and H. Cheng, *Update 2020: Management of Non-Small Cell Lung Cancer.* Lung, 2020. **198**(6): p. 897-907.

11. Awad, M.M., et al., *Long-Term Overall Survival From KEYNOTE-021 Cohort G: Pemetrexed and Carboplatin With or Without Pembrolizumab as First-Line Therapy for Advanced Nonsquamous NSCLC.* J Thorac Oncol, 2021. **16**(1): p. 162-168.

12. Xia, L., Y. Liu, and Y. Wang, *PD-1/PD-L1 Blockade Therapy in Advanced Non-Small-Cell Lung Cancer: Current Status and Future Directions.* Oncologist, 2019. **24**(Suppl 1): p. S31-s41.
13. Chalmers, Z.R., et al., *Analysis of 100,000 human cancer genomes reveals the landscape of tumor mutational burden.* Genome Med, 2017. **9**(1): p. 34.
14. Barnfield, P.C. and P.M. Ellis, *Second-Line Treatment of Non-Small Cell Lung Cancer: New Developments for Tumours Not Harbouring Targetable Oncogenic Driver Mutations.* Drugs, 2016. **76**(14): p. 1321-36.
15. Gaiser, R.R., *Postdural Puncture Headache: An Evidence-Based Approach.* Anesthesiol Clin, 2017. **35**(1): p. 157-167.
16. Kennedy, L.B. and A.K.S. Salama, *A review of cancer immunotherapy toxicity.* CA Cancer J Clin, 2020. **70**(2): p. 86-104.
17. Schoenfeld, A.J. and M.D. Hellmann, *Acquired Resistance to Immune Checkpoint Inhibitors.* Cancer Cell, 2020. **37**(4): p. 443-455.
18. Arroll, B., et al., *Antidepressants versus placebo for depression in primary care.* Cochrane Database Syst Rev, 2009(3): p. Cd007954.
19. Friedman, W.A. *Something Awesome: A Life in Nuerosurgery.* 2021; Available from: https://www.kirkusreviews.com/book-reviews/william-friedman/something-awesome/.
20. Florida, L.S.W.D.o.N.a.t.U.o. *William A. Friedman* 2022; Available from: https://neurosurgery.ufl.edu/faculty-staff/our-faculty/william-a-friedman-md/.
21. al-Rodhan, N.R. and P.J. Kelly, *Pioneers of stereotactic neurosurgery.* Stereotact Funct Neurosurg, 1992. **58**(1-4): p. 60-6.
22. Lasak, J.M. and J.P. Gorecki, *The history of stereotactic radiosurgery and radiotherapy.* Otolaryngol Clin North Am, 2009. **42**(4): p. 593-9.
23. Spiegel, E.A., H.T. Wycis, and H.W. Baird, 3rd, *Long-range effects of electropallidoansotomy in extrapyramidal and convulsive disorders.* Neurology, 1958. **8**(10): p. 734-40.
24. García Ruiz, P.J. and E. Meseguer, *[Short history of L-Dopa].* Neurologia, 2002. **17**(4): p. 214-7.
25. Fahn, S. and W. Poewe, *Levodopa: 50 years of a revolutionary drug for Parkinson disease.* Mov Disord, 2015. **30**(1): p. 1-3.

26. Leksell, L., *The stereotaxic method and radiosurgery of the brain.* Acta Chir Scand, 1951. **102**(4): p. 316-9.

27. Lunsford, L.D., et al., *Stereotactic radiosurgery of the brain using the first United States 201 cobalt-60 source gamma knife.* Neurosurgery, 1989. **24**(2): p. 151-9.

28. Kooy, H.M., et al., *Treatment planning for stereotactic radiosurgery of intra-cranial lesions.* Int J Radiat Oncol Biol Phys, 1991. **21**(3): p. 683-93.

29. Bova, F.J., W.A. Friedman, and W.M. Mendenhall, *Stereotactic radiosurgery.* Med Prog Technol, 1992. **18**(4): p. 239-51.

30. Friedman, W.A. and F.J. Bova, *The University of Florida radiosurgery system.* Surg Neurol, 1989. **32**(5): p. 334-42.

31. Koh, K.A., et al., *The hunger-obesity paradox: obesity in the homeless.* J Urban Health, 2012. **89**(6): p. 952-64.

32. Al-Toubah, T., B. Morse, and J. Strosberg, *Capecitabine and Temozolomide in Advanced Lung Neuroendocrine Neoplasms.* Oncologist, 2020. **25**(1): p. e48-e52.

33. Aykan, N.F. and T. Özatlı, *Objective response rate assessment in oncology: Current situation and future expectations.* World J Clin Oncol, 2020. **11**(2): p. 53-73.

34. Greene-Schloesser, D., et al., *Radiation-induced brain injury: A review.* Front Oncol, 2012. **2**: p. 73.

35. Mokri, B., *The Monro-Kellie hypothesis: applications in CSF volume depletion.* Neurology, 2001. **56**(12): p. 1746-8.

36. Hartgerink, D., et al., *Stereotactic Radiosurgery in the Management of Patients With Brain Metastases of Non-Small Cell Lung Cancer: Indications, Decision Tools and Future Directions.* Front Oncol, 2018. **8**: p. 154.

37. Johnson, D.B., M.J. Lopez, and B. Kelley, *Dexamethasone*, in *StatPearls*. 2022, StatPearls Publishing
Copyright © 2022, StatPearls Publishing LLC.: Treasure Island (FL).

38. Ryken, T.C., et al., *The role of steroids in the management of brain metastases: a systematic review and evidence-based clinical practice guideline.* J Neurooncol, 2010. **96**(1): p. 103-14.

11

Pouched and Cracked

Any fool can carry on, but only the wise man knows how to shorten sail.
Joseph Conrad, Message to Tusitala.

After my slough of radiation during the spring of 2020, I was pleased to be going back to my adopted home and family in Indianapolis. Over the past few months, I had received a Chernobyl-sized onslaught of radiation, or at the very least, approaching the upper limits of what the radiation oncologists considered safe. The radiation dose was lifesaving, at the very least life-*extending*, and certainly not without some measurable degree of harm.

On my return to the Hoosier state, I realized that there was no way that I could return to residency, this year at least. *Still delusional.* I figured it would take another year of clean scans and maybe some additional treatments before I could, with complete confidence, continue with my life. My residency program remained steadfast in their support, allowing another research and *treatment* year. Even though my program lacked a research track, they created the option at everyone's inconvenience, keeping me gainfully employed with health insurance and stipend.

Because the Accreditation Council for Graduate Medical Education, or the ACGME, only allows for a certain number of residents per class per program per specialty, my absence clinically, rotating on services taking care of patients and operating, left a large void in our group's working capacity. Instead of 10 cardiothoracic residents rotating to the different

298

hospitals in Indiana University's healthcare system, there were only 9. It doesn't seem like a lot, but trust me, my absence was felt. Although, I never heard any grumblings or expressions of malcontent. Revealing another reason why I had chosen Indiana University: character. However, their collective grit wouldn't absolve me of any guilt, leaving my fellow residents bombarded with extra call shifts amid work-hour restrictions tightening in recent years. How one maintains a proper surgical education without lying about your work hours remains a mystery to me.

Over the following few months, my vitality and energy would somewhat return as the radiation glow began to fade. *No, you don't actually start glowing.* Yet, even though my atoms were likely gyrating at higher valences due to the remnant effects of radiation, my energy for a sustained work capacity had been forever reduced. My daily invigoration for life had evaporated into the ether, replaced by the damage from high-energy Gamma rays. I maintained a profound fatigue; some internal manna was siphoned, never to return. I lacked the inner drive that had once allowed me to push through that last set on the bench press or sprint. Reluctantly, I'd do it anyway, but the desire was not there. My thirst for a living needed a little less quenching. Where I was once a healthy voluptuous grape, my slowly desiccating hopes left me a crackled raison forgotten in the sun.

As time progressed, I would shuffle between work, doctor's appointments, and spending time with friends and Jen. I'd attempt to enjoy my break from treatment but was interrupted by the monthly CAPTEM (capecitabine – temozolomide) regimen for chemotherapy. Chemotherapy remained blurry as it became a major part of my life and routine.

Thankfully, I did not experience any major side effects other than fatigue and an upset stomach, at least with the capecitabine portion of CAPTEM. The worse part of the month was the temozolomide portion of therapy, where the cytotoxic therapy crossed the blood-brain barrier, inciting headaches, fatigue, and dizziness. As a result, however, I could predict the days I would have energy (CAP only days) and the days I would spend most of my time in bed (CAP and TEM days). Fourteen days out of the month would be accompanied by oral chemotherapy, the rest of the month, I was free and clear to recover.

As the warm spring morphed quickly into the sweltering summer, my right lower visual field began to fade into the intensifying summertime haze like a distant mirage. The area became annoying when working on my computer as a constant blemish obstructed a slight but noticeable portion of my field of view. It appeared as if I had stared at the sun for too long. Of course, I would write it off; there was nothing I could do about it anyways. Moreover, I was determined to get off high-dose steroids placing myself on a rapid wean. They say physicians are their own worse doctors; I would prove that notion valid.

An odd aura consumed me when I walked up the stairs to my condo in late spring after a strenuous circuit workout in my unattached garage. Suddenly, I collapsed while climbing my stairs, although maintaining consciousness. I lost control of all motor function on my right-side body and was having trouble articulating any form of coherent speech. Crawling with the side of my body that remained functional, I reached my neighbor's door, who, thank God, was home, and I did my best to knock on the door.

Luckily, we were friends, having shared a cordial on several evenings; he knew about my developing condition. He sprang into action to get me into his car and rushed me to Methodist Hospital. By now, you and MH should be well-acquainted.

Once again, I entered that all too familiar emergency department, the site of my and other residents' *'Rite of Passage'*; this time, however, I remained trapped within myself. I was fully aware, but I had lost all powers of speech and most motor control of my right-side body. Immovable, fear ensued. A similar affliction had me trapped within myself during episodes of *'Sleep Paralysis'* nearly ten years earlier.

Would I ever be free of this? Was I having a stroke? I certainly had all the symptoms thereof. During the short drive to MH, my condition deteriorated rapidly. By the time I was booked and parked in one of the crowded hallways, with no rooms available, my panic reached a new high. When Jen showed up, I was writhing in discomfort and confusion on a plastic-wrapped bed with a weathered hospital sheet and pillow knocked on the tile. Each effort to explain what had happened would leave me increasingly frustrated, sending my anxiety to new heights.

After Jen succeeded in calming me down and a handful of benzodiazepines, a quick brain scan ruled out a stroke. Thank God! However, the scan did reveal one of two things: 1) My cancer was growing despite my radiation treatments, or 2) I had received such a whopping dose(s) of brain radiation I had developed radiation necrosis or *death of healthy brain tissue due to the radiation treatment, and it was expanding like cancer itself. I imagine my poor brain melting like the witch in the Wizard of Oz.*

A certain degree of radiation necrosis, or cell death, was *not unexpected*, especially after the sheer amount of radiation received at the turn of the year. *Note the double negative.* SRS is a more focused, intensified form of radiation and more likely subject to collateral damage to brain tissue. Every lesion treated with SRS carries a 5 – 26% rate of radiation necrosis and up to 17% rate of causing symptoms. [1] EACH LESION. I had 12 to 13 treated. This complication was virtually guaranteed, and I was attempting to wean off steroids which was the primary agent controlling swelling and inflammation. Why? Pride and foolishness. I loathed the fact that I needed medication to maintain homeostasis. Each time I looked in the mirror at my swollen chipmunk cheeks, a consequence of the high-dose steroids, I was motivated to rapidly wean my dose, throwing caution to the wind.

Preemptive whole brain radiotherapy (WBR) only increased my risk that much more. Brain cells are typically more resilient to radiation injury, but those protective mechanisms become overwhelmed when the insult is too great. [1] Healthy brain tissue becomes collateral damage. An apt description of my brain wouldn't be a fried egg as in the previous chapter, but more a poached one marked by liquefactive necrosis.

Jen continued to console my nerves; I slowly regained my powers of speech and ambulation. This would be one of the handful of seizures awaiting my future. I blame myself; I had been too encouraged by how well I was recovering despite the minor scotoma. Due to my recent thirty percent or more loss in lung capacity, I was eager to get back in tip-top shape, pushing myself with high-intensity workouts in lieu of long-distance running; the pain from the thoracotomies would be a friendly reminder to breathe deeper. Despite my lack of pulmonary reserve and mental endurance, I was determined to make it back to the operating room with a clean bill of health.

However, what I truly needed was complete rest. With reckless disregard, I continued to push my physiology to the upper limits of what was normal for me now, with each workout increasing cerebral blood flow (CBF) in the summer heat, inciting a dangerous cycle of swelling and inflammation. *Inflammation begets inflammation.* The day I experienced the seizure was a scorching, steamy day in Indianapolis. This ding-dong decided to go out to my dojo, my detached garage I transformed into a gym, for hefty circuit training. The fact is, I hadn't gone a week without working out since I started high school, save for surgeries and injury. Taking days 'off' was a foreign concept. In hindsight, this was very ill-advised, as was my 5-mile run the evening before my chest surgery at MSKCC, which could have played a role in my right thigh compartment syndrome. Although, these complications, in all probability, would have happened anyway.

Between a Rock and a Hard Place...
Dialect Notes V, 1921.

Following the seizure spell, I was promptly re-started on anti-seizure medications and began to pack. I could no longer be away from my treatment team at the University of Florida; I require consistent and frequent follow-up. My subsequent therapy bevacizumab, [2], or a recombinant human monoclonal antibody that binds to vascular endothelial growth factor (VEGF), would be needed to reduce the brain swelling. VEGF is a signal protein released naturally following tissue injury and aids in neovascularization or blood vessel formation. In tissue damaged by radiation, the healing process is dysregulated, causing fragility in the architecture of these newly formed vessels, which cannot provide the much-needed oxygen to hypoxic tissues propagating swelling. [2] In lieu of oxygenation, further tissue injury results. *And remember, inflammation begets inflammation. Bevacizumab discourages the growth of new blood vessels.*

Bevacizumab, also called Avastin, would require close monitoring and intravenous infusion re-evaluated monthly with laboratory analysis, which meant I needed to be closer to the University of Florida. Before the Avastin took effect, I continued having daily headaches despite enough Tylenol to send me into liver failure. *Kidding.* However, the daily headaches were mind-numbing until a month after my first infusion. I inquired as to whether or not Avastin could also be purposed for the treatment of brain metastases, and I was affirmed by my neuro-oncologist that it could. [3] Possibly, killing two birds with one stone; I was happy to hear it.

How much were we treating remnant radiation necrosis versus lingering cancer? How can we possibly be sure to direct further therapy? We needed a biopsy of the brain, meaning brain surgery. As frightening as it was, there were multiple reasons to do this. One of the primary reasons was that a large brain met resection would help alleviate my symptoms, reducing the space my tumor or foci of radiation necrosis was occupying, minimizing the effects of swelling. *Recall the Monro-Kellie hypothesis.* Secondarily, we would procure actual tissue squashing arguments as to whether it was cancer versus necrosis. Dr. Rahman, neurosurgeon at UF and protégé of Dr. Friedman, assured me this was the way to go. At this point, if Dr. Rahman said jump, I'd say, "How high?" And it is still this way, although I wouldn't do so well with jumping anymore.

She presented the options between a traditional brain surgery or one that involved awake monitoring to increase the chance that I would retain all of my faculties, like speech and walking. A major obstacle was that the largest met, the one likely causing the majority of my symptoms, was positioned at the *arcuate fasciculus*, a tract of brain fibers positioned on the left parietal brain connecting speech production and speech comprehension respectively Broca's and Wernicke's areas.[4] Talk about being stuck between a rock and a hard place. I was still under the delusion that I would be a surgeon again, so of course, I would choose awake brain surgery.

I saw no choice if I ever wanted to operate again. I had to proceed with the surety that radiation necrosis was the cause of my symptoms and not growing cancer. The only way to answer that question while simultaneously preserving any hope of maintaining my motor function and God-given manual dexterity was to consent to awake brain surgery where they could actively test my faculties in real-time. Who better than Dr. Rahman to grant me that shot? *None.* I felt safe under her knife on September 8th, 2020.

Before the awake brain surgery, I had to undergo cognitive and psychological testing to ensure I wouldn't freak out during the operation. They would ask me about depression and mood, "How are you coping?" I would unabashedly retort, "I am 29 years old. I have stage four lung cancer with metastases to my brain. I was in the middle of making my dreams come true when I was diagnosed. I had just met my fiancé and was ready to start a new life. How do you think I feel? I think I am allowed to be a little pissed and sad. Before you ask, no, I don't want any anti-depressants."

You are not awake the entire surgery. They place you under anesthesia, and they wake you up when they need to test some of your faculties. Even though I remember my experience, it wasn't unsettling. As long as I held the hand of the neuropsychologist's who had conducted the pre-surgical counseling, I was as calm as a Hindu cow. If that cow swallowed a handful of Xanax along with a handful of THC-infused gummies, of course. Hell, I was even joking around through a portion. Although when Dr. Rahman entered my ventricle, or fluid-filled cavity within the brain with pain receptors present, merriment was quickly transformed into intense pressure and pain. My only outlet was clenching the hand of the neuropsychologist until our knuckles turned white. Thankfully, Dr. Rahman responded quickly and put back to sleep.

Although, results from the pathological analysis of the brain specimen would solidify that the expanding lesions in my brain were NOT cancer but expanding radiation necrosis. *Or not cancer anymore. Relief! Well, of a kind.* Let me explain: it was very likely that any growth in the other lesions littered throughout my brain would follow suit as far as their expansion. However, there was only so much we could do to interrupt the evolving necrosis. Between high-dose steroids and Avastin, options were waning. Indeed, I desperately needed Avastin back on board, but I could not receive another dose to curb the edema unless I wished to bleed out![5] *As previously mentioned, Avastin interferes with normal wound healing and blood vessel formation, which is essential directly after surgery.*

Under the impression that my life had been difficult up to the brain surgery, the journey following the craniotomy and parietal brain resection would release an entirely new suite of challenges, including burying my hopes of being a surgeon or even being a doctor again. The true battle would begin twenty-four hours later, following the establishment of inflammation and remnant deficits.

Not at all can tell Whether I mean this day to end myself, Or lend an ear to Plato where he says, That men like soldiers may not quit their post Allotted by the Gods
Tennyson, Lucretius, 1. 145.

The inflammation naturally and expectedly began settling in, causing me to lose all motor control in my right-side body, all powers of speech, and some higher order processing. *I was operated on my left brain, and due to the decussation of nerve fibers around your brainstem from your brain to your feet, my entire right side was affected. By higher order processing, I mean doing my time tables, reading, and forward planning.* I couldn't quite process my intention or plan for any particular task. For instance, I was unable to do simple tasks like putting on socks or making a pot of coffee. I knew *how* to do it but putting the plan into action was nigh impossible. Brushing my teeth…forget about it. *Don't worry about these pearly whites; I eventually relearned.*

Transferred to a rehab facility within four days postoperatively, the swelling would heighten, and, subsequently, my right-side body became virtually unusable, especially my right hand. As the swelling peaked, so too was the civil unrest within my morning bowl of oats which had decidedly taken up arms! Reminded of the microscopic cancer cell whose overproduced genetic material and products had ruined a clean bathtub, mutated oats were engaged in tiny skirmishes throughout my room, which had turned into a battleground. At the height of the insurrection, the mutant oats and fellow activists would clash their shields across my face, hospital gown, and my mom's blond hair. After the morning insurrection had simmered down, my patient room and gown were littered with casualties. The battles would continue throughout the first week. God bless my mom for the collateral damage she endured.

I can only imagine what a passerby thought hearing the grunts and hollers that marked those first few mornings in the rehab facility. These hands that had not so long ago cannulated a delicate aorta; now only gave rise to fingers that couldn't grasp a spoon. Needless to say, I was frustrated. Frustrated that I couldn't express my frustration. Subsequently, spoons and forks would litter the ground consistently at mealtimes, joining in on the social unrest. Utensils were modified with large cushions accommodating my poor grip as if giving them body armor during the riots. Eventually, my favorite time of day was receiving a nice smoothie, cooling down my revolting irritation and dissatisfaction.

You must understand; I was not aware of the full gravity and intensity of this tortuous postoperative course. *Honestly, I don't think anyone can describe it; it must be endured. I'd do it again, but I would have been much more hesitant to acquiesce. Again, I didn't have a choice. Why dwell?*

Postoperatively, the first four days were the most painstaking. My headache was unrelenting and uncontrolled, so much so that they considered placing a ventricular shunt to decrease the cerebral pressure. Every shunt I had seen in practice had some issue in its function; adamantly, I was opposed to receiving one. Could I express that? *No.* After the fourth day, my cerebral pressures normalized; thankfully, a shunt wasn't necessary.

With my whole right side body paresis, I needed to learn to walk again. During my first week at rehab, I would spend most of my time in a wheelchair. Eventually, I would graduate to a walker and quickly a cane, but only for short periods of time. Remaining on bed precautions, alarms announced to the floor when I snuck into the bathroom for late-night relief. The alarms were fit for the Gulag. My captors implored me to use the bedside urinal, but I couldn't properly relieve myself sitting sideways on the edge of the bed. I had to micturate with gravity as the good Lord intended. Additionally, because of my lack of dexterity, I couldn't work the buttons on the automated bed, much less understand them, to position myself for satisfying relief. Pain medicine certainly didn't improve matters.

Powered by stale rehab eggs and thin slices of bacon with occasional Otis Spunkmeyer muffins, I would have speech therapy sessions which would continue for four months and beyond by myself.

In fact, I would have a litany of therapy sessions for the next four months: physical therapy, occupational therapy, and speech therapy. *From every day onward, you could count on me doing some type of therapy for a minimum of three hours each morning.* PT/OT previously was a phrase that I would conclude a clinical note within a patient's electronic medical record.

Virtually all patients are prescribed some form of rehabilitation when discharged from a surgical floor, whether something as simple as walking three times a day or range of motion exercises for an affected limb. Now, PT/OT was about to become my entire life's existence, and I had completely underappreciated its importance after surgical therapy. The operation is but a small piece in the larger story of a patient's road to recovery.

Occupational therapy (OT) involves dexterity of the hands, to which I hadn't given much thought. As part of my OT, which included charging my hands with various tasks like picking up and releasing tiny objects onto rings or simply writing, I started surgical knot tying, still under the delusion that I could train my hand to have better dexterity than before. Naturally gifted at knot tying, I thought I could re-train myself with better technique from the ground up. My own little *come back better* plan. *Again, delusional, a mirage of fading hopes and dreams. But then again, delusion and farfetched dreams had carried me this far...right?*

In the months after leaving the rehab hospital, I would sit at my desk for hours upon hours: tying and writing. Writing and tying. Tying and writing. In doing so, I compounded my dexterity practice with my language skills. After all, I also needed to learn to read and write again. I needed to be systematic to be effective. Systematic and relentless.

I devised a system, a mind-numbing system. I would press 'play' on a language application on my iPad with a bank of common phrases to be read out to me, "The dog is running." By hearing the phrase, I comprehended what was said. Check. By writing the phrase and filling up an entire column on computer paper, I practiced my fine motor control in directing my pen.

310

Check. I was also exercising memory, remembering the phrase. Check. Reciting them audibly helped with speech fluency and comprehension. Check and Check. Each round and sentence column was interspersed with 100 surgical knots employing my cool, numb hand, which was still affected by my stunned autonomic nervous system. Tying and writing. Writing and tying. Next phrase. Repeat. Typing and writing. Relentless.

Eventually, I would graduate myself to reading a page in a book. Well, not so far, more like a paragraph. After about a week, I was able to graduate myself to a full page. What was my book of choice? TSRA (Thoracic Surgery Residents Association) book. A book, collection rather, of surgical vignettes that allows you to study for cardiothoracic surgery board examination. I figured that if I was going to be reading, I might as well prepare, as I still had it in my hard head that I could be a cardiothoracic surgeon. *Again, delusional, thinking I'd turn this ship around, especially with all the extra time I had to hit the books. More study time, I thought to myself!*

In hindsight, it paid to be. Delusional, that is. Delusional or simply ignorant. With ignorance, I could enjoy the bliss of not fully appreciating the severity of my prognosis. Mood, stress, and mental state have profound effects on cancer patient outcomes. [6, 7] Although I knew all too well the implications of my diagnosis so that only left delusion… and hope. Quite the fine line. Delusions and hope kept me ferociously in the fight to regain all I had lost. Everything is impossible until it isn't.

My speech therapist at the rehab facility, Jackie, was nothing short of a godsend. She lifted my spirits when they were low, assuring me that my speech would improve. Realize that during rehab, simple naming of ordinary, inanimate objects was challenging for me, like desk or car. Imagine my frustration as a former medical student, having once memorized the labyrinth of all biochemical pathways in the body with their associated diseases, to being reduced to being unable to describe what a chair was. Jackie would have me reflect on all my progress in a short span; she reassured me that things would only improve.

She was more of my emotional therapist than a speech therapist. I would begin and end the first few sessions in tears, but she had a way of curbing my labile demeanor. She was a petite brunette which contrasted greatly with her pregnant belly, and she had a hint of a lisp which I suspect motivated her to enter the field. Each session was a rollercoaster of emotion and frustration; Jackie was there to slow the ride down and center my focus. Recovery like this was a long game. Luckily, I had her as my primary speech therapist before I returned to Jacksonville, and she went on maternity leave. I am so grateful our paths crossed, if for only a brief time.

My speech would slowly recover over the next year or more, but the one thing that never fully was restored was my ability to run and walk normally. *In fact, nothing came back normally.* I had developed classic spastic foot drop, [8], an unexpected consequence of the brain surgery. The same right leg that underwent fasciotomies due to compartment syndrome from my 13-hour chest surgery was now irreversibly maligned by peroneal foot drop. Despite countless hours of stretching, directed walking, and strength building, nothing seemed to make a difference. *What more can one manage?*

You can think of nerve injuries affecting upper or lower motor neurons depending on the location of the injury. Lower motor neuron injuries, like having a large crush injury from a cement wall falling across your leg, would create a flaccid paresis; the target muscle would be mostly void of muscular tone. Upper motor neuron injuries, like a brain operation, cause a spastic paresis causing increased tonicity, or contraction, in the target tissue or muscle. Because my injury affected only one side of my body, it is termed *hemiparesis*. Therefore, I had, and still battle, spastic, hemiparetic foot drop, which has far-reaching implications. I am forced to load my body asymmetrically, placing an uneven load on my back and lower extremities, causing alignment issues. The effects of this asymmetry over time can be visibly noted in the relative musculature on either side of my body. Where I might be able to load 100 pounds on my left leg, I can only manage 20 pounds on my right leg. Not for lack of trying; that's the best I can do.

The contraction extends far deeper than you would expect past striated or skeletal muscular control. Smooth muscle control, like the ones surrounding your blood vessels, would also be affected. On cooler days, the vasculature on my right constricts, restricting normal blood flow to my fingers and toes. It is almost as if I have acquired or secondary Raynaud's phenomenon marked by poor blood flow to the digits. [9] My right fingers and toes always feel a few degrees colder compared to my left, and on extremely cold and windy days, I must walk with a cane if I can walk at all. *So much for those marathon hopes.*

If you needed to tell a secret to someone and have them never repeat it, I was your man. Although I'd like to think of myself as a trustworthy individual, the truth is I couldn't remember jack. I couldn't remember what day of the week it was, more or less, a secret. My short-term memory took a huge hit. I could have explained the pathophysiology of coronary artery disease or staging in lung cancer in extraordinary detail, but I couldn't tell you what I had for breakfast. Being naturally forgetful didn't help my cause, but now I had an excuse! *A silver lining, perhaps?*

Any silver linings were eclipsed by dark days laid up in the University of Florida rehabilitation hospital. Amid the COVID-19 pandemic, I was only allowed to have one visitor a day, who, of course, was my mom, the innocent victim of several attacks by those mutated oats and flying cushioned utensils. *Someone at the rehab hospital should check on the status of that.* Isolation was intensified by my poor dexterity and eyesight in attempts to communicate by phone. It would take around a month before I could text anything meaningful, recall I could barely speak. Telephones might as well have been just a high-dollar paperweight.

My brother, Josh, and his girlfriend, now wife, Katie, came down to visit from Orlando. Because this was the height of the COVID epidemic, they were forced to walk around to my window as they were not allowed to enter the facility. Like a couple of prisoners attempting to converse across non-vented glass, communication difficulties were further compounded by my speech issues. Elated to see another human who wasn't my mom or one of my therapists, my excitement would be short-lived as what was a faint mist would turn into a downpour. As the rain pattered against the glass, they were forced to leave. As if the fates hadn't punished me enough, I couldn't enjoy a simple interaction with my brother.

People, family members, and the like would express concern for my mood. Thinking I had arrived at rock bottom, I kept discovering new depths; I needed to be left alone to digest the enormous pill that life had given me to swallow. A pill of regret, heartbreak, and immense pain that only time and quiet reflection could aid in its passage. This was my pain, hard-won and valiantly fought over. I sought to own it as searing as it was. Despite the entreats from my mom to console her boy in visible struggle, I needed solitude to contemplate and prepare myself to push further into whatever was necessary. Unfortunately, this translated into some less than favorable interactions with the one that birthed me.

Why was I pushing forward? Was the juice worth the squeeze? Especially if the squeeze left me handicapped and unemployed for the rest of my life?

Suicide had crossed my mind on this occasion and on others. Honestly, I would need additional occupational therapy to pull that off successfully. I couldn't eat a bowl of oatmeal; it was highly unlikely that I could pull a trigger. *It's okay to laugh.* Suicide, at this junction, wasn't an option in any depressive way but in a more practical sense. I loathed not being able to be independent. Moreover, I loathed not having the ability to provide anything of value to society at large. Would I be another weight on the healthcare and financial system? My sudden absence would resolve future medical bills, and I could leave behind a small little nest egg for my brother and sister. The proposition became more and more inviting as days of constant physical, mental, and spiritual anguish wore on.

At the brink of thirty years old, I was comfortable leaving this place. I had reached a space where I wasn't afraid to die anymore. When it comes, I will welcome it like an old friend. Parts of me had already died; flesh had already been taken from me. Yet, I still had fight in me despite the endless cycle of pain. Fear, though, was no longer a concern. I was ready to go to a place free of suffering where I could be complete and whole again.

I hold it true, whate'er befall; I feel it, when I sorrow most; 'Tis better to have loved and lost Than never at have loved at all.
Tennyson, In Memoriam. Pt. xxvii, st. 4.

On a glorious summer day in Gainesville, Florida, I was discharged from the inpatient rehab hospital and continued *organized* PT, OT, and speech therapy in Jacksonville for the next four months. Writing and tying. Tying and writing. Ad nauseam. Despite my hard work after the brain surgery, my delusions of still becoming a cardiothoracic surgeon slowly became realized. As much as they helped me recuperate manual skills in occupational therapy, surgical knot tying fell out of my daily practice. Dr. Ceppa had gotten me a picture of me operating signed by my fellow residents, motivating me to tie one more knot, but the heartfelt gesture became less of a source of motivation and more of a reminder of what was lost. It remains on my wall but with an entirely different purpose. My dream would remain just that, a dream.

However, I might remain a practicing doctor; once I receive a clean bill of health. Half of cardiothoracic surgery is managing sick patients in the intensive care unit by applying all aspects of cardiothoracic physiology, for which I was obsessed. Even though I had four years of postgraduate training between research and clinical work, I wouldn't have enough clinical experience to sit for any board examination to be properly certified. Imagine the years of hard work now seemingly flushed down the drain. How do I provide for myself? How would I manage to pay for health insurance when Indiana University would be inevitably forced to let me go? These thoughts raced through my mind towards the terminus of my employment at IU; the idea of an early grave sounded more inviting as my future prospects ran slim.

Perhaps I could apply to a shorter residency to remain a physician and translate my skills to another specialty? One of the shortest residencies is family medicine: typically, three years. Up until my diagnosis, I was focused solely on cardiothoracic surgery and the perioperative care thereof. Although I lacked intimate knowledge of family medicine, I imagine at least one of my clinical years in CT could be devoted to another residency tract. Given my seizure history, however, what program would allow me to work as one of their residents? Lack of sleep is one of my most potent inciting factors in lowering seizure threshold. [10] Although I haven't had many, and I had been seizure free for well over a year, taking overnight call was well out of the question. I wouldn't want someone within the resident's ranks who couldn't take their fair share of call. I didn't want to handicap another program.

Thoughts like these were invading my worried mind when Jen came to live with me down in Florida, finding work as an ICU nurse at a local hospital in Jacksonville, Fl. It had been months after my brain surgery and well into 2021; Jen and I had been out of consistent contact for almost a year. After some minor faculties returned, I wrapped up any lingering research obligations with IU before the institution was forced to let me go. Understandable. Despite pressing on computer keys, I wasn't good for much else. Recall, that they had essentially created a position for me at the inconvenience of everyone in the program, residents and staff alike. Despite my progress in my recovery, moving back to Indiana was an impracticality. I had already sold my condo, and there was no way to predict when I could return to the clinical arena. With over a hundred thousand dollars in student debt and no way to provide for myself, my reality was sadly crystalizing. Moreover, Jen's was sure to be shaken.

After Jen made her way down to Jacksonville Beach and settled into a new nursing job, she was stunned about how working at a teaching hospital, like Indiana University, differed from working at a county hospital. One of the principal differences was that residents were not in attendance to share in the workload. In teaching hospitals, you have residents racing the halls of the hospital, filling the void of communication between nurses and attending physicians. Effectually, teaching hospitals spoil nurses. Sorry ladies and gents, but it's true. You think you work hard but wait until you have that resident rug pulled out from underneath you, when the hospital's near-free labor gets yanked away.

Every time Jen came home, she'd huff and puff about how haphazard the communication was amongst healthcare teams and how difficult it was to get anything done. *Basically, every resident's intern year.* Of course, each hospital is different, so I am wary of generalizations, but you had better hope you have an excellent nurse to advocate for your health as a patient.

Lacking an additional layer of the workforce, many patients fall through the cracks, and avoidable mistakes are made, i.e., the substantial need for advanced healthcare providers, physician's assistants, and nurse practitioners. *Recall the delay in pain medicine administration for my first week at MSKCC, resulting in pain crises within my first three days postop from a major thoracic operation and compartment syndrome. This boiled down to a lack of effective communication via computer systems or interpersonal.* I am proud to say that Jen, my little sister, and my stepmom are all wonderful, skilled nurses. Despite her new work environment, Jen was astute and capable, and work became a non-issue.

Unfortunately, even after several months following the move down south to sunny Florida, Jen fell increasingly homesick, longing for the comfort of familiar Indy despite crashing waves greeting her each morning out our window. Formerly, I imagined this might've been a dream for her or any girl. Blinded by concerns of my cancer, I assumed that she would adjust to the change in locale smoothly, only requiring a short adjustment period. That had proved true with her job, at least. After a few months, adapting was taking longer than expected; her overall disposition would begin to decline. I soon realized something much deeper was evolving. Before her move, she still lived at home without much responsibility. As endearing as her family was, she had never experienced any long period out on her own. I was operating under the false presupposition that she was prepared for a significant lifestyle change; if fact, I thought it might've been a fun change-up, an adventure we'd both share.

Sadly, Jen never embraced the prospect that I, in all probability, would never return to the Midwest. I assumed such was evident as I had already sold my Old Northside condo and moved all my things to Florida as maintaining gainful employment was no longer feasible. But both of us were guilty of not clearly communicating the facts of our situation and intention. A specific location was of the utmost importance to acquire proper medical care, University of Florida. Doctors who waged to save my life needed to conduct and direct all my future medical care; I had lost all trust in any other stewards. Rightly so, if I stayed where I was, I'd likely be dead. Although we were in the sunshine state, this was my cold reality. However, instead of welcoming a new way of life down south in our partnership sealed by engagement, it became abundantly clear that she was seeking every opportunity to return to Indiana and her comfort zone.

Believe you me, I wanted that as well, but I was hamstrung. Another valuable aspect of growing up in a broken home by traditional standards and moving to at least five different homes before I was seventeen years old, I developed good coping skills early, socially and otherwise. If I kept looking back on what *was*, I would miss what *could be*. This rang as true now as it did when growing up. I would soon drive myself mad with each glance in the rearview mirror especially given the events of the past few years. As Matthew McConaughey says matter-of-factly in Dazed and Confused, the only thing to do was, "Keep Livin.' L-I-V-I-N."

As the months wore on, coinhabiting in our condo by the beach, her constant longing for Indiana grew ever more worrisome and palpable. And like a pulse, I could sense her discontent like a dagger in my chest cavity with impending penetration. I was doing my best fighting for my life, having no preeminence over geography. I would never dream of discouraging her from returning home for a short visit, even though I knew it wasn't good for her. However, her frequent trips illustrated her wants clearly, twisting the knife with each turnaround.

All I wanted for her was happiness; countless cancer treatments had drained all my vitality, making me a poor partner, admittedly. There were days when I couldn't get out of bed; I no longer considered myself an immortal with boundless energy. Up to that point, since I had left for brain radiation, most of our relationship had been long distance, due to COVID and other logistics. Jen had never experienced what I had to live every day. Facetime failed to capture my suffering during brain radiation or my time in the rehab hospital. Although, I would applaud anyone with that much imagination, Stephen King perhaps.

Every trip home to Indiana tore at the tethered laces loosely holding our relationship together. Eventually, it wouldn't be more than a week after arriving from a trip back home before sinking deeper into a depression, twisting that dagger another degree. Feeling helpless, I'd question, "Wasn't I enough?" We were planning a life together; why was she running away, especially when I needed her the most? "Through sickness and health..." right? Undeniably, the brain surgery, and cancer, had changed me. I was, am, sick after all. Couldn't she see that? *Maybe, I failed to recognize the sickness developing in her.*

Communication through radio waves and internet connections in no way encapsulated the severely watered-down version of what I was experiencing prior to our sharing a home. Therefore, due to the reality of our circumstances for which we lacked any control, she hadn't *seen* it, if only intermittently, my daily torture. She hadn't worn the mutated oats in her hair from the plastic bowl that flew across the room, hadn't bore the brunt of my frustration of being unable to speak, or steadied me with a safety belt while I wiped the shit clean from myself. Her eardrums weren't still ringing from my cries of pain from my right thigh compartment syndrome. I did my best to safeguard her from the raw reality that had become my life.

For almost a year, we had lived apart throughout this unfortunate scenario: producing two versions of the same movie. The G-rated version, on the one hand, and R-rated on the other. Her struggling with the emotional pain of having a loved one battling some esoteric foe hidden behind operating room doors, clinic office curtains, and travel distances, I, experiencing every tangible piece of suffering. *No one can truly know.* Even though we were together in a gestalt sense, in no way were we on the same emotional page with these differential realities. Analogous to slow continental drift, the movement apart from each other was so infinitesimal it went unnoticed. After a year of a widening divide, the distance between us became so insurmountable that it would take a large cargo ship, *probably topped off with mustard gas*, to cross the divide. Between cancer and her developing mood issues, I saw very little chance this large tanker finding safe harbor.

And it wasn't for lack of trying. I enticed her to have friends come visit Florida to help ease the transition. When she had a friend visit for a week's time, her mood took a complete 180 degrees. Hope, it seemed, maybe peaking over the horizon. As soon as he left, she fell right back into her emotive entanglement within days. I'd further attempt to arrange some 'dates' with other couples, thinking she just needed a group of solid gal pals to integrate. Every attempt failed. Jealous of the happiness I saw in her with the short visit with a close friend, why couldn't I make her the same degree of happy? We used to share in that happiness; I longed to share in it again. The knife slowly twisted another few degrees.

Believe it or not, I was more scared for her than myself. My fate was already clear, likely an early grave, for which I had accepted with some surety. I didn't want this flower to be uprooted in the process; I loved her too much. Her petals wilted in the Florida sun, and I lacked the strength to water them. Some days she wouldn't ascend from the couch. Walking into our condo, one would be confused about who was undergoing cancer treatment. On her days off, three screens were between her and the real world: her cellphone, her computer, and the television. Despite my constant coaxing to engage with the world on my good days, she'd rather vege out with audible winds reverberating against the window, calling out in attempts of rescue.

Jen continued to slip into a darkness that, frankly, I wasn't equipped to manage, still grasping onto the same tethered ropes of hope and delusion. Shouldering both of our griefs was far too immense a task. Like every dumb dude, I minimized my feelings in an effort to be tough, perhaps to shield her, perhaps to shield myself from its acknowledgment. Our relationship continued to suffer from lack of communication. When we finally had honest conversations about how we were doing, we were beyond repair.

At a loss of options on how to proceed, feeling utterly helpless in combatting her declining mood, I called her sister, who apparently shared in my concerns of her worsening depression. In fact, both she and her mother were concerned, relieved that I wasn't alone, heartbroken by its actuality. Her sister reassured me to just stick with it! Busy raging through my own battle, I knew what was necessary, what was required for both our sakes. A decision that would not be easy or popular but absolutely necessary. I know she wouldn't suggest it herself and would even combat the idea. But in her heart, both our hearts, we knew. One terminal event sealed the fate of our relationship, at least for me.

Jen decided to take yet another trip back home, and her flight was scheduled for 5:30 in the morning. Like every southern gentleman, I'd, of course, insist on driving her to the airport despite her offer of taking an Uber. Unfortunately, I needed to also drive down to Gainesville for follow-up doctors' appointments which was around an hour and a half away from the Jacksonville airport. My appointment was in the mid-morning. Even though I was in no danger of missing my appointment, I didn't have enough time to return home and take a nap before my drive. Therefore, I headed directly to Gainesville after dropping Jen off.

The issue was that I had gotten zero sleep; I am normally a light sleeper conditioned from being on call for a couple years, but, moreover, from being on chronic steroids. Jen had the terrible habit of taking her phone in bed, interrupting the small window of time I had to fall asleep. When that window passes, I am up for another hour or so. Her cell phone light and giggles at Tik Tok videos were enough to keep me awake. As she fell right to sleep, I remained alert, not to mention angry.

After getting around two to three hours of sleep and dropping Jen off at the airport, I made the drive highly caffeinated across highway 301, connecting Jacksonville to Gainesville, surfing on a massive sugar high. I went to my scheduled appointments and had my labs checked as I was active oral chemotherapy and planned my sugar-infused wave to crash right at the stairs of the beach condo. My only pitstop was procuring a few Krispy-Kreme doughnuts whose sole purpose was to provide me the energy to reach my destination and certainly not because they are undeniably delectable.

Thirty minutes after my attempted return home, I blacked out. I awoke to the rumbling of thick grass in my truck's undercarriage on thankfully a soft shoulder of the country highway 301. Fortunately, the country highway was desolate. I went to place my truck in park, but all my right-sided deficits had returned with a vengeance on my attempt. Managing to stop my white Colorado despite my hemiparetic right side transitioning to near total paralysis, I was so disoriented that I didn't know what direction I was facing and how to proceed.

After regaining most of my faculties and assessing the minimal damage to my truck, I felt the unfortunate and reckless need to get back on the road and get home. In retrospect, this was one of the most foolish things I have ever done. *Well, my parents may argue otherwise.* After driving in the wrong direction for a short time, a wiser Caleb took hold. I stopped at a familiar rest stop and called for help.

A full week would pass before all my lingering symptoms dissipated: hemispatial neglect, trouble with concentration, inability to read, and headaches. My ability to tolerate minor stress through sleep deprivation or otherwise was virtually absent. From that point on, I devoted myself only to entirely to recovery; my recovery had no end in sight. Damn everything else. I could not risk another incident for the sake of my life and the life of other people. My actions were so irresponsible. After all the work I had put into recovery, writing and tying, tying and writing, months of PT/OT and speech therapy, the pain, was I willing to throw that all away? When Jen returned to Florida from another unnecessary trip, we no longer shared a bed, further increasing the space between us.

One of the largest reasons for our schism can be attributed to the COVID epidemic. My being on active cancer treatment and the travel restrictions and her being an intensive care nurse at the worst peaks of the global disease prohibited us from seeing each other for almost. Be that as it may, she was not able to be there during the most critical points of therapy. In hindsight, different decisions could have been made to salvage our relationship. An ICU nurse is needed anywhere; however, I wanted her also to be on those frontlines and not hitched to me. But this would come heavy expense, our survival.

Each month apart was another hammer to the wedge to our once firm and solid oak. Don't get me wrong. I shoulder the blame. I didn't want to talk about how frustrating it was to go to the bathroom without someone holding you with a stabilizing belt at the waist or how poorly my headaches were being controlled. In no way did I want to share my human dignity and modesty being flushed away. Painful months lived through the beginnings of each period of multiple recoveries I never wanted to revisit. Like a World War II veteran, I never wanted to speak of them again. Communication might've saved us, but maybe not. Jen's love for the Midwest and her love of home tucked away in a comfy cul-de-sac were too great for me to overcome.

I detail these things not because I want to explain some festering malcontent for someone whom I still have immense love for but to explain how the consequences of cancer can have far-reaching ramifications. Its penumbra knows no boundaries and is indiscriminate in its destruction. Cancer wrapped its chelipeds around my relationship until it was crushed. We were perfect for each other; anyone could see it. Where my cancer brought much unification to my immediate family, its pincers tore apart Jen and I's. We missed some potentially edifying months that would have solidified our bond if different choices had been made. But she was absent, and to no fault of our own, we couldn't come back from that.

I am glad, for the decision undoubtedly would have been made in the future as my condition continued to deteriorate. Worse months were soon to come, some that I am happy to save Jen from. I lament anyone taking up the charge for taking care of me in the near future. She doesn't know it, but she was rescued from something I wouldn't want for any young lady at the edge of the greatest years of her life. If I needed to be the bad guy and break things off, so be it.

Nonetheless, I needed to be selfish if I wanted the chance to recover. This meant pouring everything I had, every ounce of every day, into recovery if I wanted the chance of beating cancer. This involved: overhauling my diet, receiving adequate sleep, yoga, and a litany of other adjuvant therapies. My body would need to become a temple, and I realized I wasn't doing enough.

Whoever or wherever they are, have been, or ever shall be, fools, blockheads, imbeciles, idiots, dunderheads, dullards, blunderers, I alone far exceed them all in folly and want of sense.
Plautus, Bacchides, 1. 1087. (Act v, sc. 1)

In the early months of 2021, my life in Indiana had officially come to a painful end, and my relationship with Jen would follow suit in those that followed. Not only did I mourn a relationship with quite possibly the most perfect girl I had ever met, but I would soon be out of a job. Not surprisingly, though, I could hardly string two sentences together in any coherent fashion after brain surgery. My walking was just as handicapped as my speech; my spastic foot drop had me tripping over my feet just as much as my words. All my sense of self-worth and pride was tied to my hard-won pride of being a doctor. My life had become a slow-moving trainwreck with the linked cars continually piling up at the rear. The only question was how many cars were there and how much collateral damage could be accrued?

In medical school, we had a professor say that we have won the cosmic lottery as students. We were *privileged* to be in our positions in have the opportunity to be doctors. For the longest time, I agreed with that contention. How lucky are we to be in America, receiving a top-notch education with almost the guarantee of future job security, and, most of all, helping people while you're at it!? However, that statement has a slight implication: *you didn't earn it.* Never mind where you come from, never mind everything you did to get here, never mind your personal sacrifice: your presence within the lecture hall is evidence of your *privilege.*

A braver man might've argued, but I was a measly first-year medical student unaware of how to tie my shoes at a new institution. Best not to ruffle any feathers. Now with the prospect of an early death, who really cares? Let no pompous professor minimize your personal struggle in what you have achieved. Let no bureaucrat convince you that your journey through medical education or training in any profession, for that matter, is underserving or misplaced. The audacity of that admission counselor speaks to the rampant disarray of education, medical and otherwise. Who is this individual to make sweeping judgments unwittingly downplaying another individual's struggle? And I stand in full awareness of my own hypocrisy; I am writing about *my story; how* insufflated is that? Indeed, life is just one big contradiction. I digress.

Having a slow-growing cancer like carcinoid allows one to view the trainwreck in a slow, stepwise torture with a sequential downtrend in function and quality of life. I often consider if it would have been better to actually have had small cell lung cancer? At least my death would have been marked with surety and haste. Instead, I am left to suffer slowly as the railway cars multiply and pain builds.

In summation, I first lost probably 30 – 35% of my pulmonary reserve following lung surgery with the removal of most of my left lung. Thoracotomies resulted in chronic pain on either side of my chest; right thigh compartment syndrome led to fasciotomies and unreplaceable muscle resection. Secondly, I received an onslaught of lifesaving brain radiation, both whole and targeted. Such extensive measures will undoubtedly lead to secondary malignancies and other issues in the future, likely dementia. Thirdly, the intense radiation regimen necessitated brain surgery due to radiation necrosis which unfortunately resulted in speech difficulties, right spastic foot drop, and hemiparesis. Fourthly, one of the railway cars held a passenger; my love life had become a causality in the tragic pileup. None of these events or complications can be attributed to anything but talons of cancer. And that damned spiteful crustacean was not finished.

The first day after I had settled into the beach condo in Jacksonville Beach, I hobbled my way out to the beach, stood favoring my left side, took a deep breath of the salty Atlantic Ocean air, and said to myself, "I can heal here." I imagined the immense blue swallowing all my pain and suffering, every memory of desperation and fear along with all my hopes and dreams, every goal and aspiration, being dissolved and washed away by the vast salty blue. And I with it. What was my pain but a grain of sand in the perpetuity of time and space? Toes gripping those ancient and inconsequential particles left at the whim of the constant oscillating current, I was reminded of my front porch stoop in Indy, where I had experienced *ekstasis*. As the sea foam dissolved around my toes with each wave, my ego and pride followed. I corrected myself, "I could die here."

Nobody can deny but religion is a comfort to the distressed, a cordial to the sick, and some times a restraint on the wicked; therefore, whoever would laugh or argue it out of the world, without giving some equivalent for it, ought to be treated as a common enemy.
Mary Wortley Montagu, Letter to the Countess of But, 1752

At the turn of the year between 2020 and 2021, I received a heavy package from Tom, Dr. Tom Martin. Within this lofty package was a Life Application Study Bible accompanied by a read-along note-taking guide to direct daily devotions. Over the years, I had numerous books gifted to me, some religious and others not, to encourage me along the road of recovery— literally stacks of books sent to bolster my spirits. However, I found them an empty gesture as most hadn't read them themselves. As well-meaning as these offerings were, they usually ended up unread and gathering dust in my closet.

No stranger to the Bible, I was baptized and raised in a Christian home. However, as previously mentioned, during my college years, I had fallen away from the *practice* of religion and became lukewarm and indifferent but maintained a distant respect for faith. Remaining content in my current spiritual station, I saw no need to dig further for any truth or comfort. Or maybe, I was too scared to move that stone for fear of what I might discover.

A month later, as the Good News sat unsung at the corner of my desk, something possessed me to finally crack open Tom's lofty gift. What I found so unique about this Bible, besides its sheer mass, was the detailed historical context that augmented the spiritual text. For example, each chapter would begin with an overarching summary, complete with estimated timelines and significant players in each book. Central take-home themes are emphasized in the beginning and throughout the chapters driving home a unified message. Maps relevant to the time are included to breathe life into the geopolitical context. As far as the actual text of the Bible, I'd estimate that there are at least three sentences of accompanying explanatory text for each verse. Hence, the weight upon my lap.

After my long hiatus from religious study and reflection, I opened directly to a random chapter in Psalms which, in my opinion, reads like a cheerleading section for those who are distraught and wanting. Within the first couple of sentences, I began inconsolably sobbing. Even though this massive piece of work sat heavily on my lap, I felt the weight of the world lifted from me. What was this feeling? Floodgates of pain and grief suddenly were released. After just one small passage, my thirsty spirit was finally experiencing a long-awaited quench.

Why had I abstained for so long from this simple daily ritual? I was disappointed for having deprived myself of a long-held consecrated daily practice that has the power to set an individual in a positive frame of mind, despite uncontrollable circumstance. A positive state of mind has a powerful effect on cancer outcomes, although less tangible and harder to appreciate. But this fact is superfluous in the grand scheme of life. Life, indeed, is suffering. The plight of every human being is the self-realization and inevitability of suffering. The challenge is to greet that suffering with a welcoming smile and willful acceptance, with the 'enveisié,' so to speak.

Thus, my epiphany: I believe that is what God, or whatever ineffable reality you subscribe, from Abrahamic religions spanning to those in the far East, hadn't been the focus in my life. Instead, I was tirelessly pursuing worldly things like knowledge and empiricism, perfecting one's craft in occupation, and reaping the rewards thereof. I had made a false god out of these material endeavors, as highly deserved and hard-won as they may have been. I wasn't, however, paying homage to what had breathed life into what is otherwise a clay molding of existence. Clearly, we aren't meant to understand an entity that exists outside our understanding of space and time, but it is with surety that there is comfort within and through Him. Through what avenue do you subscribe? I entreat you not to wait as long as I to find a suitable mode of comfort. For rest assured, hard times are inevitable; best be prepared.

My understanding of the mystery of God will undoubtedly mature as I continue to grow and learn. In our increasingly secular society, we need spiritual healing more than ever. I had ignored that crucial component of personal development for over a decade; emphasis on the spirit needed to be restored—mind, body, and spirit. And if I ever were to heal, I would need this trinity of my being—each buttressing the next. The process would have to begin with self-forgiveness and grace, acknowledging and relinquishing guilt and feelings of inadequacy that haunted my past. God loves and accepts all. By reciprocating love for God, you can better love and accept yourself. In turn, you can better love others.

1.   Lee, D., et al., *Brain Metastasis Recurrence Versus Radiation Necrosis: Evaluation and Treatment.* Neurosurg Clin N Am, 2020. **31**(4): p. 575-587.
2.   Zhuang, H., et al., *Bevacizumab treatment for radiation brain necrosis: mechanism, efficacy and issues.* Mol Cancer, 2019. **18**(1): p. 21.
3.   Garcia, J., et al., *Bevacizumab (Avastin®) in cancer treatment: A review of 15 years of clinical experience and future outlook.* Cancer Treat Rev, 2020. **86**: p. 102017.
4.   Ivanova, M.V., et al., *Functional Contributions of the Arcuate Fasciculus to Language Processing.* Front Hum Neurosci, 2021. **15**: p. 672665.
5.   Chung, C., A. Bryant, and P.D. Brown, *Interventions for the treatment of brain radionecrosis after radiotherapy or radiosurgery.* Cochrane Database Syst Rev, 2018. **7**(7): p. Cd011492.
6.   Matthews, C.R. and P.J. Hess, *Thirty-three, zero, nine.* J Thorac Cardiovasc Surg, 2020. **160**(3): p. 871-875.
7.   Hoffman, C.J., et al., *Effectiveness of mindfulness-based stress reduction in mood, breast- and endocrine-related quality of life, and well-being in stage 0 to III breast cancer: a randomized, controlled trial.* J Clin Oncol, 2012. **30**(12): p. 1335-42.
8.   Carolus, A.E., et al., *The Interdisciplinary Management of Foot Drop.* Dtsch Arztebl Int, 2019. **116**(20): p. 347-354.
9.   Haque, A. and M. Hughes, *Raynaud's phenomenon.* Clin Med (Lond), 2020. **20**(6): p. 580-587.
10.   Shneker, B.F. and N.B. Fountain, *Epilepsy.* Dis Mon, 2003. **49**(7): p. 426-78.

__12__

Heal Thy Self

If soldier, Chase brave employments with a naked sword Throughout the world. Fool not, for all may have If they dare try, a glorious life, or grave. George Herbert, The Church-Porch. St. 15.

The summer of '21 would drone on with endless hours at the gym and yoga, fighting in vain for a normal gait. Following the brain surgery, the spastic foot drop had, and still has, quite a stranglehold on my normal movements. For example, at baseline, my toes curl in response to overstimulation or attempting to walk too rapidly. Specifically, the peroneal nerve is affected; where most people can relax their foot during the normal ambulation, I am compelled to swing my entire foot around to clear the ground due to the inability to lift my toes. If I wasn't easy to pick out of a crowd with my red hair, every hobble, like a bobby at the end of a fishing line, removed all doubt.

In an attempt to wake up my little piggies, I read a book about neuroplasticity. Despite the former belief that brain neurons were static after a certain age, research indicates that the brain has the profound ability to rewire itself through intention, focus, and relentless repetitive movements. [1-3] For example, I am writing this passage with a left eye patch so that I might encourage my right eye's perpetual blemish to dissipate, a symptom from the largest met, which required brain surgery. In Norman Doidge MD's book, he highlights the impressive recoveries one can experience through the power of the mind. [3] Still inspired by the short conversation with Mr. Goggins a year earlier, I ceased feeling sorry for myself and just asked myself what would Goggins do? If I had trouble walking, well, that's exactly what I should be doing! Ad nauseam.

Simple ambulation wouldn't be enough; I needed tactile feedback with each uncoordinated trudge of my dead leg. Racking my brain for a mechanism to magnify the connection between my peripheral senses and brain, I thought, "How does any muscle get larger and more functional?" Add weight and movement. I instantly purchased a weighted vest to spark the fire in my sleeping digits. The increased pressure imposed by each step might ignite those synapses and shake the rust off my dusty axons.

To my surprise, it worked! Well, for about an hour after I walked. Proprioception and sensation in my right foot and leg were temporarily restored, and, for a short time, I was walking normally. My gait would usually correct after about half a mile, remain strong after a mile and a half, and then deteriorate at my last half mile. The bottoms of my feet would be sizzling from the stimulated axons like a freshly cooked ribeye fresh off the grill. Now, I had an effective means of teaching myself how to walk again. Insurance would allow for around an hour of rehabilitation time where most therapists would show up unprepared or late. If I wanted to get better, I knew I'd have to take matters into my own hands. The only thing that could possibly derail my progress would be progression of disease, the possibility of which was a constant worry: the fear of having all my efforts be for not.

Fear would loom ominously even on the brightest days in Florida, trudging down 1st street adjacent to the beach during my Quasimodo marches. Just as sure as afternoon showers in Jax, so too was the rising hesitation as the date of my next scan approached. The weight of the vest was a challenge in the summer heat, but not as much as the constant burden of anticipation. I imagine every cancer patient feels like this, especially after completing every form of treatment one can fathom: surgery, chemotherapy, and radiation. Flurries from butterflies, more like moths, tickled my stomach as days drew closer to a scheduled evaluation.

Was all this worth it? Being a surgeon was clearly out of the question with a bum leg and hand, but now becoming a doctor was in question. My seizure disorder precludes me from being on call; I cannot lose any sleep. Who will hire a half-trained cardiothoracic surgeon resident with a seizure disorder who didn't complete residency with a knowledge base in a specialized field that I would never enter? My prospects were becoming decidedly slim despite 12 years of higher education. *What was I fighting for again?*

With cancer, instead of birthdays, Thanksgivings, and Christmas's, the date of the scan to evaluate disease status took precedence; life had been reduced to living from scan to scan. Goals for the future were truncated from plans for the coming decade to plans for the next month. Would I even make it to my next scan? Could I make it to my little sister's matriculation from nursing school? Could I make it to my brother's wedding? Will I be functional enough to make the best man speech? "If I could just make it to, [you name it]," I will be happy, a far cry from my illustrious aim to be a skilled surgeon.

The beautiful thing about cancer, despite all the complicated schedules and navigating travels and doctors' visits, treatment regimens, pills for side effects, and the side effects of the side effects, is that cancer has a simplifying impact on your life. All I had was the day. If I woke up, it was a good day if I woke up free of pain, even better. If I woke up and didn't need to use my cane, "Hey, now it's a party!"

As horrible and heartbreaking as cancer is, I found that my relationship with my family had never been better. Through tragedy, my family came together united under a common enemy. My brother and I's relationship had never been stronger. The bond within my immediate family had never been deeper. Cancer, my cancer, in particular, grows slowly, allowing one and others to contemplate what's important, lending opportunity to restore and mend broken relationships. Personal pride is replaced with love and affection. If cancer does any good, it accomplished that.

After my slough of radiation treatments, my brain was a war zone. I imagine scattered wounded microglial cells and tattered myelin limping along the battlefield, picking up the arms and legs of the dendrites of their comrades. Medics were exasperated; surgeons overwhelmed having not eaten for days. Leukocytes lugging wheelbarrows spilling over with appendages in an effort clear the field to make room for another onslaught of inflammation brought forth by the long siege of fallout.

Despite the valiant, lifesaving efforts, in fall of 2021, my neuro-oncologists and neurosurgeons affirmed that the cancer was still on a slow and steady trajectory to take my life. I was inconsolable.

A dream Of youth, which night and time have quenched forever,
Still, dark, and dry, and unremembered now.
Shelley, Alastor, 1. 669.

I wanted everything to stop. No more treatment. No more sticks. No more scans. No more chemo. Cancer had decided my entire past two years, wrecked my dreams, maligned my body, and dissolved my personal relationship. Now, I would *decide* to stop. I was determined to maintain some semblance of autonomy before I kicked the bucket, and I would not have the cancer dictate my last few months of my life.

I traveled home back to the smell of the sweet pines and informed my family of my decision; they were in full support. They bore witness to the pain I had endured. Enduring. One let down after another. We sat together and reviewed a thick photo album of me growing up that my mother had thoughtfully made, complete with my graduation from pre-school to my matriculation from medical school and all the events in between. From me running around in diapers through sprinkler heads to the first deer I killed with my dad, each eliciting flashbacks to a happier time free of pain. In awe of the cheerful grin once tattooed on my face and the hopeful vitality of youth, this poor ginger had no idea what fate had in store.

I had long dreamt of venturing out west to run the canyon trails of Zion National Park along with a slew of other trails throughout the Southwest. After residency, I wanted to spend my vacations running and exploring one step at a time. With my disabilities and reduced lung capacity, such was a farfetched dream.

After my parents' split, my brother and I had difficult decisions as to where we would decide to live. At the age of 14, you could decide: mom or dad. There's a 4-year difference between my brother and me. When we each reached that age, we both decided to stay at our dad's. Personally, a certain vindication was felt in finally spending more than every other weekend with daddy making up for lost time. Despite my well-rooted relationships with friends and community, I felt it my responsibility to grant him well-deserved time with his son and grant myself time with my father. Although there was great sadness in leaving behind so much, I needed more time with Pop before going to college.

However, divorce meant that Josh and I would be separated, too as we were four years apart. Four years also meant that when Josh was wrapping up high school, I would be just beginning it. We would spend almost eight years out of the same household. To no fault of our own, a small thirty-minute drive between Tifton and Nashville, GA, might as well have been a trip to the next state; realize this is before cellphones and dependable internet. Indeed, divorce has far-reaching and unsuspecting sequelae, with the cracks piercing through subsequent generations. A benevolent split helps to ease the collateral damage, but with our parent's relationship, the separation was anything but. I was too young to remember much, but Josh bore the brunt of the schism.

The distance would further increase when he left for the Air Force Academy (AFA). Admittance to the AFA was no easy feat for a South Georgia boy, about as easy as it was to get into a cardiothoracic surgery program with only 37 spots per class in the nation at the time. Thankfully, there was no requirement for me to have a congressman sign off on my admission to residency. Josh had dreams of being a fighter pilot. Growing up, he would always watch the history channel, and posters of planes were littered across his walls. Once he graduated from his lego set, he put together model jet planes and could recite the specs and model by heart.

Unfortunately, Josh would be no stranger to tragedy, having his dreams swept away. While playing intramural flag football at the AFA, he took a misstep and tore every ligamentous connection in his right knee. "Nothing but meat" was tethering his lower leg to his thigh. The military orthopedic surgeon was backed up for months. Where he needed an operation as soon as possible, he would have to wait for a couple of months with the fate and integrity of his knee dangling in the balance. Imagine hobbling on the ice on crutches in an institution that is unforgiving to tardiness.

Instead of taking a year off to let his leg properly heal, he was eager to rejoin the ranks of his fellow cadets. In hindsight, he admitted this route was poorly chosen and probably would have most benefitted from taking the year off to let his knee properly heal. Like me, eager to jump back in with his comrades, he was determined to show his grit. However, each time he attempted to run or reengage in some flavor of physical activity, he would sadly reinjure his knee. I can't say that I would've done anything differently; I would've seen it as a challenge to come back stronger than before. Sooner than expected. Overcoming the odds gives one a sense of inspiration, no matter how ill-advised.

Each time my brother attempted to reestablish his physical prowess, he would further damage his knee, developing back problems requiring further operations. My brother was forced to stay another two years at the AFA before he was honorably discharged, never being able to realize his long-held dream of being a pilot. To add insult to injury, Josh had to pay back a

341

sizeable military loan that young cadets are encouraged to get when they are first accepted. With no serious prospects for employment in the civilian world, he found himself at a loss for gainful employment. *Sound familiar?*

Josh spent six years in Colorado Springs, Colorado, two more than what was required. One year for each torn ligament with not much to show for it. I can now fully empathize with how my brother was feeling at the culmination of those years; dreams ripped apart with each ligamentous tear.

I think, am sure, a brother's love exceeds All the world's love in its unworldliness.
Robert Browning, A Blot in the 'Scutcheon Act ii, sc. 1.

Needless to say, Josh knew what I was going through. Next, when he offered that we go out west for his bachelor party, just him and me, I was thrilled. We had time to make up for. Instead of going out with some close buddies, he decided he and I have our own trip. Our relationship had always been strong despite our living situations, but the past few years had proven to bolster the bulwarks. Since I decided to forgo any further treatment and Josh having saved vacation time, we finally had an opportunity to revel in fraternity uninterrupted.

We designated Las Vegas our base camp. There was no gambling or any circus events; we used this strategic location to pivot amongst the national park system from Zion, Bryson Canyon, and Grand Canyon to Death Valley, Sequoia, and Yosemite. We had covered a wide expanse of the American Southwest in a little over two weeks. Although I wasn't running it, I was having the time of my life with my big bro. I couldn't have done it without him.

The trip's difficulty became evident before we even stepped on the plane. Effects of the brain surgery hanging like thick fog affected my forward planning and organizational skills even after almost a year out. On the outside, I seemed to have been mended; there was no major change in appearance or noticeable difference in my speech. Until you place me in a stressful situation to reveal the underlying deficits. My right leg would gyrate like a hound getting its ear scratched, and headaches would quickly follow if the stimulation of the senses remained too strong for too long. Most park passes and campsites must be purchased in advance, which meant constantly oscillating between computer screen to phone to calendar, back and forth, until I was sent into a dizzying confusion. The orchestration of our 2-and-a-half-week travel would ultimately fall on my brother.

Physically, I could only limp around with my stuffed Patagonia bag of clothes and toiletries while Josh had to carry his share along with all our camping effects: tent, cooking supplies, dehydrated food, sleeping bags, and mats. The list goes on. Moreover, I could barely decipher setting up a tent proper, something I had done countless times as a kid camping out in South Georgia. My poor dexterity and body positioning left me with a few fiberglass splinters that would take a couple of weeks to leech out of my fingers. Eventually, I'd give up, overwhelmed with frustration limping away from a deflated scaffold of the tent in malcontent. Josh never said a word, only lending a hand when he saw it was needed.

Like during our first day after arriving at Zion National Park, we parked on the side of the road to stretch our legs. The clay-colored canyons reminded me of the red dirt of the Piedmont that previously muddied up our boots in North Georgia when we were kids. Josh and I, at no more than 6 and 10 years old, would spend hours trying to dam up a little creek behind our house in La Grange, Ga, sometimes forgetting to kick our mucky boots off before marching into the house and tracking our escapades on our mom's cream-colored carpet floors.

Reminiscent of dam operations down by the creek, we decided to do a little of our own exploring because, to our disappointment, Zion was incredibly commercialized. For example, a fast-food restaurant was in the middle of the park. I am sure there are less traveled areas, but none where my crippled ass could venture. We parked our blue Explorer rental, dusty with the fine desert sand, and found an area near the eastern end of the park to roam, isolated from the constant stream of travelers just like us.

Josh was there to hold me steady as I attempted to balance across the weathered grooves of the canyons. Despite my Solomon boots, any increase in the grade of the slope would throw me off balance. Any concavity of the rocks sent my hands in a rapid search for the nearest stronghold to reestablish rebalance. Grasping Josh's hand to maintain equilibrium, we made it up to some higher ground, turned to gaze through a cloudless blue sky, and breathed the dry desert air. Zion's jagged and weathered landscape stored memories of mountains worn thin by harsh conditions. And it was beautiful. Beautiful and temporary.

The carved and molded landscape stained red by leeching ionizing iron and calcium carbonate deposits was concrete evidence of an ongoing process that would leave this wonderous tourist destination eroding and disappearing into time. Soon this would be sand, nothing, immaterial. In

344

retrospect, what inspired my longing to venture out to the Southwest was more than its majestic beauty that attracts tourists from all over the world.

I felt a potent kinship with the landscape, although this was my first time here. These desert canyons and modest peaks stood in stark contrast to the distant memory of the towering mountain ranges which previously had reigned in its stead. Millions of years of erosion, insult after insult, had worn even the most durable and unyielding of foundations. Although its degradation made for an eclectic and stunning panorama, it was crumbling, nonetheless.

Voyeurs endlessly cycle through the ongoing destruction siphoning the last bit of beauty, cheapening its timeless beauty with each upload to a social media profile. The greater the erosion and harshness of its features, the more attractive it becomes, drawing more spectators to the tragic and gorgeous scene. Onlookers applaud the efforts of the prior mountain drawing inspiration from the tragedy unfolding—the inevitable millions' year tragedies unfolding naked and stripped upon an arid stage.

The tourists don't think of the anguish the mountain had endured. The ravines and ranges lay battered daily as the cars enter and exit the park to mindlessly go on to leech the beauty from the next park. The terrain wears the scars of battle. Sure, some may find inspiration in the story of the canyon, how hard it has fought to exist valiantly, defying all logic. But with a memory of a vast mountain range so vivid in its past, letting go to the ancient forces of erosion grows evermore inviting with each passing epoch.

Could I follow…the canyon and remnants of mountain ranges, into that primordial process that grinds the brown earth like coffee beans to be digested and recycled? After all that I had endured, everything I had lost, I wanted to pass into a space with no memory or pain. I wanted to be forgotten.

An open wound festering with inflammation and pus might just be desiccated by the arid desert climate. After traveling through Death Valley, we culminated our travels at Yosemite. Of all the places that we had been, Yosemite was the most awe-inspiring. Josh and I would walk, breathless, speechless, through what appeared to be a fantasy land. A scene right from a storybook.

After a serpiginous route climbing nauseating mountainous roads and through a tunnel, the sun revealed the enchantment that was Yosemite. I am surprised there weren't more accidents along the Tunnel View, because the spectacle had every car braking in awe of the scene that unfolded before each passerby. You are instantly possessed by beauty. No description can do the landscape justice.

After pausing at the height of the entry overlook, Josh had difficulty keeping his eyes on the road. Both our months hung slack as if the weight of this scene's magnificence multiplied gravity's mass which tugged at our jaws like a couple of largemouth bass being reeled in. Yosemite was a skilled fisherman; every twist and turn of the road was another pull and yank never snapping the heavy test line on the road. Thankfully the weights on the Explorer didn't overheat as we made our hasty descent into the Yosemite Valley.

As we met the valley basin, the crystal-clear river meandering through the park revealed mountain trout jumping and frolicking, likely in celebration of their protected status within the park's confines. Josh and I would strike out on walks where nothing was said. Unlike our prison-like conversation across windowpanes during COVID while recovering from brain surgery, we BOTH had lost our powers of speech. Every fifty yards was a different vantage point of pure beauty, another portrait of astonishment and awe incarnate.

Within the valley, you are surrounded by mountains rising immediately upwards at impossible angles at such a steep grade that hiking up was a long shot. Home to some of the highest peaks in California, ranging from 12,000 to 13,000 feet, Yosemite is the resting place of the largest waterfall in North America, aptly named Yosemite Falls. My brother and I would trot between the view of the Half Dome and El Capitan with not much said between us other than some "Oh's" and "Awe's." Everywhere we paused for a break along our hike, we had to remind ourselves to continue walking. It was that captivating. We walked an estimated 7 to 8 miles on our first complete day there; by the end, my brother remarked that my wobbly gait had nearly been restored, if only for the day. Indeed, it would take nothing short of Paradise to heal these scars.

We returned to Las Vegas and had a couple of days to relax by the pool before we returned to Florida. After making possible my dream of venturing out West, Josh had one last surprise for me. He implored me to come downstairs to the hotel lobby, where he had an old AFA buddy who was working at the local Air Force base in Las Vegas. I didn't see why not; I wasn't doing much, only slightly fatigued from our many hours of driving.

We stepped outside, and Josh said his friend was just around the corner parking his car. I was looking for him, and as soon as I asked what he looked like a familiar face came running across the road. David Goggins! Someone who had been a source of inspiration for the past couple of years was standing right in front of me. "No f**king way!"

Star-struck, I did my best to thank him for taking time, probably interrupting his intense training schedule, to come to give me a little encouragement. By this time, Mr. Goggins had become increasingly popular and easily recognizable by everyone on the sidewalk. We had a short exchange and snapped a quick picture, but a crowd was growing by the second. He simply stated in classic Goggins fashion, "I gotta go! Stay Hard." I wanted to express to him how much his book and lifestyle had motivated me through some of the worst portions of cancer treatment. During the worst days, his voice, his story would echo through the dark chambers of misery, enticing me to, "Get Up! Get going!" Power through the lethargy, power through the nausea, power through the pain. He had motivated me since that phone call when I was first diagnosed three years ago. Goggins is the real deal, but more than that, he is a good person.

Tell me what you eat, and I will tell you what you are.
Brillat-Savarin, Physiologie du Gout. Ch. 36.

Reinvigorated by the trip with Josh and meeting one of my heroes, I returned determined to figure this cancer thing out. Come hell or high water. Sometime late in the summer of 2021, I was at an acupuncturist; yes *I was willing to try everything* when I was reminded of a specific diet that I had employed during my medical school days which used a certain

348

proportion of macronutrients (carbohydrates, protein, and fat) to optimize athletic performance.

By engineering metabolism, or the way in which your cells process energy, one can experience less fatigue perception and improved cellular respiration. Lactate acid turnover and thresholds are increased along with VO_2 max, [4], or the maximum amount of oxygen consumption an individual can manage before becoming completely exasperated. *Your cells are more resilient to stress, breath better, and lactic acid, which makes your muscles burn when running low on oxygen in tissues, is recycled faster.* Per one *specific* macromolecule, one can achieve 31% more energy per carbon unit than the primary and preferred energy alternative, glucose. [5-7] Despite more energy consumed due to a resultant higher resting metabolic rate, muscle mass is spared or even increased with escalations in testosterone (in men) while fat mass is decreased in men and women. [4, 8-10]

Moreover, there are several reports of improved cognition and memory, [4, 8, 11], and as a dumb country boy, I needed all the help I could get during interminable study sessions and long runs. Another benefit was consuming equal the food mass as your standard diet but gaining double the energy. With this nutrient-enriched diet, if I weren't the smartest tool in the toolshed, I'd undoubtedly be the hardest working. What was my dietary modification to accomplish this? The Ketogenic Diet (KD)

I can feel eyes rolling. And I understand; most do not do it the proper way. Along with all the controversy that a *"perfect diet"* entails, *whatever that is*, the KD seems to spark the most controversy. Where there's smoke, there doesn't always have to be fire. The true implications and applications of KD on health and well-being have only now been realized by popular media and more explored by the scientific community. But like with any new "fad," I cringe when it's dubbed a fad since it's been around since the early 1900s, nuance is failed to be appreciated leading to polarization into camps: overzealous ketokickers and stark denialists. Like most things, the truth lies in the middle, most of which should align with your personal goals.

If you are exploring KD and have preexisting health issues, I recommend speaking with your doctor or nutritionist who is knowledgeable in the KD. For example, if you have any problems with fat metabolism or any operations altering the normal anatomy of your digestive tract. Note, that many healthcare workers have no idea what they are talking about regarding diet. When asked what to eat, most would say something very general, "A balanced diet,' or, "I diet high in fruits and vegetables." What does that even mean?! Moreover, simply observe the body habitus of whom you are asking for advice; the proof is in the pudding or the hips. Politely seek another opinion. When done correctly, the Ketogenic Diet is safe despite some negative press. It took me months before I fine-tuned the diet removing all potentially harmful items that attempt to sneak into your dinner.

But first, what is the Ketogenic Diet?

KD is a diet where your principal means of energy production is sourced from fat. FAT. A standard American diet is 55% carbohydrates, 15% protein, and 30% fat. KD flips that standard on its head; one eats 75 to 90% fat as a primary fuel source and limits carbohydrates to 20 to 50 grams.[12]

The energy currency substitutes glucose for fat by the metabolism of 3 molecules: Acetoacetate, Beta-hydroxybutyrate (BHB), and acetone; the chief circulating ketone is BHB. These ketone bodies are produced in your liver. [7] Once BHB enters the cell, it is broken down to two molecules of acetyl-CoA, similar to glycolysis, and enters the Krebs cycle and ultimately to the mitochondria, the powerhouse of the cell, where energy gets multiplied severalfold. [4] A beautiful and redundant cycle. *So fat is broken down into simple energy molecules called ketone bodies that are used like glucose.*

Hold on to that bit of information as that will become important when we get to cancer.

Historically, the KD was employed to treat juvenile epilepsy and related epileptic syndromes, [13] before the invention of pharmaceuticals, like phenytoin (1938). This simple dietary intervention was introduced in the 1920s to ameliorate the multitudes of seizures these kids would experience in a single day. [11] The diet successfully increases seizure thresholds demonstrably, meaning it takes more neural excitement to unleash one. [14-16] provides at least an efficacious adjunct to help control refractory seizure syndromes. [17-19] *This high-fat diet and ketone metabolism can treat seizures.*

Benefits to the brain do not stop at seizure control. Utilizing ketone metabolism has also been studied in other neurological conditions from Alzheimer's to autism, all with significant benefits. [4, 11] Indeed, it would not be the athletic benefits that drew me back to the diet. The neuroprotective effects and my desire for a better quality of life first

351

rekindled my intrigue. I had no desire to have another seizure driving down state road 301 in Florida, for my sake or another's.

Anecdotally, I was always in a constant brain fog after all my treatment, especially after my brain surgery. I would've forgotten my head if it wasn't loosely screwed on. My speech was constantly jumbled, and actions were always disorganized. After three days of being on the diet, I felt like a veil had been lifted. My speaking had improved, cognition and memory enriched. There was less walking to the kitchen, forgetting what I had wanted to eat. Additionally, my walking was smoother. Also, at the time of this writing, it has been eight months since I started the KD, and I remain seizure-free.

Who by intemperance in his diet, in some sort, digged his grave with his own teeth.
Thomas Fuller, Church History. Bk. iv, sec. 3. (1655)

Let's face it, folks, us Americans are fat. Most of our health problems are self-made. In the 20th century, where we made great strides in medicine through antibiotics [20] and public health initiatives [21], the next century was brewing new problems for ourselves: obesity and obesity-related conditions. As I limp down the street or through a supermarket, almost half the people I see are overweight or obese, consistent with the current reported burden of disease. According to the CDC (Center for Disease Control), with data from 2017-2018, 42.7% of Americans are obese. Almost half! "From 1999 – 2000 through 2017 – 2018, US obesity prevalence increased from 30.5% to 42.4%. During that same time, the prevalence of severe obesity increased from 4.7% to 9.2%. Obesity-related

352

conditions include heart disease, stroke, type 2 diabetes and certain types of cancer [, and] these are among the leading causes of preventable, premature death."[22] *I think it more apropos to say that we are sick. We are a sick nation.*

Obesity is hurting our pocketbooks and waistbands while our ever-stressed health care system tries to keep up. Based on a Medical Expenditure Panel Survey between 2005 to 2010, medical costs per obese adult rose 14.3 percent. The cost overall to the adult in the United States "...rose from $212.4 billion to $315.8 billion, an increase of 48.7 percent."[7, 23] As obesity becomes more prevalent and costly, encouragement by plus-size models and popular media in acceptance of unhealthy lifestyle seems a little sinister and misguided. Where we should be awarding good behaviors, we are acting in antipathy.

We would soon pay for our over-embellishment. For nigh forty years, we ate and ate until nature would remind us that ignoring respect for ourselves would have dire consequences. The World Health Organization (WHO), on March 11, 2020, declared the novel coronavirus (COVID-19) a global pandemic. [24] And what population of patients did this virus plague the most, other than the elderly? More plainly, who is more likely to wind up dead from the virus? Those with obesity and the associated conditions thereof: hypertension and diabetes. [25, 26] Indeed, research would indicate that COVID causes vascular endothelial dysfunction, [27] and, with it being well established that diabetes is both a micro- and macrovascular disease, it only stands to reason that this population would have compounded risks and consequences after contracting the virus. [28,

29] *People already battling weight issues are primed to have worse outcomes following contracting COVID.*

Metabolic syndrome, also syndrome X, characterized by "...central and abdominal obesity, systemic hypertension, insulin resistance (or type 2 diabetes mellitus), and atherogenic dyslipidemia," causes the body to be in a widespread inflammatory state...at baseline! [30] Those with metabolic syndrome are already immunosuppressed due to the nature of the syndrome. One study indicated that patients infected with COVID-19 with preexisting metabolic syndrome had higher mortality, more ICU admissions, and a greater need for mechanical ventilation. [31] *Those affected by metabolic syndrome are like walking time bombs of inflammation with the virus acting as the match.*

Beginning in the 1970s, we began to eat our way to epidemic proportions until it was declared as such in America in 1999, [32] and a pandemic not shortly after. This means we have had almost twenty years to curb our appetite, live healthier, and make better choices. Indeed, as Benjamin Franklin said, "An ounce in prevention is worth a pound of cure." We have been subject to a lifestyle obsession of excess. More is always better. What made COVID-19 so virulent, apart from the viral dynamics and mode of spread, [33] was our insatiable appetite, just lambs led to slaughter by our *insatiable palate.*

But that isn't completely true now, is it? The food we have so easily at our disposal is maligned, mutated by the whims of our post-industrial market pressures ultimately designed for us to take one more bite. One more bite turns into another. And another. Until our designer foods have commandeered our pleasure reward pathways. [34]   Our foods are engineered for excess. Sugar is hidden in almost everything you pick off the shelf. Despite the deleterious effects to our health, it's so satiable, so satisfying, that we consume it anyways. Sugar, high-glycemic products, and processed goods stimulate ancient and primordial reward pathways sending dopamine levels sky-high postprandially. [35]   The more those products fly off the self, the market will respond accordingly: more.

Placing blame on large food corporations for producing what an open, free market demands speaks to our blind laziness. It's like doing a rain dance and cursing the heavens for the thunderstorm. Companies are only entities responding to market pressures looking to survive amongst their fellow competitors. Free market principles have given us the quality of life we all take advantage of every day. Dr. Rand Paul's book, "The Case Against Socialism," highlights the value of free market capitalism, *not crony capitalism*, including but not limited to us not being forced to eat our own pets, which has been cited in societies whose governments are rot with corruption. [36] I hope we wake up to the realization that we are the masters of our own fate, and *you can control what you put in your mouth*. As people change and their wants change, the market will mold and shift to an individual's wants or die altogether, the way it shalt.

The simple fact is, however, sugar is addicting [34], and our processed diet is making us sick. [37] Don't believe me; try going without it for a few days. Like most addictions, they are marked by *binging*, like eating an entire bag of chips in one sitting. You find it hard to resist the delectable salt crunch of eating more than the recommended serving. As you are

355

coming down from your sugar high, you may experience moodiness, fatigue, and irritability. Welcome to *withdrawal.* When you go without that sugar high, you *crave* your next fix, even when your daily metabolic needs have already been met. *Realize that sugar is a carbohydrate, but not all carbohydrates interact with your metabolism in the same way as sugar. For the purposes of this discussion and the KD, consider them one and the same.*

There is good news: sugar addiction can be broken by employing the Ketogenic Diet where, again, you primarily use the breakdown of fats, formally known as lipolysis, as your primary energy source! Eat fat to lose fat, only if the diet is scant on carbohydrates. Seems counterintuitive. Not much about our bodily metabolism is straightforward, making it so fascinating.

Another name for the KD is the low-carbohydrate, high-fat (LCHF) diet. I suppose this name was an effort to corral all the dietary studies under one umbrella to easily compare methods also acting to remove the stigmas associated with diets like KD and Atkins. After many years and continued research, some of the confusion about the Ketogenic, Atkins, LCHF diets are dissolving however it's not my goal to dive into semantics or popular opinion. Know that this diet typically indicates a dramatic reduction in carbohydrate intake to below 20 – 50 grams per day, forcing the body into a state of ketosis. [12, 38] *Twenty grams of carbohydrates is like eating half a bagel; fifty grams is like eating three skinned moderate-sized potatoes.*

Once you burn off excess carbohydrates in your skeletal muscle and liver, generally in about three days if sedentary, more rapidly if active, the body shifts gears in its metabolism from a glucocentric to a ketocentric mode. The glucocentric mode of metabolism promotes insulin resistance, storing triglycerides and free fatty acids, lower energy expenditure, and increased inflammation, ultimately culminating in cardiovascular disease and other obesity-related illnesses. [7, 39, 40] When in a ketocentric mode, however, fat stores are mobilized [8, 41] and has an overwhelming anti-inflammatory effect, having even been reported to ameliorate autoimmune disease like multiple sclerosis. [42] Instead of *your body being in an active mode of storage packing potent energy into those hips and belly*, through the influence of insulin and IGF-1 (insulin-growth-factor-1), *your body is setting fire, catabolizing excess storage bins resting in those love handles.*

Those stored and ingested forms of fat are processed by your liver to form ketones, or ketone bodies, as the primary energy currency of your body. [43] When ketones enter a cell, they are obligated to be processed by the mitochondria, or the energy powerhouse of the cell. Glycolysis, sugar/carbohydrate metabolism, occurs exclusively OUTSIDE the mitochondria in the cell cytosol. Very important point! Once within the cell, Ketones are transformed into acetyl-CoA to enter the Kreb's cycle and, finally, the electron transport chain in the mitochondria where it can produce energy. [7, 44] *Fat molecules are broken down into ketones in the liver and can only be metabolized by the mitochondria for energy.*

When not in a ketogenic state, carbohydrate metabolism is preferred by the mitochondria. In a carbohydrate-starved state as in ketosis, ATP production, or energy, depends on mobilized fats. There are other organs that produce ketones outside of the liver and kidneys, but we have complicated this enough.

Clogged with yesterday's excess, the body drags the mind down with it, and fastens to the ground this fragment of divine spirit.
Horace, Satires, Bk. ii, sat. 77.

A multitude of clinical studies and systemic reviews, as hard as it is to conduct studies on diets, support the use of the Ketogenic Diet for weight loss, [8, 38, 41, 45] if only for a short term to revitalize the metabolism and reach weight loss goals. Some people are on a diet for many years without harm, but most studies aren't longer than a couple of years. Once goals are achieved, I would still eat responsibly and continue restricting carbohydrates. The health benefits are far too substantial to be taken lightly, especially regarding cardiovascular disease. [46] Weight reduction, in and of itself, is a powerful tool to lessen an individual's overall mortality. [47]

In a sixth month uncontrolled study by Westman in 2002, [48] 51 patients were on a diet of fewer than 25 carbohydrates a day with no limit on total caloric intake. Forty-one out of the 51 patients experienced weight decreases significantly from baseline by 10.3% +- 5.9%. The participants' lipid profiles (fat profile, cholesterol profile; whatever you might refer to them as) were all improved. Total cholesterol, low-density lipoprotein (LDL), and triglycerides were lower, while HDL and triglycerides/HDL were higher. All positive changes! *The KD, despite unlimited caloric intake, had significant weight loss and favorable changes in blood fat profiles. All by eating mainly fat!*

Among the published studies by 2003, Bravata et al. concluded that the mechanisms for weight loss by the KD were most likely attributed to decreased overall intake of calories and increased adherence to a dietary regimen rather than carbohydrate restriction and lipid interactions. [49] Splitting hairs, I know. Nonetheless, by 2004, the KD had been established as a safe dietary intervention long-term. [50] Not surprisingly, this diet had been used in children for decades in treating childhood epilepsy disorders, as mentioned prior. [19, 51] I've controlled my own seizure disorder for … a year and counting. How quick we are to forget the lessons learned from the past!

In the Annals of Internal Medicine in 2004, Yancy et al. conducted a dietary study on KD versus a low-fat diet to treat obesity and hyperlipidemia (increased circulating fat in the blood) in 120 overweight patients. The KD group was allowed only 20 grams of carb a day, and the low-fat group allowed only 30% of their energy from fat along with other constraints for a total of 24 weeks. Retention rates to dietary plans were significantly higher with KD versus low-fat (76% vs. 57%).[52] Moreover, weight loss was double in the KD group, and carbohydrates were even added when they lost too much weight! *KD had lower attrition rates and was more successful at weight loss.*

In their meta-analysis, a multi-institutional study in 2006 involving University Hospital Basel in Switzerland, Duke University Hospital, and the University of Cincinnati, compared the effects of low-carbohydrate versus low-fat diets on weight loss and cardiovascular risk factors in randomized controlled trials. [53] After the comparison of 5 studies for a total of 447 patients, those in the low carbohydrate group lost more weight, experiencing lower blood pressure and significant favorable changes in circulating blood fats (triglycerides and high-density lipoprotein [HDL]), decreasing and increasing respectively. *KD improved cardiometabolic health by lowering blood pressure and inducing positive changes in fat ratios decreasing risks of heart and vascular disease. Recall, high triglycerides are considered to increase risk; high HDL is considered protective. The ratio between the two should ultimately be telling of an individual's risk of experiencing a significant vascular event, like a heart attack.*

In 2020, an Australian study at the University of Melbourne would confirm an elevated triglyceride/HDL ratio (>2.5) to be an independent predictor of mortality for all-cause mortality and strongly associated with an increased risk of major adverse cardiovascular events. [54] Higher triglyceride bad, Higher HDL good. Therefore, a lower ratio of the two metrics is ultimately positive. Basically, these were favorable blood fat changes supported by clinical observation. *Our understanding of fat metabolism is evolving and isn't as simple as once perceived.*

A 2018 study reported 20 obese (BMI 35.5 +/- 4.4) individuals on a calorically restricted ketogenic diet for 4 months. Participants maintained a moderate level of ketosis and lost 18 kilograms (40 lbs) of fat mass on average. Moreover, they reported increased physical activity, sleep, and sexual activity. *I do not know what came first. Again, all positive metrics for a good quality of life and weight reduction.*[55] What's the mechanism?

The experienced success in weight management might be a result of how energy from fat is compacted in three-dimensional space. Fat contains 9 Cal per gram versus the 4 Cal per gram from protein and carbohydrates. *Fat gives you more bang for your buck, so to speak.* Because fat is more satiating and energy-packed, you can eat less food mass, consuming equivalent energy underlining the utility in distance running. Clinically, evidence suggests that most on the KD consume fewer calories, losing more weight. *Anecdotally, I'd force myself to eat more to maintain weight.* And as mentioned, when someone enters ketosis, they typically run hotter with a higher resting metabolic rate propagating weight loss. [56]

"The proposed mechanism of the effectiveness of KD is *maintenance* of resting energy expenditure and lean muscle mass, high fat mass loss, and increased fat oxidation rate compared to isocaloric carbohydrate diets."[7, 56] Also, there may be a greater reduction in appetite due to higher proteins in diet and increased metabolic efficiency due to a greater respiratory quotient.[57] Overall, weight reduction seems to stem from reduction of appetite, reduction of lipogenesis with a concomitant rise in lipolysis (fat breakdown), and increases metabolic rate. Evidence suggests cardiovascular parameters are improved through improved blood pressure and lipid profiles. [57] In addition, the diet treats type 2 diabetes by lowering insulin dependency, sometimes reversing insulin resistance and decreasing A1c levels. [57, 58] There is also favorable changes in neurohormones, ghrelin and leptin, that influence appetite. [57] *At multiple levels, the KD acts to remodel and sculpt favorable changes in overall metabolism.* What is the experts' consensus, however?

In 2019 within the Journal of Clinical Lipidology, Kirkpatrick et al. published an exhaustive review of the current level of evidence, and strength thereof, in the recommendations of a low carbohydrate and very-low-carbohydrate (VL-CHO) (including ketogenic) in addressing body weight and other cardiometabolic factors (cardiovascular disease and diabetes). [45] Basically, this review attempted to put into scope the true benefit of the low carb, ketogenic lifestyle, which to me, concluded in an anticlimactic fashion. Admittedly the authors comment on the inherent weakness of the existing studies; conducting dietary studies is no easy task. You are waging war on peoples' primal reward mechanisms: eating. Nonetheless, they concluded the KD revealed advantages in appetite control, triglyceride reduction, and reducing medication requirements for type 2 diabetes. Still, low-carbohydrate/VLCHO/Ketogenic diets were not superior to other weight loss schemes. At six months, this diet WAS significantly more effective, but after a year, these positive results fell away in significance. [45]

In the population of overweight and obese individuals, the researchers endorsed a high level of evidence in support of the diet, for at least six months. Cardiometabolic factors, lipid profiles, and blood pressure, are met with mixed results. High-density lipids (HDL), your protective lipids or fats, are consistently increased, however. The study also supports that fat should be from unsaturated and polyunsaturated sources, like olive oil and plant fats, rather than animal sources. [45] *In summation, the KD is concluded to be a reasonable and safe weight loss option but not the only means for weight loss or reducing vascular risk.* So why have we been under the impression that fat is so bad, especially when other cultures, like the Inuit, have eaten nearly 80% fat traditionally and experienced a rapid decline in health outcomes upon the introduction of a westernized diet? [59-61]

The demonization of fat of diet has a long and misconstrued history which stems mainly from a brilliant American physiologist, nutritionist, and public health scientist, Ancel Keys. He is renowned for his diet-heart hypothesis, or dietary-fat hypothesis, of the 20th century, whereby elevated serum cholesterol increases atherosclerosis, i.e., the plaques that build in your arteries because cholesterol and lipids are what is found in the walls of diseased vessels. When atherosclerosis forms blockages around the heart impeding normal blood flow, heart attacks result or myocardial infarctions. Atherosclerosis is a systemic disease; plaques can build in any vessel. [62, 63] *In the brain, it can cause a stroke, for example.* Following the death of President Franklin D. Roosevelt from hypertension and heart failure in 1944, Keys' aided his predecessor, Harry S. Truman, in another type of war as tensions overseas were simmering over from World War II. President Truman signed the National Heart Act to get to the bottom of heart disease. [64]

Keys would provide strong correlations for coronary heart disease rising with the consumption of fat. [62] *However, correlation is not causation.* He would go on to shape dietary recommendations for our entire nation influencing public policy and popular opinion on diet, hinging much of his conclusions on large epidemiological studies, such as the Seven Country's Study (SCS) (more like a hodgepodge of 16 specific cohorts of men in seven different countries), which, again, revealed a strong correlation between dietary fat with poor cardiovascular health. The countries included in the cross-cultural study were: the United States, Italy, Finland, Greece, the Netherlands, Japan, and what is now Croatia and Serbia. [62] The public understood this to mean that all fat is bad and we must restrict all fat consumption or else we will all succumb to heart disease. *This couldn't be further from the truth; the idea of nuance in nutrition is often lost.*

Keys had made a key distinction in his studies that often goes overlooked. The *type of fat* needs to be deliberated and discerned. Not all fat is created equal. In fact, Keys noted that polyunsaturated fat lowered cholesterol while saturated fat did the opposite. Polyunsaturated fat, like omega 3 fatty acids such as alpha-linolenic acid, are protective to vascular health. Thus, Keys endorsed replacing those saturated fatty acids, namely animal fats, with fish and plant fats, NOT carbohydrates. [62] Such is supported by other researchers.[65] In other words, the type of fat matters, in keeping with the American Heart Association guidelines (2017) to replace saturated fat with unsaturated fat to lower cardiovascular disease risk. [63] Unfortunately, this message was not well communicated as the current American receives 60% of their calories from carbohydrates in efforts to maintain a low-fat diet. [66]

However, the Prospective Rural Urban Epidemiology (PURE) study would argue differently in its fat purview. Over 135,000 subjects between 35 and 70 years old were enrolled in PURE between 2003-2013 further analyzed for total mortality, major cardiovascular events (MACE), among other secondary outcomes among 18 countries on five continents. They conclude, "Total fat and types of fat were not associated with cardiovascular disease, myocardial infarction, or cardiovascular mortality."[63, 67] Saturated fats are even associated with a lower incidence of stroke. "High carbohydrate intake was associated with higher risk of mortality, whereas total fat" wasn't. [67] *This one, highly powered, iconoclastic study seems to have shaken much of our preconceived notions.* Other studies mirror such conclusions.[68] *The authors endorsed global dietary guidelines be reconsidered in light of this powerful study.*

Although Keys' assumptions of the dangers certain types of fat were somewhat founded, although as we have seen later contested in the heavily powered PURE study, he would argue later in the 1970s that the dangers of *sugar* or *sucrose* (a combination of glucose and fructose) were *unfounded*. Which I would argue was the largest disservice to our health and well-being as a nation. John Yudkin MD, a British physiologist and nutritionist, warned on the dangers of sugar (sucrose and fructose) in *Pure, White, and Deadly,* his book in 1972. [69] He advocated for a low carbohydrate diet void of sugar to deter dental caries, obesity, diabetes and heart disease, even cancers.[70-72]

Keys' was vehemently opposed to Yudkin's view on sugar. [73] Yudkin suffered heavy criticism from Keys and the sugar industry. Yudkin's reputation was smeared as Keys' would shape nutritional recommendations for the entire nation, ostensibly giving sugar a 'clean bill of health.' In 2016, Gary Taubes would write a wonderful book on the "The Case Against Sugar," highlighting the controversy and detriment that sugar has had on our well-being and society at large [74], somewhat vindicating Yudkin's position. Moreover, the EPIC study, European and Prospective

Investigation into Glycemic Index, published in 2020, involved over 330,000 men and women between 35 and 70 years of age over eight years found significant risk with high sugar consumption, especially when replacing saturated fats with sugar. Sugar and refined carbohydrates increase cardiovascular risk instead of lowering it. "This large pan-European study provides robust additional support for the hypothesis that a diet that induces a high glucose response is associated with greater coronary heart disease."[75] *In other words, our nation's previous dietary recommendations involved demonizing fats that can aid in a healthy lifestyle while supporting the increased consumption of sugar, which is implicated in heart disease and metabolic disease, i.e., diabetes.*

However, the EPIC and PURE studies were some 30 to 40 years following Keys' recommendations. During the interim, the landscape was already finely molded to the tune that fat equals bad. The risk of overindulgent carbohydrate consumption fell out of concern. The nuance of fat metabolism would be lost in obscurity, where most of those beneficial fat calories in the form of unsaturated fats were replaced with carbohydrates. Sugar entered the scene having the blessing of a nutritional giant of his time, Ancel Keys, and of course, the Sugar Research Foundation (SRF). Historical documents from the SRF in the 1960s and 1970s confirm the latter suspicion that fat consumption was purposely defamed as the harmful effects of sugar were ignored. [76] The public took fat as the end all evil. All the while, obesity would rise to epidemic proportions.

Other men live to eat, while I eat to live.
Socrates. (Diogenes Laertius, Socrates. Bk.ii, sec. 34; Stobaeus, Florilegium, xvii, 22.)

This cursory review of the benefits of the KD was an effort to remove any false or misleading preconceived notions. To review, there are benefits in weight reduction, reducing cardiovascular risks, epilepsy, neurological disease, even acne, and hormonal health, [4] not to mention our health economy. Although I had reinstituted the diet to gain proper control over my seizures and gain better control over my cognition for a better quality of life, at least for the remainder of it, the largest adjunct to my life was its activity against cancer![12]

Two prevailing theories of the origin of cancer are: (1) Cancer is a genetic disease, meaning that the cause of cancer comes from alterations of the genome in the form of a singular or multiple mutations of DNA within the nucleus coding for corrupted proteins or none at all; or (2) Cancer is a metabolic disease where the manifestations are among the *epigenome*, outside the nucleus, for example, the cytosol or mitochondria. The characteristics of the *epigenome* and the downstream effects to the nucleus and associated organelles are responsible for cancerous growth.

Cancer, seen as predominantly a genetic disease, has dominated scientific literature for nearly a century refracting viewpoints to the contrary with a narrow lens. Indeed, over time, we have become tunnel viewed in our comprehension of where or how cancer originates. Of course, like most things, the truth is somewhere in the middle as there is unmistakably a percentage of cancers that are of direct genetic origin. [77, 78] There's no argument there. However, the persistent underappreciation of how much cancer is a metabolic disease has hampered both our research efforts and progress in finding effective treatments. [79]

367

I cannot in good conscience continue with this topic without first attributing credit to the writings of Travis Christofferson, MS, "Tripping over the Truth: How the Metabolic Theory of Cancer is Overturning One of Medicine's Most Entrenched Paradigms," [80] the research of Dominic D'Agostino, Ph.D. who is presently associate professor at the University of South Florida, [81-84] and Thomas N. Seyfried Ph.D. out of Boston College whose revitalizing work has given a renewed breath of life into our understanding of cancer and its management. [79, 84-87] Not to mention, the meaningful, heartbreaking, but very informative book by Miriam Kalamian, EdM, MS, CNS, "Keto for Cancer: The Ketogenic Metabolic Therapy as a Targeted Nutritional Strategy," she describes her battle in her son's cancer as well as a comprehensive guide in implementing the ketogenic diet as a therapeutic strategy; [88] she also has co-authored many articles with the aforementioned authors about the benefits of the KD.[86, 89-91]

Most, if not all, of our understanding of the metabolic theory of cancer cell metabolism, can be attributed initially to the work of Otto Warburg and Peter L Pedersen. [92] Otto Heinrich Warburg was a German physiologist, medical doctor, and Nobel laureate for Physiology or Medicine in 1931; Dr. Peter Pedersen is a professor of biological chemistry at Johns Hopkins who has carried Warburg's torch of cancer being seen as a metabolic disease. Pederson never relented from his research efforts despite the idea's unpopularity. [92] For the sake of brevity, I have truncated their illustrious careers and achievements, but know they are many. Both have spent their careers researching cellular and cancer energetics. *In other words, what drives the uncontrollable and unbridled growth of cancer cells?*

368

Dr. Warburg discovered the "Warburg phenomenon," where cancer cells maintain high lactate acid production to produce energy despite the abundance of oxygen, so-called *aerobic fermentation*. In other words, Warburg demonstrated that cancer cells derive greater than 50% of their energetic needs by metabolizing glucose directly into lactic acid even in the presence of oxygen. [92] *That shouldn't happen; lactate acid production from the fermentation of glucose is not necessary when oxygen is abundant.* In fact, energy production through lactic acid production is inefficient and only necessary in times of metabolic stress. [93] Fermentation typically occurs during anaerobic biological processes, like brewing a beer, making sauerkraut from cabbage, or producing energy for muscles beyond your metabolic capacity. *Cancer prefers this primitive pathway.*

Cancer ferments constitutively or nonstop and at a higher rate than normal cells resulting in unchecked cellular growth. Over-utilizing the glucose-lactate pathway in the cytosol (*not in the mitochondria*) provides cancer cells' energy for unbridled progression despite using an older metabolic pathway. Other mutations in important enzymes, like Hexokinase II and mitochondrial receptor (VDAC), are vital to spur on the process. [92] Moreover, cancer's overproduction of lactic acid creates an acidic microenvironment, which disables immunoregulatory mechanisms, evading the host's immune system. [94] Note, cancer's reliance on glucose metabolism is responsible for the utility of imaging modalities like the 2-(^{18}F)-flouro-2-deoxy-D-glucose (FDG) by positron emission tomography (PET), FDG-PET scan. [95] Areas of hypermetabolic activity, increased glucose turnover, signal scans to increased cellular turnover, i.e., cancer.

Cancer metabolism is marked by overwhelming lactic acid production to fuel growth.

Prevailing theories of carcinogenesis would indicate that cancer comes from a disorder in the regulation and maintenance of a tightly controlled genome within the nucleus of a cell, so-called the somatic or germ theory of cancer. Stated differently, the central issue is that something has gone awry with the expression of genes within the nucleus. However, the metabolic theory of cancer would indicate that the root cause of cancer is disordered or dysregulated *mitochondria* within cancer cells. Disordered genes within a cancer cell nucleus are merely a side effect of a more extensive metabolic problem, problems within the powerhouse of the cell. In Thomas N. Seyfried's pioneering book, "Cancer as a Metabolic Disease: On the Origin, Management, and Prevention of Cancer," he provides a bolstering case for why cancer should be seen in a different light, a metabolic light. [79]

Hanahan and Weinberg comment on the hallmarks of cancer in 2000 in the journal Cell: "evading apoptosis [cell death], self-sufficiency in growth signals, insensitivity to anti-growth signals, tissue invasion and metastasis, limitless replicative potential, and sustained angiogenesis [blood vessel growth]." [83, 96] It was only added later that altered metabolism, *aerobic fermentation*, was a major player despite being one of the first characteristics discovered, as well as evading immune destruction. [97]

So, cancer cells have altered metabolism. They produce energy for their cells differently than our normal cells. Instead of producing ATP, the energy currency of the cells, through the mitochondria, cancer cells have

370

dysfunctional mitochondria crippling normal cellular metabolism and respiration. Well, in fact, they do not respire at all; they *ferment*. Because of their disordered and malfunctional mitochondria, they are forced to rely on a simpler biochemical pathway for energy: the glycolytic-lactate pathway, as previously mentioned. This pathway is conserved or common to all cancers!

So, can we target that Achilles heel of cancer's metabolism, its dependency on carbohydrate/sugar metabolism? *Yes!* Through a high-fat, low-carbohydrate diet, i.e., the Ketogenic diet. Cancer cells must ramp up their glycolytic processes to satisfy their uninhibited and destructive growth. Without functional mitochondria, they cannot metabolize fat. *Recall, fat metabolism is restricted to the mitochondria.* By restricting your diet to predominantly fats with scant intake of carbohydrates and limited protein, you can essentially starve cancer out! This dietary scheme is a siege on cancer energetics until the cancer cells undergo apoptosis or programmed cell death.

The KD acts in other ways to discourage cancer growth. They include, as outlined by Poff et al. [83]: "reduction in glucose and insulin" signaling driving growth, "modulation of oxidative stress" spurring free radical damage to tissues, "reduction of inflammation," "enhancement of anti-tumor immunity," "alteration of gene expression," and finally the "sensitization of tumors to standard of care therapies," like radiation and chemotherapy. *The diet is like putting on an extra layer of metabolic armor to fight cancer.*

What I think is most interesting is that you can use the KD to add to the efficacy of already established therapies that are standard of care: radiation, chemotherapy, and surgery. In a lung cancer model, the KD was shown to amplify the effects of chemotherapy and radiation, sensitizing cancer to the effects of the treatment. [12, 98] The diet has also been investigated in neuroendocrine cancers and malignant gliomas within the adjuvant setting, among other cancers like pancreatic and breast cancers. [99-102]

The anti-tumor effects of KD have been studied and are continued to be investigated. [83, 103] A systemic meta-analysis of 29 animal and 24 human studies revealed the KD's anti-cancer properties in almost three-quarters of the studies. Although the human studies were lacking and randomized controlled trials remain wanting. [12, 104] As mentioned previously, diet studies are challenging to conduct. Employing the diet as a targeted metabolic strategy has been found to increase progression-free and overall survival, [12, 105] at the very least increasing quality of life, especially in brain cancer patients. [106]

However, it must be stated that there is no *conclusive* evidence as to the therapeutic efficacy of KD as metabolic cancer therapy. Romer et al. in 2021, in a systemic review of 39 studies with 770 patients, showed no clear benefit of utilizing the KD in the treatment of cancer even though admittedly, the authors, again, comment on the poor quality of conducted studies lacking in stringent methodology. [107, 108] Remember that one must consider that although the extension of life may not be perceptibly bolstered, the quality of life may be improved, especially during cytotoxic cancer treatment. [106, 109] *Trust me, that is a huge deal.*

372

Until there are some major, well-controlled, randomized studies on the efficacy of KD in the treatment of cancer, as a primary intervention or in the adjuvant setting, I am afraid that most of us cancer patients will be left to wonder as to the potential benefits the KD despite the evidence I have presented here. Not until you implement it yourself will you experience the real, tangible difference. No scientific paper can properly convince you until it is felt. In my opinion, the increase in quality of life has been well worth the effort. At the very least, it has allowed me to coherently write these pages. *Well, as best as I can manage.*

Placing a metabolic vice on your cancer crippling its metabolism and subsequent growth, might lend time for your cure to be found. You never know what could happen, what breakthroughs will be made. For example, I was diagnosed in 2019. Solid evidence for the CAPTEM regimen, the cytotoxic therapy I responded so well to for treating lung neuroendocrine cancer, emerged in 2020. [110] CAPTEM is usually used to treat gastroenteropancreatic neuroendocrine cancers. [111] By all metrics and estimations, I shouldn't be alive right now. I attribute my still breathing to both God and the diet, *not to mention all the people involved in my treatment over the years.* Through dietary modifications, however, you can work to tip the scales in your favor by molding an inhospitable cancer microenvironment. As you buy time, your cure may be right around the corner.

We must not sit down, and look for miracles. Up, and be doing, and the Lord will be with thee. Prayer and pains, through faith in Christ Jesus, will do anything.
John Eliot, Indian Grammar Begun: Post-Script.

Instead of boring you with more observational studies about the supposed efficacy of the diet, let me explain my experience with the ketogenic diet. Preceding years before my treatment, I was generally healthy, but regrettably, I had no significant limitations on my diet. The previous years of treatment had worn on me; however, the last thing I was worried about was being over-picky about what I ate. Moreover, I would go weak in the knees when the sweet smell of Firehouse deli meat journeyed through my nostrils, especially while on chemotherapy. Pregnant with odd cravings throughout chemo, Firehouse was my welcomed failing.

After Josh and I returned from our trip out West, as previously mentioned, from the encouragement of my acupuncturist, I thought I would give KD another try, if only to curb my propensity for seizure activity. Within three days, my cognition and mental capabilities were improved. My memory was boosted; I would no longer lose myself in mid-conversation. There were no more trailing off into miscellaneous ramblings. After three days! It became abundantly clear that there was something to this diet. Proof of its power was evident when I came off the keto kick. A one- or two-day diet sabbatical would immerse me in a thick mental fog. My noodle running on anything other than ketones was like running my system on crude, unrefined oil.

I began to experiment with the diet, ensuring consistent levels of maximal ketosis that would be actively fighting cancer growth, a therapeutic level of ketosis. There are essentially three levels of ketosis: (1) No Ketosis, $0.0 - 0.6$ mmol/L, (2) Nutritional Ketosis, $< 0.6 - 3.0 <$ mmol/L, or (3) Therapeutic Ketosis, > 3.0 mmol/L. Multiple apps and devices aid in tracking macromolecule intake to ensure adequate fat intake to maintain ketosis. A blood analyzer for measuring circulating ketones is the most reliable tool. Consult your physician or nutritionist who is cognizant of the benefits and minor risks of the KD; some people may have issues with fat metabolism, which may preclude one from the diet.

As previously mentioned, I stopped having seizure activity after transitioning to a ketogenic lifestyle. More importantly, the mental clarity and increased energy allowed me to come off high-dose dexamethasone, which has its own suit of exciting side effects. Namely, affecting my overall mood and behavior; I would get upset at the most menial of situations. My round steroid-infused facies finally deflated as I was able to downgrade to a less potent regimen with hydrocortisone beginning the long process of an uncomfortable steroid wean. Despite the lethargy, weaning off steroids is necessary due to the long-term consequences of prolonged use. [112]

After my positive experience with the diet, I began to counsel other patients and acquaintances with the diet. The diet was empowering, a way to play an active role in treating your own cancer instead of sitting in the backseat while a busy, distracted doctor does much of the driving. Remember, no one will care about your life more than you!

Due to how good I was feeling, I decided to forgo more scans until late November 2021, nearly five months after my last scan. Checking earlier didn't make sense. After being informed that any more radiation would kill me, what would we do if the scan results were less than reassuring? Since I was doing well clinically, turning over rocks looking for snakes didn't seem to serve anyone. Additionally, I was engaged in alternative therapies outside of the restricted ketogenic diet; they included hyperbaric chamber oxygen therapy (HBOT) three times a week and multiple hot sauna therapies to boot.

I modeled this ancillary approach after Iyikesici [102] of Altinbas University in Istanbul, Turkey. He took forty-four end-stage non-small cell lung cancer (NSCLC) patients with distant metastases. He administered metabolically supported chemotherapy (MSCT: 12 hours of fasting and insulin administration), active counseling on the ketogenic diet, applied hyperthermia treatments, and HBOT. The protocol is effectively directly killing the cancer with chemotherapy, starving it from fuel sources with insulin, fasting, and the KD, exploiting the heat sensitivity of cancer cells with local hyperthermia to 42 Celsius (107.6 Fahrenheit) and administering supra-atmospheric pressures oxygen levels (HBOT) combatting the anoxic environment created by the tumor microenvironment. *Literally, he was declaring war on all fronts responsible for cancer growth.*

After eight months, he found some impressive response rates. The overall response rate (complete and partial response rates) was 61.4%. To a lesser extent, 15.9% had stable disease. [102] This was even with 40.9% having brain metastasis. Overall survival was 42.9 months; at the termination of the study, 15 had died, and 29 were still alive. Recall that NSCLC (lung cancer) and breast cancer consistently compete in lives claimed from cancer each year.

The combination of treatment modalities was perfectly logical to me. Although I was not on chemotherapy at the time, I could certainly employ some of these other strategies with no problem. Costly, yes. Doable, sure.

376

Inspired by the aforementioned study, I would create my own protocol: forcing unwanted oxygen into my cancer cells with HBOT *three times a week*, [113] maintaining a constant concentration of therapeutic ketones, and whole body hyperthermia surviving the sauna for at least thirty minutes or as long as I could stand at least the times a week. [114, 115] These modifications were the best I could manage with the resources at my disposal.

After already having been on the KD for many months, the addition of HBOT and sauna sessions, not to mention a blistering Bikram yoga practice, were revitalizing. I hadn't felt better in the past couple of years. Despite how good I felt, scans were awaiting in the near future. Therefore, I pushed all my chips into the pot and into this alternative treatment plan. Every ounce of my day in some form of therapy, either actively or passively, hoping to crack this crab's shell.

Even though I was satisfied with my efforts, I had a contingency plan. I planned to purchase my own 3-BP (3-Bromopyuvate), a small, selective anticancer agent developed by Young H Ko [116] with Peter L Pederson that selectively inhibits the growth of large animal tumors by the manipulation of two key enzymes, Hexokinase-2 and mitochondrial ATP synthasome. [117, 118] 3-BP works alongside the KD in targeting cancer cell metabolism. There had been some impressive results with preclinical data and an isolated case study with its utilization in a liver cancer patient. [80, 119-122]

However, at this point, 3-BP has not had illustrious, widespread FDA approval in the States save for a small clinic out in Arizona. *Or at least at the time of this writing.* Research from this small clinic is pending, with most information on the current website mostly anecdotal in success. One of the earliest studies investigating 3-BP was conducted in the 1990s. But research stagnated for some ludicrous reasons described in "Tripping over the Truth;" [80] this small molecule's discovery had been over 30 years ago. Time was/is not a luxury for me. How could I get a hold of this anti-cancer agent, which successfully targets cancer cell metabolism? I would remove all doubt in my affinity for delusion if I believed that the powers that be would gear research and drug development towards a cancer as rare as mine. Rare cancers are not priori. But was I delusional enough to consider purchasing my own 3-BP and self-administering the medication? Yes, I even had plans on where to purchase the product from overseas.

I agree; that would have been a disaster. I am no more a molecular chemist than a horse is a basketball. But it wouldn't be necessary to take up an entirely different scientific trade because that November of 2021, my scans were *clean*. What does that mean, *clean*? Well, with the dedicated CT of my chest, abdomen, and pelvis, with the exception of the remnants of previous radiation to my left hip, *something I hadn't mentioned before but needed nonetheless*, the scan was clear of active cancer. As far as my brain disease, where we thought my brain disease had continued to progress, my neurooncologist informed me that my brain had stabilized, *no signs of growth*.

No signs of growth. No progression. Chest clear. Metastases not visualized.

Bear good fortune modestly.
Ausonius, Epigrams. No. ii, 1. 8.

Stunned, completely. For the first time in two and a half years, hope seemed to have poked a stream of light into my dark-lit canopy. These alternative therapies might have potentiated the effects of my previous treatments or have their own therapeutic efficacy altogether. There was no way to know for sure, but I had found a sustainable play in, at the very least, seriously halting my cancer's growth. Very work intensive and moderately costly, but so were hefty hospital bills. I began looking to the future again, devising ways I could make a life for myself and maintain a stranglehold on my cancer. Being a surgeon was out of the question, but as I stacked up clear scans and continued to live seizure-free, I might assume confidence to continue my path in being a physician in some shape or form.

In the meantime, I could counsel patients or anyone on the benefits of the ketogenic diet. With my educational background and personal experience, dietary counseling could be a fun stepping-stone. And it was! For months after the good news, I worked on my business model and directed a handful of patients looking to make a change in their lives. I counseled many cancer patients looking to gain advantages in exploiting cancer metabolism. As I started this service, I never had the heart to charge despite phone conversations lasting hours. I quickly realized the insatiable need to not only speaking and teaching on healthy diets within and outside of the cancer world but also navigating the complicated scope of clinical trials available around the United States featured on websites like clinicaltrial.gov. Many do not have the health literacy to discern up and down; a knowledgeable resource is needed to steward patients in the right direction.

Excited by the prospects and the success I had already had, I purchased some textbooks on cancer nutrition in preparation for what might be a temporary occupation. I wanted to know everything! Meanwhile, I completed all the requirements to be a physician in the state of Florida, although I wouldn't be board certified. What's a certification other than a sheet of paper anyway? I can teach myself. The next year as I rack up clean scans, I could continue with my self-made treatment plan, counsel patients on nutrition, and perhaps re-enter a nearby residency to complete my training.

There was no silver lining to look to anymore, only blue skies.

1.   Mattson, M.P., et al., *Intermittent metabolic switching, neuroplasticity and brain health.* Nat Rev Neurosci, 2018. **19**(2): p. 63-80.

2.   Gulyaeva, N.V., *Molecular Mechanisms of Neuroplasticity: An Expanding Universe.* Biochemistry (Mosc), 2017. **82**(3): p. 237-242.

3.   Norman Doidge, M.D., *The Brain's Way of Healing: Remarkable Discoveries and Recoveries From the Frontiers of Neuroplasticity.* 375 Hudson Street, New York, New York 10014: Penguin Books.

4.   Paoli, A., A. Bianco, and K.A. Grimaldi, *The Ketogenic Diet and Sport: A Possible Marriage?* Exerc Sport Sci Rev, 2015. **43**(3): p. 153-62.

5.   Veech, R.L., *The therapeutic implications of ketone bodies: the effects of ketone bodies in pathological conditions: ketosis, ketogenic diet, redox states, insulin resistance, and mitochondrial metabolism.* Prostaglandins Leukot Essent Fatty Acids, 2004. **70**(3): p. 309-19.

6.   Laffel, L., *Ketone bodies: a review of physiology, pathophysiology and application of monitoring to diabetes.* Diabetes Metab Res Rev, 1999. **15**(6): p. 412-26.

7.   Kuchkuntla, A.R., et al., *Ketogenic Diet: an Endocrinologist Perspective.* Curr Nutr Rep, 2019. **8**(4): p. 402-410.

8.   Bikman, B.T. and K.H. Fisher-Wellman, *The Metabolic Effects of Ketones.* Int J Mol Sci, 2021. **22**(15).

9.   Wilson, J.M., et al., *Effects of Ketogenic Dieting on Body Composition, Strength, Power, and Hormonal Profiles in Resistance Training Men.* J Strength Cond Res, 2020. **34**(12): p. 3463-3474.

10.   Vargas-Molina, S., et al., *Effects of a ketogenic diet on body composition and strength in trained women.* J Int Soc Sports Nutr, 2020. **17**(1): p. 19.

11.   Hallböök, T., et al., *The effects of the ketogenic diet on behavior and cognition.* Epilepsy Res, 2012. **100**(3): p. 304-9.

12.   Dowis, K. and S. Banga, *The Potential Health Benefits of the Ketogenic Diet: A Narrative Review.* Nutrients, 2021. **13**(5).

13.   Nangia, S., et al., *Is the ketogenic diet effective in specific epilepsy syndromes?* Epilepsy Res, 2012. **100**(3): p. 252-7.

14.   Westman, E.C., et al., *Low-carbohydrate nutrition and metabolism.* Am J Clin Nutr, 2007. **86**(2): p. 276-84.

15.   Kossoff, E.H. and J.L. Dorward, *The modified Atkins diet.* Epilepsia, 2008. **49 Suppl 8**: p. 37-41.

16.   Ułamek-Kozioł, M., et al., *Ketogenic Diet and Epilepsy.* Nutrients, 2019. **11**(10).

17.   Zhang, Y., et al., *The Anticonvulsant Effects of Ketogenic Diet on Epileptic Seizures and Potential Mechanisms.* Curr Neuropharmacol, 2018. **16**(1): p. 66-70.

18.   Neal, E.G., et al., *The ketogenic diet for the treatment of childhood epilepsy: a randomised controlled trial.* Lancet Neurol, 2008. **7**(6): p. 500-6.

19.   Rezaei, S., et al., *Short-term and long-term efficacy of classical ketogenic diet and modified Atkins diet in children and adolescents with epilepsy: A systematic review and meta-analysis.* Nutr Neurosci, 2019. **22**(5): p. 317-334.

20.   Hutchings, M.I., A.W. Truman, and B. Wilkinson, *Antibiotics: past, present and future.* Curr Opin Microbiol, 2019. **51**: p. 72-80.

21.   Parascandola, J., *From marine hospital to public health service.* Med Secoli, 1999. **1**(1): p. 197-207.

22.   (CDC), C.f.D.C.a.P. *Overweight and Obesity.* 2022 [cited 2022; Available from: https://www.cdc.gov/obesity/data/adult.html.

23.   Biener, A., J. Cawley, and C. Meyerhoefer, *The High and Rising Costs of Obesity to the US Health Care System.* J Gen Intern Med, 2017. **32**(Suppl 1): p. 6-8.

24.   Cucinotta, D. and M. Vanelli, *WHO Declares COVID-19 a Pandemic.* Acta Biomed, 2020. **91**(1): p. 157-160.

25.   Peña, J.E., et al., *Hypertension, Diabetes and Obesity, Major Risk Factors for Death in Patients with COVID-19 in Mexico.* Arch Med Res, 2021. **52**(4): p. 443-449.

26.   Richardson, S., et al., *Presenting Characteristics, Comorbidities, and Outcomes Among 5700 Patients Hospitalized With COVID-19 in the New York City Area.* Jama, 2020. **323**(20): p. 2052-2059.

27.   Rovas, A., et al., *Microvascular dysfunction in COVID-19: the MYSTIC study.* Angiogenesis, 2021. **24**(1): p. 145-157.

28.   Madonna, R., et al., *Diabetic microangiopathy: Pathogenetic insights and novel therapeutic approaches.* Vascul Pharmacol, 2017. **90**: p. 1-7.

29.   Viigimaa, M., et al., *Macrovascular Complications of Type 2 Diabetes Mellitus.* Curr Vasc Pharmacol, 2020. **18**(2): p. 110-116.

30.   McCracken, E., M. Monaghan, and S. Sreenivasan, *Pathophysiology of the metabolic syndrome.* Clin Dermatol, 2018. **36**(1): p. 14-20.

31.   Lohia, P., et al., *Metabolic syndrome and clinical outcomes in patients infected with COVID-19: Does age, sex, and race of the patient with metabolic syndrome matter?* J Diabetes, 2021.

32.   Dietz, W.H., *The response of the US Centers for Disease Control and Prevention to the obesity epidemic.* Annu Rev Public Health, 2015. **36**: p. 575-96.

33.   Leung, N.H.L., *Transmissibility and transmission of respiratory viruses.* Nat Rev Microbiol, 2021. **19**(8): p. 528-545.

34.   Avena, N.M., P. Rada, and B.G. Hoebel, *Evidence for sugar addiction: behavioral and neurochemical effects of intermittent, excessive sugar intake.* Neurosci Biobehav Rev, 2008. **32**(1): p. 20-39.

35.   Volkow, N.D., R.A. Wise, and R. Baler, *The dopamine motive system: implications for drug and food addiction.* Nat Rev Neurosci, 2017. **18**(12): p. 741-752.

36.   Paul, R., *The Case Against Socialism* 2019: Broadside Books.

37.   Lustig, R.H., *Ultraprocessed Food: Addictive, Toxic, and Ready for Regulation.* Nutrients, 2020. **12**(11).

38.   Feinman, R.D., et al., *Dietary carbohydrate restriction as the first approach in diabetes management: critical review and evidence base.* Nutrition, 2015. **31**(1): p. 1-13.

39.   Heymsfield, S.B. and T.A. Wadden, *Mechanisms, Pathophysiology, and Management of Obesity.* N Engl J Med, 2017. **376**(3): p. 254-266.

40.   Ludwig, D.S. and M.I. Friedman, *Increasing adiposity: consequence or cause of overeating?* Jama, 2014. **311**(21): p. 2167-8.

41.   Walton, C.M., et al., *Ketones Elicit Distinct Alterations in Adipose Mitochondrial Bioenergetics.* Int J Mol Sci, 2020. **21**(17).

42.   Bahr, L.S., et al., *Ketogenic diet and fasting diet as Nutritional Approaches in Multiple Sclerosis (NAMS): protocol of a randomized controlled study.* Trials, 2020. **21**(1): p. 3.

43.   Westman, E.C., et al., *A review of low-carbohydrate ketogenic diets.* Curr Atheroscler Rep, 2003. **5**(6): p. 476-83.

44.   Xiong, J., *Fatty Acid Oxidation in Cell Fate Determination.* Trends Biochem Sci, 2018. **43**(11): p. 854-857.

45.   Kirkpatrick, C.F., et al., *Review of current evidence and clinical recommendations on the effects of low-carbohydrate and very-low-carbohydrate (including ketogenic) diets for the management of body weight and other cardiometabolic risk factors: A scientific statement from the National Lipid Association Nutrition and Lifestyle Task Force.* J Clin Lipidol, 2019. **13**(5): p. 689-711.e1.

46.   Gregg, E.W., et al., *Association of the magnitude of weight loss and changes in physical fitness with long-term cardiovascular disease outcomes in overweight or obese people with type 2 diabetes: a post-hoc analysis of the Look AHEAD randomised clinical trial.* Lancet Diabetes Endocrinol, 2016. **4**(11): p. 913-921.

47.   Chen, C., et al., *Weight change across adulthood in relation to all cause and cause specific mortality: prospective cohort study.* Bmj, 2019. **367**: p. l5584.

48.   Westman, E.C., et al., *Effect of 6-month adherence to a very low carbohydrate diet program.* Am J Med, 2002. **113**(1): p. 30-6.

49.   Bravata, D.M., et al., *Efficacy and safety of low-carbohydrate diets: a systematic review.* Jama, 2003. **289**(14): p. 1837-50.

50.   Dashti, H.M., et al., *Long-term effects of a ketogenic diet in obese patients.* Exp Clin Cardiol, 2004. **9**(3): p. 200-5.

51.   Sampaio, L.P., *Ketogenic diet for epilepsy treatment.* Arq Neuropsiquiatr, 2016. **74**(10): p. 842-848.

52.   Yancy, W.S., Jr., et al., *A low-carbohydrate, ketogenic diet versus a low-fat diet to treat obesity and hyperlipidemia: a randomized, controlled trial.* Ann Intern Med, 2004. **140**(10): p. 769-77.

53.   Nordmann, A.J., et al., *Effects of low-carbohydrate vs low-fat diets on weight loss and cardiovascular risk factors: a meta-analysis of randomized controlled trials.* Arch Intern Med, 2006. **166**(3): p. 285-93.

54.   Sultani, R., et al., *Elevated Triglycerides to High-Density Lipoprotein Cholesterol (TG/HDL-C) Ratio Predicts Long-Term Mortality in High-Risk Patients.* Heart Lung Circ, 2020. **29**(3): p. 414-421.

55.   Castro, A.I., et al., *Effect of A Very Low-Calorie Ketogenic Diet on Food and Alcohol Cravings, Physical and Sexual Activity, Sleep Disturbances, and Quality of Life in Obese Patients.* Nutrients, 2018. **10**(10).

56.   Ebbeling, C.B., et al., *Effects of dietary composition on energy expenditure during weight-loss maintenance.* Jama, 2012. **307**(24): p. 2627-34.

57.   Paoli, A., et al., *Beyond weight loss: a review of the therapeutic uses of very-low-carbohydrate (ketogenic) diets.* Eur J Clin Nutr, 2013. **67**(8): p. 789-96.

58.   O'Neill, B. and P. Raggi, *The ketogenic diet: Pros and cons.* Atherosclerosis, 2020. **292**: p. 119-126.

59.   Senftleber, N.K., et al., *Diet and physical activity in Greenland: genetic interactions and associations with obesity and diabetes.* Appl Physiol Nutr Metab, 2021. **46**(8): p. 849-855.

60.   Akande, V.O., et al., *Determinants of dietary behavior and physical activity among Canadian Inuit: a systematic review.* Int J Behav Nutr Phys Act, 2015. **12**: p. 84.

61.   Tvermosegaard, M., et al., *Cardiovascular Disease Susceptibility and Resistance in Circumpolar Inuit Populations.* Can J Cardiol, 2015. **31**(9): p. 1116-23.

62.   Montani, J.P., *Ancel Keys: The legacy of a giant in physiology, nutrition, and public health.* Obes Rev, 2021. **22 Suppl 2**: p. e13196.

63.   Forouhi, N.G., et al., *Dietary fat and cardiometabolic health: evidence, controversies, and consensus for guidance.* Bmj, 2018. **361**: p. k2139.

64.   *NATIONAL Heart Act.* Public Health Rep, 1948. **63**(33): p. 1059-63.

65.   Kuipers, R.S., et al., *Saturated fat, carbohydrates and cardiovascular disease.* Neth J Med, 2011. **69**(9): p. 372-8.

66.   Lennerz, B.S., et al., *Management of Type 1 Diabetes With a Very Low-Carbohydrate Diet.* Pediatrics, 2018. **141**(6).

67.   Dehghan, M., et al., *Associations of fats and carbohydrate intake with cardiovascular disease and mortality in 18 countries from five continents (PURE): a prospective cohort study.* Lancet, 2017. **390**(10107): p. 2050-2062.

68. Ravnskov, U., et al., *Lack of an association or an inverse association between low-density-lipoprotein cholesterol and mortality in the elderly: a systematic review.* BMJ Open, 2016. **6**(6): p. e010401.

69. Bray, G.A., *Fructose: pure, white, and deadly? Fructose, by any other name, is a health hazard.* J Diabetes Sci Technol, 2010. **4**(4): p. 1003-7.

70. Yudkin, J., *PATTERNS AND TRENDS IN CARBOHYDRATE CONSUMPTION AND THEIR RELATION TO DISEASE.* Proc Nutr Soc, 1964. **23**: p. 149-62.

71. Yudkin, J., *Sugar and disease.* Nature, 1972. **239**(5369): p. 197-9.

72. Panyagharm, Y., *[Sugar and dental caries].* J Dent Assoc Thai, 1981. **31**(5): p. 244-53, 255.

73. Keys, A., *Sucrose in the diet and coronary heart disease.* Atherosclerosis, 1971. **14**(2): p. 193-202.

74. Taubes, G., *The Case Against* 2016: Knopf Doubleday Publishing Group.

75. Sieri, S., et al., *Glycemic index, glycemic load, and risk of coronary heart disease: a pan-European cohort study.* Am J Clin Nutr, 2020. **112**(3): p. 631-643.

76. Kearns, C.E., L.A. Schmidt, and S.A. Glantz, *Sugar Industry and Coronary Heart Disease Research: A Historical Analysis of Internal Industry Documents.* JAMA Intern Med, 2016. **176**(11): p. 1680-1685.

77. Roukos, D.H., *Genome-wide association studies: how predictable is a person's cancer risk?* Expert Rev Anticancer Ther, 2009. **9**(4): p. 389-92.

78. Roukos, D.H., S. Murray, and E. Briasoulis, *Molecular genetic tools shape a roadmap towards a more accurate prognostic prediction and personalized management of cancer.* Cancer Biol Ther, 2007. **6**(3): p. 308-12.

79. Seyfried, T.N., *Cancer as a Metabolic Disease: On the Origin, Management and Prevention of Cancer.* 2012, John Wiley & Sons, Inc.,Hoboken, New Jersey: A John Wiley & Sons, Inc., Publication.

80. MS, T.C., *Tripping Over The Truth: How the Metabolic Theory of Cancer Is Overturnnig One of Medicine's Most Entrenched Paradigms.* 2017, White River Junction, Vermont

London, United Kingdom: Chelsea Green Publishing. 3.

81. Seyfried, T.N., et al., *Metabolic therapy: a new paradigm for managing malignant brain cancer.* Cancer Lett, 2015. **356**(2 Pt A): p. 289-300.

82. Poff, A.M., et al., *Ketone supplementation decreases tumor cell viability and prolongs survival of mice with metastatic cancer.* Int J Cancer, 2014. **135**(7): p. 1711-20.

83. Poff, A., et al., *Targeting the Warburg effect for cancer treatment: Ketogenic diets for management of glioma.* Semin Cancer Biol, 2019. **56**: p. 135-148.

84. Poff, A.M., et al., *The ketogenic diet and hyperbaric oxygen therapy prolong survival in mice with systemic metastatic cancer.* PLoS One, 2013. **8**(6): p. e65522.

85. Seyfried, T.N. and L.C. Huysentruyt, *On the origin of cancer metastasis.* Crit Rev Oncog, 2013. **18**(1-2): p. 43-73.

86. Khodabakhshi, A., et al., *Effects of Ketogenic metabolic therapy on patients with breast cancer: A randomized controlled clinical trial.* Clin Nutr, 2021. **40**(3): p. 751-758.

87. Seyfried, T.N., et al., *Cancer as a metabolic disease: implications for novel therapeutics.* Carcinogenesis, 2014. **35**(3): p. 515-27.

88. Mariam Kalamian, E., MS, CNS, *Keto for Cancer: Ketogenic Metabolic Therapy as a Targeted Nutritional Strategy*, ed. J. Lipfert. 2017, White River Junction, VT 05001: Chelsea Green Publishing.

89. Khodabakhshi, A., et al., *Feasibility, Safety, and Beneficial Effects of MCT-Based Ketogenic Diet for Breast Cancer Treatment: A Randomized Controlled Trial Study.* Nutr Cancer, 2020. **72**(4): p. 627-634.

90. Khodabakhshi, A., et al., *Does a ketogenic diet have beneficial effects on quality of life, physical activity or biomarkers in patients with breast cancer: a randomized controlled clinical trial.* Nutr J, 2020. **19**(1): p. 87.

91. Seyfried, T.N., et al., *Provocative Question: Should Ketogenic Metabolic Therapy Become the Standard of Care for Glioblastoma?* Neurochem Res, 2019. **44**(10): p. 2392-2404.

92. Pedersen, P.L., *Warburg, me and Hexokinase 2: Multiple discoveries of key molecular events underlying one of cancers' most common phenotypes, the "Warburg Effect", i.e., elevated*

glycolysis in the presence of oxygen. J Bioenerg Biomembr, 2007. **39**(3): p. 211-22.

93.   Kroemer, G. and J. Pouyssegur, *Tumor cell metabolism: cancer's Achilles' heel.* Cancer Cell, 2008. **13**(6): p. 472-82.

94.   Hinshaw, D.C. and L.A. Shevde, *The Tumor Microenvironment Innately Modulates Cancer Progression.* Cancer Res, 2019. **79**(18): p. 4557-4566.

95.   Mankoff, D.A., et al., *Tumor-specific positron emission tomography imaging in patients: [18F] fluorodeoxyglucose and beyond.* Clin Cancer Res, 2007. **13**(12): p. 3460-9.

96.   Hanahan, D. and R.A. Weinberg, *The hallmarks of cancer.* Cell, 2000. **100**(1): p. 57-70.

97.   Hanahan, D. and R.A. Weinberg, *Hallmarks of cancer: the next generation.* Cell, 2011. **144**(5): p. 646-74.

98.   Allen, B.G., et al., *Ketogenic diets enhance oxidative stress and radio-chemo-therapy responses in lung cancer xenografts.* Clin Cancer Res, 2013. **19**(14): p. 3905-13.

99.   Muscogiuri, G., et al., *Ketogenic diet: a tool for the management of neuroendocrine neoplasms?* Crit Rev Food Sci Nutr, 2022. **62**(4): p. 1035-1045.

100.   Woolf, E.C., N. Syed, and A.C. Scheck, *Tumor Metabolism, the Ketogenic Diet and β-Hydroxybutyrate: Novel Approaches to Adjuvant Brain Tumor Therapy.* Front Mol Neurosci, 2016. **9**: p. 122.

101.   Plotti, F., et al., *Diet and Chemotherapy: The Effects of Fasting and Ketogenic Diet on Cancer Treatment.* Chemotherapy, 2020. **65**(3-4): p. 77-84.

102.   Iyikesici, M.S., *Long-Term Survival Outcomes of Metabolically Supported Chemotherapy with Gemcitabine-Based or FOLFIRINOX Regimen Combined with Ketogenic Diet, Hyperthermia, and Hyperbaric Oxygen Therapy in Metastatic Pancreatic Cancer.* Complement Med Res, 2020. **27**(1): p. 31-39.

103.   Dąbek, A., et al., *Modulation of Cellular Biochemistry, Epigenetics and Metabolomics by Ketone Bodies. Implications of the Ketogenic Diet in the Physiology of the Organism and Pathological States.* Nutrients, 2020. **12**(3).

104. Klement, R.J., *Beneficial effects of ketogenic diets for cancer patients: a realist review with focus on evidence and confirmation.* Med Oncol, 2017. **34**(8): p. 132.

105. Klement, R.J., N. Brehm, and R.A. Sweeney, *Ketogenic diets in medical oncology: a systematic review with focus on clinical outcomes.* Med Oncol, 2020. **37**(2): p. 14.

106. Panhans, C.M., et al., *Exploring the Feasibility and Effects of a Ketogenic Diet in Patients With CNS Malignancies: A Retrospective Case Series.* Front Neurosci, 2020. **14**: p. 390.

107. Römer, M., J. Dörfler, and J. Huebner, *The use of ketogenic diets in cancer patients: a systematic review.* Clin Exp Med, 2021. **21**(4): p. 501-536.

108. Sremanakova, J., A.M. Sowerbutts, and S. Burden, *A systematic review of the use of ketogenic diets in adult patients with cancer.* J Hum Nutr Diet, 2018. **31**(6): p. 793-802.

109. Klement, R.J., et al., *Ketogenic diets consumed during radio-chemotherapy have beneficial effects on quality of life and metabolic health in patients with rectal cancer.* Eur J Nutr, 2022. **61**(1): p. 69-84.

110. Al-Toubah, T., B. Morse, and J. Strosberg, *Capecitabine and Temozolomide in Advanced Lung Neuroendocrine Neoplasms.* Oncologist, 2020. **25**(1): p. e48-e52.

111. Cives, M. and J.R. Strosberg, *Gastroenteropancreatic Neuroendocrine Tumors.* CA Cancer J Clin, 2018. **68**(6): p. 471-487.

112. Johnson, D.B., M.J. Lopez, and B. Kelley, *Dexamethasone*, in *StatPearls*. 2022, StatPearls Publishing
Copyright © 2022, StatPearls Publishing LLC.: Treasure Island (FL).

113. Chen, S.Y., et al., *Hyperbaric oxygen suppressed tumor progression through the improvement of tumor hypoxia and induction of tumor apoptosis in A549-cell-transferred lung cancer.* Sci Rep, 2021. **11**(1): p. 12033.

114. van der Horst, A., et al., *The clinical benefit of hyperthermia in pancreatic cancer: a systematic review.* Int J Hyperthermia, 2018. **34**(7): p. 969-979.

115. Kurashova, N.A., I.M. Madaeva, and L.I. Kolesnikova, *[Expression of heat shock proteins HSP70 under oxidative stress.].* Adv Gerontol, 2019. **32**(4): p. 502-508.

116.   Ko, Y.H. and B.A. McFadden, *Alkylation of isocitrate lyase from Escherichia coli by 3-bromopyruvate.* Arch Biochem Biophys, 1990. **278**(2): p. 373-80.

117.   Mathupala, S.P., Y.H. Ko, and P.L. Pedersen, *Hexokinase-2 bound to mitochondria: cancer's stygian link to the "Warburg Effect" and a pivotal target for effective therapy.* Semin Cancer Biol, 2009. **19**(1): p. 17-24.

118.   Ko, Y.H., et al., *Advanced cancers: eradication in all cases using 3-bromopyruvate therapy to deplete ATP.* Biochem Biophys Res Commun, 2004. **324**(1): p. 269-75.

119.   Ko, Y.H., et al., *A translational study "case report" on the small molecule "energy blocker" 3-bromopyruvate (3BP) as a potent anticancer agent: from bench side to bedside.* J Bioenerg Biomembr, 2012. **44**(1): p. 163-70.

120.   Geschwind, J.F., et al., *Novel therapy for liver cancer: direct intraarterial injection of a potent inhibitor of ATP production.* Cancer Res, 2002. **62**(14): p. 3909-13.

121.   Cal, M., et al., *The Anticancer Drug 3-Bromopyruvate Induces DNA Damage Potentially Through Reactive Oxygen Species in Yeast and in Human Cancer Cells.* Cells, 2020. **9**(5).

122.   Cal, M., et al., *Mitochondrial Function Are Disturbed in the Presence of the Anticancer Drug, 3-Bromopyruvate.* Int J Mol Sci, 2021. **22**(12).

_____13_____

The End's Beginning

He dies every day who lives a lingering life.
Pierrard Poullet, La Charite 'Tis solitude should teach us how to die It hath no flatterers; vanity can give No hollow aid; alone --- man with his God must strive.
Byron, Childe Harold. Canto iv, st. 33.

I reveled at the notion of the doors of my future being reopened. However, this is no fairy tale. This is a story about someone afflicted with cancer, metastatic lung cancer that had gone to brain and bone by the time I was diagnosed in 2019. If the past is any indication of what the future holds, one can simply make an educated guess of the events to follow. I am writing this particular passage near the summer of 2022, exactly three years from the week I was officially diagnosed, or misdiagnosed rather. My chances of survival to five years are well below 10%.

Even though I am naturally positive, and as we have seen somewhat delusional, the years of constant disappointment and pain had worn on my native constitution. In a stepwise fashion, I had witnessed much of my function slowly wither away either by the cancer or the treatment thereof. I should have learned my lesson from the many times I'd open the stable doors and allow the mustangs of optimism roam freely the pastures of my potential future. Once again, I'd allow the wagon roll in front of the horse never looking over my shoulder for any worrisome signs of nascent disease. Particularly, my right shoulder.

During my latest follow-up where both a brain magnetic resonance imaging (MRI) and dedicated computed tomography (CT) scan were conducted, we failed to retrieve a positron emission tomography (PET) scan. Remember that a PET scan indicates areas of hypermetabolic activity, or rapidly dividing cells, i.e. cancer. If we had, we would have clearly noted a metastasis that was slowly brewing in my right shoulder.

My right shoulder had been aching for months, although I had assumed that it had been a result of my poor walking mechanics and long treks by the beach with my weighted vest. After the brain surgery, my entire right side was, for lack of a better word, wonky. As my spastic gait attempted to correct over time, I assumed my shoulder pain would follow in course, or at the very least stay the same. At any rate, the dull ache was only an ache, and as such was tolerable.

I had taken an interest in calisthenics; I figured this would be a way to exercise while working on proprioception, balance, and strength. The combination of very simple movements like pushups and pull-ups with painstaking detail to form and muscle activation was a new challenge for me. Due to all my newly acquired disabilities, basic gymnastic moves were all I could muster anyways. However, between calisthenics and TRX bands, I maintained a respectable workout routine.

While balancing on a waist high bar lifting myself from the ground, I would slowly dismount landing safely and carefully back on the ground. This was an isometric hold I would practice each time I was in the gym; one of my chief moves to my upper body routine. However following the completion of the static bar hold, I decided to stretch backwards deviating from my normal sequence of movements. Suddenly, the bar slipped from its sturdy resting place and me along with it. In order to catch myself from my backwards trajectory, my arms swung wildly which elicited severe pain in my right arm.

Being in corner of the gym and most bystanders actively entranced by either phones or music, none noticed the severe pain the short fall had elicited. My right arm was screaming at me which I thought was odd because the distance from me and the ground was modest at best. Luckily, a friend was present and drove me to the emergency department half a block down the round. I assumed a dislocation. Despite the piercing pains, the x-ray revealed no such finding. If fact, it was a completely normal scan. *Embarrassing, am I that much of a wuss?*

The following couple of weeks I stayed away from loading my right shoulder hoping that the lingering ache would improve. Unfortunately, the twinge remained persistent and annoying. All my efforts at stretching provided no relief. Eventually, I had an orthopedist order an arthrogram, where they inject dye directly into the joint space to get a clear picture as to what was going on. Unfortunately and very unexpectedly, the nagging pain for upwards of six months was a 3 to 4 centimeter (grape or walnut-sized) metastasis well bedded in the humeral head with further mets tracking down my right arm.

This would be crippling for both my body and state of mind. The resulting treatment regimen via radiation directly to the shoulder left me with a paralyzing frozen shoulder, or adhesive capsulitis, taking months of ongoing rehab to address. Imagine your shoulder joint being tightly fixed surrounded by stiffened cobwebs; cobwebs that are innervated and incite sharp pains for each degree of articulation regained. For two months, I hadn't moved my shoulder because of weakness and pain caused by the invasive cancer; all the while those spiders were spinning their webs around my joint being actively fibrosed by radiation treatment. Once the cancer pain was replaced by the pain of immobility, *you begin to learn the difference in pain profiles,* I would begin another long journey of rehabilitation. Rehabilitation that involved daily unravelling of those cobwebs like barbed wire fences scratching and screeching across my arm and shoulder. Hours are spent knocking down those painful webs only to find the spiders had spun another pattern by the next morning. Meanwhile, I was forced to link back up with a familiar friend: chemotherapy.

Additionally, we would welcome another addition to the treatment team. Bisphosphonates were infused to harden my bones as they were weakened by the incessant cancer. Following its administration, I had almost every negative reaction to the infusion listed on the drug information pamphlet. For two days, I felt like I came down with a horrible bout of break bone fever;[1] every inspiration ignited a fire in each rib space. From head to toes, every joint carried the singe. As if I procured a private maître d' of pain serving sizzling steaks fresh off the grill, the hot grease would baste each joint capsule with searing hot sauce traveling from around my knee to my elbows, from my elbows to my shoulders, and every combination in between. A blistering performance of interdigitating immolation made for an imaginative ballet across my body for which no amount of Tylenol could sprinkle an iota of relief. Unable to make it to my bed, I laid in sweat and misery for two long days. My mom had to change the sheets twice on the sofa.

Because I now have two appendages unable to perform normally, both my right arm and leg, I can no longer compensate to account for the pain on my right arm and the movement disability in my right leg. Therefore, until my functionality improves with countless hours of rehabilitation, I will remain wheelchair bound. Out my window I can hear and see the crashing waves not 200 meters away, but they might as well on another planet. Sure, I could have assistance in getting out there and enjoying some sunshine, but that's not the point. It's the fact that I need assistance to do something so simple which irks me so.

While immobile, other pains and injuries began to remerge. All the progress experienced with improving my gait pattern had all but been abolished after the first couple of weeks of forced inactivity. Familiar pains in my ribs, which were former sites of metastases, had returned as well as pain deep within my pelvis from multiple previous areas of cancerous outcroppings. One of which had needed spot radiation; others had previously gone away with chemotherapy. The metastatic lesions, particularly in the pelvis, kept no secrets as to their presence as turning my hips in bed would randomly incite piercing pains.

Not being able to move freely has been one of my greatest fears. Ever since I was a kid, I was always on the move. Whether it was a bike, skateboard, running, you name it, I never stopped moving. Throughout my entire treatment journey, I thought as long as I can keep moving, then I won't die. Afterall, an object in motion will remain in motion unless acted upon by another force. I never expected that such a force would present itself as a large shoulder met.

It would appear the last lesson for me to learn from this experience is a lesson in being still. Being still. Being still and letting go of any power or control remaining in my life. For me, being still might be the worst torture of all. Perhaps, a final lesson?

All writing comes from the grace of God.
Emerson, Essays, Second Series: Experience

Since my diagnosis on May, 31st 2019, I had been misdiagnosed leading me off on an entirely separate treatment paradigm which would have left me with irreversible chest radiation and far-reaching long term sequalae, and likely, an earlier grave. If my pathology was not reviewed and changed from small cell lung cancer to atypical carcinoid of the lung, suggesting surgical therapy over chest irradiation as the preferred therapy, undoubtedly, I wouldn't have made it as far as I have. Indeed, the risks of a thoracic operation on a freshly irradiated chest, which ended up requiring thirteen hours of operative time, could've ultimately culminated in an early death due to increased operative risks.

The hesitation in the interpretation of the minute brain lesions when a definitive biopsy was out of the question and subsequent staging disagreements surrounding my case fostered uncertainty among consulting teams resulting in designating my cancer stage 3III instead of stage 4. This fortunate downstaging would allow for me to go under the knife. My chest operation, left lower lobectomy with lingulectomy with full mediastinal lymphadenectomy, allowed for the debulking of the tumor mass even though there were remnant cancerous lymph nodes nascent in my chest. *Debulking of the tumor burden itself might've proven therapeutic allowing for more treatment time and less chance for an obstructive process within the lung or major vessel.*

During the 13-hour thoracic operation on August 8th, 2019, I spent eight hours on my right-side causing compartment syndrome which comprised the survival of my right leg due to the extended period of lack of blood flow. Fasciotomies were performed to release the building pressure as well as a generous section of my lateral thigh muscle. Seven additional washouts and debridements were required to ultimately close my leg. A weekend in New York City, NY for one operation, quickly changed into a month.

After licking my wounds from the thoracic operation, five months later during a follow-up, my chest scan was reassuring, however not nearly resolved. The feared punctate lesions in my brain were growing having almost doubled in size confirming their malignant potential. Thus, the lesions confirmed my stage 4 cancer status. Quickly, I was started on chemotherapy. Due to the multitude of brain metastases, a lifesaving volume of radiation would be called for. Subsequently, I underwent whole brain radiation along with two rounds of radiosurgery culminating in three months of radiation therapy, radiation that would forever alter my energy levels, cognition, and eyesight.

Downstream effects of high dose radiation were inevitable. Areas of the brain delivered the most potent arcs of therapy began to expand in a process called radiation necrosis, but at the time it was hard to distinguish active necrosis from growing cancer. Nonetheless due to my increasing frequency of seizures, an operation was indicated for diagnosis and treatment purposes. To preserve motor function, I elected to undergo awake brain surgery on September 9th, 2020. The expanding lesion was confirmed to radiation necrosis, yet I was still maimed with right hemiparesis and spastic foot drop despite my efforts of sustained rehabilitation. Despite the reassuring evidence from the brain biopsy, new lesions were noted on a follow-up scan. In turn, I was informed nothing more could be done. Another ounce of radiation could kill me.

At this point in time, I continued with chemotherapeutic regimen completing 8 rounds of a CAPTEM regimen as well as Avastin to discourage cancer growth and brain swelling. I was hopeful that the moderate amount of brain penetration of the CAPTEM regimen might just be what I need. Systemically, or outside the brain, the regimen showed great signs of success having already cleaned up much of my lymph node basins in my chest. I had pelvic metastasis, especially in my left hip, but those had been radiated and had responded well.

Despite the wishful thinking and countless prayers, the brain's metastatic growth still marched along undeterred into the summer of 2021. Although I was stable systemically, I decided to stop all treatment. Maimed and discouraged, I questioned the point of a clean body scan if my brain disease was not under control?

My brother and I struck out west for a vacation, and I would return revitalized with plans for a last stitch effort in treating the cancer in alternative ways. I employed a restricted Ketogenic diet supplemented by hyperthermia, Bikram yoga practice, hyperbaric oxygen chamber therapy for four to five months. My next computed tomography (CT) scans and brain scans were stable. To our dismay however, we had failed to retrieve a PET scan which might've revealed our next obstacle.

Unfortunately, a shoulder metastasis had been lingering despite my plans in turning my future around. A small ache in my right shoulder was the only indication that anything was awry. Until I injured my arm at the gym, there was no reason to investigate something so infinitesimal. Reluctantly I received an arthrogram, which revealed a large four-centimeter metastasis with other metastases tracking down my arm. *Luckily, I had caught it at a crucial junction*; any more time without treatment would have left me with a high risk of a pathological break and/or a possible shoulder replacement if I decided to acquiesce to continued treatment. Only time will tell how it heals or if the tumor burden is too much.

Humanity and Immortality consist neither in reason, nor in love; not in the body, nor in the animation of the heart of it, nor in the thoughts and stirrings of the brain of it; — but in the dedication of them all to Him who will raise them up at the last day.
Ruskin, Stones of Venice, Vol. i, ch. 2.

Unsure on what this account would ultimately become, I was mostly fearful of what might be unveiled about myself. Writing had always been a way for me to organize and illuminate thoughts and actions to provide a much-needed sense of clarity. Usually, these ponderings would find a home in the trash bin once that had served their purpose. During these three years and ongoing treatments, I never gave myself time for pure self-reflection only focusing on schemes to return valiantly to practice, no more than a

399

daydream now. My treatment, just like all my education and athletic endeavors prior, was always centered on what was the *next step*. Instead in reverence of the now, I was always concerned with the future and how I could *control* it.

As much as I love medicine, more specifically cardiothoracic surgery, I wouldn't have spent countless hours writing about my battle with the very cancer I had been training to treat just for the sake of an educational exercise. There are far better and smarter teachers. Nearing a truncated life myself, what would be the point? Especially while battling the effects of hemi-spatial neglect while typing, my right hand will annoyingly trail off the keyboard just like me in conversation prior to my dietary changeup instituting the ketogenic diet.

As I remain nearly immobile on my couch before I continue my daily routine of hours of rehabilitation, I question what it is exactly I am holding on to? Why have I been clinging to this life? I imagine my aunt, who I never met, having similar thoughts prior to her taking her life after her fight with breast cancer. Why keep going? Despite my disarming demeanor, I have contemplated suicide if only to escape the pain, metaphorically and literal, of the reality that had become my life. Multiple instances people had applauded me for my unyielding positivity and motivation that I provided for their everyday life. However, this was only a quarter of the story, part of the story that I let them see. Like a best friend has always said to me, "Never let them see you sweat."

As I began to recount the events of the past few years and further, I began to pick up on these cookie crumbs left behind for me to note reassuring me that my coordinates in life were true as heartbreaking as the journey would prove to be. No matter how dire the straits, I always felt a comfort in being where I needed to be and doing what I needed to be doing throughout every bit of treatment. Assuredly, I was made for this struggle; I was made for this pain. And I was made to show people *why*, to the best of my approximation. These cookie crumbs assured me that something good was happening here even though it wasn't completely obvious at the moment. But these events couldn't have occurred in any other way.

The unlikelihood to my current survival and all the seemingly inconsequential events leading up to my diagnosis and treatment create a myriad of loosely associated events which would have profound effects on my ultimate outcome. One may not contend to my interpretation of these events and the conclusions thereof, but I can find no other reason. The events throughout the past years were too tenuous to be attributed luck or happenstance. I understand if people do not agree with these conclusions. Remarking upon things with a retrospective lens can lead to bias attributing significance to events when there isn't any. I get that.

As the story in these pages were unfolded to me, I was enlightened to their significance. I hope I can relay the significance in the most articulate way I can. I know most will write this off and chalk it up as mostly conjecture, and again that's okay. But the reality is, *I should be here. Even though my life has been immensely shortened in all probability, I should have died many moons ago.* I am living on borrowed time. There is little room for deviation or error in the sequence of events in the prior pages. I am convinced that there is a larger story at play here, one that transcends ego and suffering. The repeated happenstances and coincidences were, in fact, anything but. Things happened in precisely the way they were supposed to. Seemingly, the events of my life were a top-heavy Land cruiser traveling down a narrow mountain road tittering left and right with falling rocks and collapsing overpasses, but, yet, managing to stay on course. Meanwhile, I was blindfolded, ignorant to the significance and weight of the boulders tumbling around me.

I maintain that these events can only be attributed to God. Indeed, I do appreciate the argument that what I lay out as evidence of the ineffable reality, you may see as figments of my imaginative conjuring and purely circumstantial. Attributing anything more is disingenuous or misleading. Where I see an act of God, several in fact, you may only see conjecture and pontification, a culmination of thermodynamically favorable chemical interactions crystallizing into events that could only settle into one structure. And that's okay.

But could that be another manifestation of God? For an individual who has wavered in belief consistently throughout much of their life and, in retrospect, realizing the fragility of the situation(s) and decision(s), giving *chance* credit becomes just as unlikely as it is ignominious. A less religiously inclined person might find my efforts to attribute significance of the events ridiculous, perhaps egotistical, in their interpretation. Which is also ok. Believe me. I had much hesitancy in owning these words as the message within may not be widely accepted. But that is also ok. I only hope that it will reach the most people it can. A message of hope in suffering. We've made it this far, so hear me out. *It won't be as bad as me discussing the difference between atypical carcinoid and small cell lung cancer.*

Remember. With my current understanding of God, which I will always be maturing, God is outside of time. God is outside of existence as we know it; His true nature is unknowable, yet He reveals himself, for lack of a better characterization, to us. The lens I find lends me to the greatest understanding is through that of Jesus Christ, God, and the Holy Ghost. Our linear understanding of time limits our understanding, and we are left to depend on faith to fill in our gaps in understanding. Our ape-like consciences can only shoulder so much, more like a bum right shoulder. However, keeping our human machinery geared to keep a lookout for cookie crumbs, we may find a renewed appreciation to not alone the good and the bad, but in God altogether.

But give me, Lord, eyes to behold the truth; A seeing sense that knows the eternal right; A heart with pity filled, and gentlest ruth; A manly faith that makes darkness light.
Theodore Parker, The Higher Good

To the best of my recollection, I did not want for much as a child leading a somewhat semi-charmed life with loving parents and siblings. However, few and isolated incidences of trauma at the hands of peers would imprint a deep-rooted sense of inadequacy. One instance where peers stripped me bare and made a mockery of my prepubescent features in between lashes of a wet towel scarred the deepest. Years later, forgiveness was requested and granted but the welts lingered red in my memory. Moreover, navigating the confusion that accompanies having divorced parents who are only

403

consistently rocky terms would undoubtedly seed distrust in developing strong interpersonal relationships.

Joggling lives between Tifton and Nashville, GA after making the transition from my mother's home to my father's proved to be much more difficult than anticipated. I quickly learned the fallacy of thinking you can be in two places at once. Everything from friends to sport would suffer in the constant flux in location. However, such a setup would diversify me as an individual. I learned to be comfortable in everchanging social settings slowly building emotional intelligence and a fortified ego reinforcing a previously injured confidence. Moreover, less than sturdy foundations in home life and an early sense of insufficiency would bless me with a work ethic unmatched from my peers. The internal drive to compete in both school and sport was fulfilling, but alternatively was a pathway to exact my own flavor of revenge: success.

Quickly however, revenge turned to passion. My early interest in health working with the town doctor in the Agrirama in South Georgia germinated into an early inspiration in entering the healthcare field. Additionally, passion for soccer mixed with discontent in performing a juggling act between expectations and lives ultimately hampered both friendships and athletic development. Thus, I was driven to seek greener pastures at the expense of my familial relationships, particularly my father and I's. My move to Florida from Georgia indicated my willingness to double down on my work ethic and athletic development to reach the next level as isolating as my senior year of high school might become. Pressure to preform mounted with the move especially as time between reciprocal communications with my father continued to be flatlined.

Prior to my move, my natural tendency to overload myself served me well between school and sport teaching me good time management. All of which stemmed from my dad's unrelenting work ethic as he showed me the value of sweat upon your brow on those hot summer afternoon erecting fences and tending to cattle. Constant work was had to be done at the farm. Learning how to effectively utilize one's hands in making a tangible change in the world gifted a special satisfaction that money cannot provide. Not unlike sewing a perfect row 6-0 prolene for a coronary anastomosis, seeing a line of perfectly arranged fence posts you've slaved over the entire weekend builds hard won self-pride.

Fatigued from playing three sports including a traveling soccer team an hour and a half away, I fell asleep at the wheel. I wrecked my top heavy Landcruiser on a narrow country road. The margins for error were infinitesimal as I was passing over a bridge adjacent to deep embankments on either side. I flipped my truck a couple of times from overcorrecting in the process totaling the cruiser with no seatbelt. However, not wearing a seatbelt allowed me to fall into the passenger seat during the 70 mile/hour tumble and into the only open space in the cabin that was not crushed like a coke can. I walked away in shock with only a scratch on my leg. Believe it or not, I had seen an angel once while riding my bike around our neighborhood as a child but was not sure as to what I was looking at being so young. With not a cloud in the sky, the vivid white robes and scepter in hand contrasted unmistakably from the pearly blue surrounding its distant silhouette. Indeed, there was no doubt what was guiding my passage through the cruiser's cabin as I was tossed around like a ragdoll in a washing machine.

These few instances were major influences in my early development as menial as they appear. The stage was set to acquire and continue to develop tools that would serve me well especially as I encountered disease: confidence, social malleability, self-drive and belief. A hardworking and rebellious desire to live in the face of cancer had germinated from an early, perhaps misconceived, inadequacy, perhaps a negative self-evaluation, serving me well, nonetheless. This God-given upbringing bequeathed the topsoil to fodder strong roots of constitution.

A man's "religion" consists not of the many things he is in doubt of and tries to believe, but of the few he is assured of, and had not need of effort for believing.
Carlyle, Latter-Day Pamphlets. No. 8

My experience with the metaphysical wouldn't be limited to just angels but something somewhat more sinister shortly after my move from South Georgia to Jacksonville, Florida. The incubus or succubus charged with my torment likely was signaled by the stress of my recent move, the rocky status my Father and I at the time, and entering a new school system my senior year in a foreign beach town. With the heaviness of guilt looming constant and the unsurety in my decisions, my consciousness was primed for sleep paralysis. SP has plagued the human mind for centuries and are well-reported cross-culturally. As unsettling SP may reveal itself, I find it reassuring in that something more profound and ethereal beyond what we can touch, perhaps hinting to mankind to arise from our spiritual slumber.

The ultimate significance of this phenomenon I will leave to the readers' interpretation.

Prior to and up to my time at Stetson University (SU), I was introduced to some challenging inconsistences with Abrahamic religions challenging my original assumptions about religion. As I learned more becoming more self-critical as to religion and belief, a passion for theology grew in the midst of unanswered questions. Originally, I experienced an existential crisis of sorts being a well-worn notch on Georgia's bible belt. Forming a healthy critique of my makeshift religious purview over time, I would slowly attain a more edifying relationship with the ultimate reality via a lens through which I was raised. Also throughout my time at SU, I continued to exercise a solid work ethic broadening my research interests and bolstering my resume prior to acceptance to medical school. Furthermore, my college relationships provided heartfelt support during my cancer treatments in the years to come

The reverence for religion's role in my life was always present but not fully appreciated. Indeed, I wrestled consistently with its overall implications in my life after college. Was God present or merely a passive bystander? What was I amongst all of time and humanity? Clearly there's something else out there, but in what capacity? God would soon remove all doubt.

Religion is the dominion of the soul. It is the hope of life, the anchor of safety, the de- liverance of the soul.
Napoleon I. (O'Meara, Napoleon in Exile)

After being accepted to University of Florida's College of Medicine after SU, my classmates and I received our white coats after we pledged the Hippocratic Oath officially declaring us physicians. Like I imagine many in the crowd felt, I did not feel like a doctor. My '*Rite of Passage'*, as stated above, occurred in a solitary month of my 2ⁿᵈ year of residency when I felt like I could capably take care of another human being. At the end of that month, I felt like a capable doctor, at least, with some hedges to trim.

On my last evening of clinical work as a resident physician on the edge of D-day, I regrettably encountered a patient who tested every clinical skill I had learned up to that point. Having handled every aspect of care of this victim of multisystem trauma from a motorcycle accident, it was clear that we would have to withdraw care. At the precipice of the week, I felt an overwhelming sadness fall over me as I pronounced him dead. Grateful for everything that he taught me and devastated at the outcome on the eve of my diagnosis no less, I had finally felt the raw ache of becoming a physician. At last, realizing my dream, and loathing it all the same. Through his struggling last heart beats, the magnified percussions in my stethoscope were like punches in my stomach for what I knew was awaiting come dawn: my final day as a physician. *This itself was a blessing; I was granted the wish for which I had dreamt for numerous decades.*

When that fateful diagnosis came, a small army stood at the ready. The ranks of which were filled with the closest of friends from grade school to residency, colleagues and mentors, and, last but certainly not least, my family. The illustrious support was constant and overflowing from people who had played central roles in my personal and professional development, but moreover, were baseline *good* people willing to lend a hand someone was in need. With all my contacts I was never without a place to stay when traveling to seek opinions and explore options for clinical trials. The care and concern of Dr. Ceppa, the wisdom of Dr. Beckman, the undying support of Dr. Hess, the continued support of Dr. Everett and his family: all provided a constant well to replenish my spirit. Indeed, from Chance and David Goggins, I had endless motivation to siphon. *I wish I had the ink to name everyone. God places people in your life when you need them most.*

For example and chief among them, Dr. Thomas Beaver would allow for my earliest exposure to cardiothoracic surgery planting an early passion for the field supporting with research opportunities and facetime in the operating room. Although he also provided opportunity of a young medical student in research and networking, he would eventually connect me with my future oncologist, Dr. Frederic Kaye, whose relentless attitude in fighting cancer would forever change my overall trajectory in survival. Dr. Kaye led to the recruitment of an effective treatment regimen as well as physicians, like Maryam Rahman MD and Alan Friedman MD, neurosurgeons at the University of Florida, who would push the bounds on what is seen as acceptable toxicity for treatment. Dr. Beaver also provided opportunity back at UF when I had to be let go from IU in their research department, although that status of my cancer would not allow any big-time commitments. *This all stemmed from one lecture by Dr. Beaver given during my 1st year of medical school.*

Dr. Beaver and Dr. Hess, both having trained at UF, would lead to me having probably the most important conversation of my life with Dr. Tomas

Martin, or Tom, who had trained each of them. Tom and I's poolside conversation reinvigorated my love for Christ gifting me a version of the Bible that would change the way I consumed the Word. The gift came when I needed it the most as thoughts of suicide started to creep into cognizance whilst my dreams for this life began to crumble. I recall his tantalizing question of "How are you preparing for the next life?" I don't know where I would be if it wasn't for our poolside discussions.

Grief is to man as certain as the grave: Tempests and storms in life's whole progress rise, And hope shines dimly through o'er-clouded skies; Some drops of comfort on the favour'd fall, But showers of sorrow are the lot of all.
George Crabbe, The Library, 1. 641.

Perhaps, the most important character in this journey was my medical school roommate, aptly named Michael, who subsequently attended Colombia University following UF and took a job at the Mayo Clinic in Jacksonville, Beach not five minutes from where I live. Due to the improbability of my original diagnosis, Michael implored me to get a second opinion before I received life altering chest radiation that would inextricably change my overall survival. Subsequently at Memorial Sloan Kettering, my pathology was changed, from small cell lung cancer (SCLC) to atypical carcinoid of the lung (AC), completely uprooting the treatment paradigm that I had embarked upon at my home institution. *Oddly, a team of friends from medical school had made a propitious trip to Indianapolis and were present when I received the good news.* I was one week away from receiving mediastinal radiation which would have put me at increased risk of receiving a large operation. Despite suffering a limb threatening complication of compartment syndrome to my right leg, I was able to walk without issue suffering no nerve injury only mild muscle loss. *Without Michael's adamance, I would have likely passed long ago.*

Tracking back to the time of my diagnosis, I was denied from the family medicine clinic at my home institution as a busy surgical resident having no '*room*' in their schedule, and, by surprisingly, a former medical school colleague working in the ED when requesting a simple chest X-ray. Despite my frustration, the next day I was seen by a more caring and knowledgeable physician; who's attending so happened to be the next-door neighbor of Jen, my ex-fiancé. Initially I was released with a diagnosis of Histoplasmosis. Thanks to the persistence of Dr. Ceppa, the diagnosis was changed with bronchoscopic examination not a week later. No one else could have delivered that kind of news but a mother to a mother. *Angels come in all different shapes and sizes, even Mimi size. Moreover, it is difficult to evaluate the value of time not wasted in deliberation and pontification cut short by the bronchoscope. It certainly is not nil.*

The importance of the unsurety of the minute lesions of the brain scan that were too small to biopsy cannot be understated. The question remained, "Was it a past resolved infection versus cancer that had traveled to the brain?" The window of time created allowed for me to be down staged from stage 4 to stage 3 cancer, in other words, no operation vs. operation. Leaving me a small window to have massive debulking of the tumor. Even though Dr. Rudin and ol' Davey Jones (Dr. David Jones) at MSKCC agreed to, with me, pull the trigger to give me the best chance of survival, resulting surgical margins were not clear. The atypical carcinoid cancer had already

411

begun growing larger in my brain. Although, Dr. Jones was successful in preserving as much lung function where other surgeons said they couldn't. *I had been stage 4 all along. Being stage 4 would have precluded me from receiving what ended up being, likely, a life prolonging operation. Only God could've have worked within these narrow margins of time and uncertainty.*

Additionally, we cannot discount what *didn't* happen during my treatment journey. Along with the timing being impeccable as far as the indecision of the cancer's pathology and staging, my diagnoses sat on the edge of the COVID epidemic. There is no way to adequately evaluate: (1) my risk of contracting severe pneumonia from the virus or (2) the preemptive value of taking daily steroids during cancer treatment combatting the virus prophylactically. As a cardiothoracic resident, I would have been on the frontlines in the intensive care units. If I would have gotten sick while working, one can only imagine my outcome having undiagnosed metastatic lung cancer superimposed with a viral infection. *I might've avoided a premature death sooner than I originally estimated. Six months before the epidemic, I was already enacting some recommended precautions and was clinically inactive, i.e. spending little to no time at the hospital.*

Although not absolutely necessary, awake brain surgery was the only option if I wanted the best chance in preserving brain function while simultaneously making a ruling on the growing mass in my brain: expanding radiation necrosis following brain radiation or expanding cancer. The procedure also addressed my seizures disorder which developed after

412

the life-saving amount of brain radiation was delivered. This vital information would come at the price of the function of my entire right side and speech centers leaving me with mild speech and computational issues, hemiparesis, and spastic foot drop at more than 2 years postop. Despite my efforts at rehabilitation, no amount of surgical knot tying could address my occupational injuries laying to rest any hope, or delusion, of me being a surgeon. The biopsy would prove to be radiation necrosis, although other areas showed signs of continued growth. But I am happy to report, time and the Ketogenic Diet have served me well. Brain scans have been stable.

As my dreams of being a surgeon died, my relationship with Jen soon followed becoming another form collateral damage. Depression is both insidious and infectious also well known to effect cancer survival. With no choice, I had to sacrifice further and focus on all aspects of recovery. Relentless attempts of regaining my all my faculties through all flavors of rehabilitation would be largely in vain. It wasn't long after my brain surgery when I relinquished my loupes and various cardiothoracic textbooks to my closet. Now, only a memory of my dream exists in the form of a picture hanging solemnly depicting me dissecting a mammary artery with the signatures of all my residency class adjacent. The hours upon hours that I had dedicated to master a time-honored craft will never come close to the amount I grieve today.

And we shall be made truly wise if we be made content; content, too, not only with what we can understand, but content with what we do not understand — the habit of mind which theologians call — and rightly — faith in God.
Charles Kingsley, Health and Education On Bio-Geology

Typing this passage, I am forced to depend on a wheelchair to maintain minimum mobility throughout my home. Due to the metastasis that has taken root in my right shoulder and further radiation and chemotherapy in treatment, I am unsure whether my body can sustain a further hit. No longer can I engage in my daily psychotherapy through the ability to exercise freely. Between my bum leg and bum arm, the wheels I am forced to use to escort my meat vessel about the living room does not exempt me from physical pain. In fact, it exacerbates the near constant pain I awake in each day. No longer can I use exercise to escape the pain, emotional and physical. No longer could I run away from my problems and reality. I always said to myself, "An object in motion would stay in motion unless acted on another force. If I keep moving, how could I die?"

Because cancer had robbed me of my ability to move freely; I had no choice but to face ultimate reality before me. I had run from God for so long racing to hide from the light before me. The light I had once known as an unknowing child, the light that I would meet again in the years to come. Always moving, Always looking for the next step in career, in physical challenges, instead of sitting back and giving praise to what brought me into existence. Ignoring the events as mentioned above, I neglected to recognize the entity which gave me life. Some would say, "What God would allow for his child to sustain so much pain and suffering?" In the context of all eternity and little ol' me, what is my suffering but a drop of water in the ocean?

God exists outside time. God was neither created nor destroyed; God just *is*. The ineffable reality far supersedes our feeble attempts of conjuring true understanding among dogmatic perversions. We must attempt to nonetheless. Feeling in touch with the divine through struggle, pain, and strife, was what was required of me. However, I was encouraged with the peculiarity of my experiences involving revolving *deva vu* throughout my life and *ekstasis* near the time of my cancer diagnosis. These were taken as signs, however heartbreaking, that my path remained traveled and true.

The sequence of events however linear or serpiginous to follow might be chocked up as being complete conjecture from someone who is reaching to find significance in their remaining life. I understand that reasoning. However, I wouldn't have been compelled to spend so much time on writing; there are better things to do before I die rather than hunch over my keyboard for several months while undergoing cancer treatment. I only hope that my story will at least bring a newfound appreciation and respect to belief in general. God forbid, you do not have any major tragedy befall you and your family, but strength found in the Spirit will aid in the inevitable trying times to come. I do not claim that the medium for which I appreciate the ultimate reality in a Judeo-Christian fashion to be the only way, but it is important to have a way. You cannot find solace in knowledge and the physical when it is the spirit that needs quenching.

Of course, some may say it's a matter of perspective. You can view the fortuitous events as hinging only on chance occurrences. Or that, events settled out in the most thermodynamically favorable way crystallizing into reality. Or, I just got lucky to have lived as long as I have with a death sentence. Or, I was well-connected with abundant resources. Maybe. But I am not entirely convinced. In retrospect, my life has been too much of a tight-rope to walk especially during the mishaps of treatment. I just hope you would open your heart and mind to the possibility that the same power that dictated the events of my life is in power of yours too.

I am fortunate enough to have to time to commit these words to black and white while turning an analytical lens inward so that I might better understand the greater reality outward, God. I will continue to focus in maturing myself spiritually in preparation for what is to come. If you are reading this, you have enough time too. And remember: *"Faith is not about everything turning out ok, Faith is about being ok no matter how things turn out." -Anonymous*

1.   Senftleber, N.K., et al., *Diet and physical activity in Greenland: genetic interactions and associations with obesity and diabetes.* Appl Physiol Nutr Metab, 2021. **46**(8): p. 849-855.

CPSIA information can be obtained
at www.ICGtesting.com
Printed in the USA
LVHW032119201122
733501LV00011B/658